# Hunter Series Owners Workshop Manual

## John Fowler

**Models covered**
All Saloon and Estate versions of Hunter and Minx,
Singer Gazelle and Vogue, Sunbeam Vogue and Arrow,
Humber Sceptre, 1496 and 1725 cc

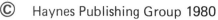

ISBN 0 85696 518 9

Printed in England

**HAYNES PUBLISHING GROUP**
**SPARKFORD YEOVIL SOMERSET ENGLAND**
*distributed in the USA by*
**HAYNES PUBLICATIONS INC**
**861 LAWRENCE DRIVE**
**NEWBURY PARK**
**CALIFORNIA 91320**
**USA**

# Acknowledgements

Thanks are due to the Talbot Motor Company Ltd for their assistance with technical information, to Castrol Ltd who supplied lubrication data, and to the Champion Sparking Plug Company who supplied the illustrations showing the various spark plug conditions. The bodywork repair photographs used in this manual were provided by Holt Lloyd Ltd, who supply 'Turtle Wax', 'Dupli-Color Holts', and other Holts range products.

Finally thanks are due to all those people at Sparkford who helped in the production of this manual, particularly John Austin and Paul Hansford who edited the text and Stanley Randolph who planned the layout of each page.

# About this Manual

## Its aim

The aim of this manual is to help you get the best value from your car. It can do so in several ways. It can help you decide what work must be done (even should you choose to get it done by a garage), provide information on routine maintenance and servicing, and give a logical course of action and diagnosis when random faults occur. However, it is hoped that you will use the manual by tackling the work yourself. On simpler jobs it may even be quicker than booking the car into a garage, and going there twice to leave and collect it. Perhaps most important, a lot of money can be saved by avoiding the costs the garage must charge to cover its labour and overheads.

The manual has drawings and descriptions to show the function of the various components so that their layout can be understood. Then the tasks are described and photographed in a step-by-step sequence so that even a novice can do the work.

## Its arrangement

The manual is divided into twelve Chapters, each covering a logical sub-division of the vehicle. The Chapters are divided into Sections, numbered with single figures, eg 5; and the Sections into paragraphs (or sub sections), with decimal numbers following on from the Section they are in, eg 5.1, 5.2, 5.3 etc.

It is freely illustrated, especially in those parts where there is a detailed sequence of operations to be carried out. There are two forms of illustration; figures and photographs. The figures are numbered in sequence with decimal numbers, according to their position in the Chapter; eg Fig. 6.4 is the 4th drawing/illustration in Chapter 6. Photographs are numbered (either individually or in related groups) the same as the Section or sub-section of the text where the operation they show is described.

There is an alphabetical index at the back of the manual as well as a contents list at the front.

References to the 'left' or 'right' of the vehicle are in the sense of a person in the driver's seat facing forwards.

Unless otherwise stated, nuts and bolts are removed by turning anti-clockwise, and tightened by turning clockwise.

**Whilst every care is taken to ensure that the information in this manual is correct, no liability can be accepted by the authors or publishers for loss, damage or injury caused by any errors in, or omissions from, the information given.**

# Introduction to the Hillman Hunter and variants

Since the introduction of the Hillman Hunter in 1966 there has been a profusion and confusion of models, all of similar basic shape. When one considers the Sunbeam and Singer marques also, the permutation of names and engines becomes complex, and the manufacturing company are to be commended upon the rationalisation of the range implemented in 1970. The names Singer, Vogue, Gazelle and Minx disappeared as part of this process. Additional models as felt necessary were introduced subsequently, these variants employing the remaining basic names of Hillman Hunter, Sunbeam, and Humber Sceptre.

The car is conventional in mechanical layout, drive from the engine being transmitted to the rear axle via a four-speed manual gearbox or a three- or four-speed automatic transmission, and a one- or two-piece propeller shaft.

A range of engines is employed, and the basic equipment can be found to vary quite widely, this being governed by the model and by the intended market.

# Contents

| | Page |
|---|---|
| Acknowledgements | 2 |
| About this manual | 2 |
| Introduction to the Hillman Hunter and variants | 2 |
| General dimensions and weights | 9 |
| Buying spare parts and vehicle identification numbers | 10 |
| Tools and working facilities | 11 |
| Jacking and towing | 13 |
| Recommended lubricants and fluids | 15 |
| Safety first | 16 |
| Routine maintenance | 17 |
| Chapter 1 Engine | 19 |
| Chapter 2 Cooling system | 53 |
| Chapter 3 Fuel and exhaust systems | 60 |
| Chapter 4 Ignition system | 91 |
| Chapter 5 Clutch | 104 |
| Chapter 6 Manual gearbox, overdrive and automatic transmission | 111 |
| Chapter 7 Propeller shaft | 142 |
| Chapter 8 Rear axle | 146 |
| Chapter 9 Braking system | 150 |
| Chapter 10 Electrical system | 165 |
| Chapter 11 Suspension and steering | 206 |
| Chapter 12 Bodywork and fittings | 221 |
| Conversion factors | 240 |
| Index | 241 |

Hillman Hunter GL

Hillman Hunter GL Estate

Hillman Hunter GT

Humber Sceptre

Hillman Hunter GLS

# General dimensions and weights

| Dimensions | Minx, Hunter, Gazelle, Vogue | Hunter De-Luxe, Super and GL | Hunter GLS and GT | Sceptre |
|---|---|---|---|---|
| **Wheelbase** | 98.5 in (250.2 cm) | 98.5 in (250.2 cm) | 98.5 in (250.2 cm) | 98.5 in (250.2 cm) |
| **Track (front and rear)** | 52 in (132 cm) | 52 in (132 cm) | 52.50 in (133 cm) (GLS) 52.75 in (134 cm) (Later GLS) 51.75 in (131 cm) (GT) 52.5 in (133 cm) (Later GT) | 52 in (132 cm) † 51.75 in (131 cm) |
| **Overall length** | 168 in (426.7 cm) (Minx/Gazelle) 169.5 in (430.5 cm) (Hunter & Vogue) 172 in (436.9 cm) (Estate cars) | 168 in (426.7 cm) 171 in (434.3 cm) (Later cars) 170.75 in (433.7 cm) (Estate cars) 173 in (439.4 cm) (Later Estate cars) | 168 in (426.7 cm) 171 in (434.3 cm) (Later cars) | 169.5 in (430.5 cm) 171 in (434.3 cm) (Later cars) 173 in (439.4 cm) (Estate cars) |
| **Overall height (at kerb weight)** | 56 in (142.2 cm) | 56 in (142.2 cm) 56.5 in (143.5 cm) (Later cars) 55.75 in (141.6 cm) (Later Estate cars) | 56 in (142.2 cm) 55.75 in (141.6 cm) (Later GT) 104.75 in (142.9 cm) (Later GLS) | 56 in (142.2 cm) 55.75 in (141.6 cm) (Later cars) 58 in (147.3cm) (Estate car) ** |
| **Overall width** | 63.5 in (161.3 cm) | 63.5 in (161.3 cm) | 63.5 in (161.3 cm) | 64.75 in (164.5 cm) 63.5 in (161.3 cm) (Later cars and all Estate cars) |
| **Minimum ground clearance** | 6.75 in (16.8 cm) | 6.5 in (16.5 cm) | 6.5 in (16.5 cm) 5.5 in (14.0 cm) (Later GLS) 5.75 in (14.6 cm) (Later GT) | 6.75 in (16.8 cm) 5.5 in (14.0 cm) (Later cars and all Estate cars) |
| **Turning circle** | 33 ft 6 in (10.2 m) | 34 ft 0 in (10.36 m) | 34 ft 0 in (10.36 m) 34 ft 2 in (10.40 m) (Later cars) | 33 ft 6 in (10.2 m) |

*Towing capacity (max) — all models*
**Braked** ...... 17 cwt (864 kg)

**Unbraked** ...... 10 cwt (508 kg)

*Roof rack load (max)* ...... 100 lb (45 kg)

| *Kerb weights* | Saloon 2035 lb | Saloon (overdrive) 2065 lb | Saloon (automatic) 2062 lb | Estate 2170 lb |
|---|---|---|---|---|

*Kerb weights are approximate only, and subject to variation between different models*

† from Serial No LH 090-7
** including roof rack

# Buying spare parts and vehicle identification numbers

## Buying spare parts

Spare parts are available from many sources. Talbot have many dealers throughout both the UK and the rest of the world, and other dealers, accessory stores and motor factors will also stock Talbot spare parts. Our advice regarding spare part sources is as follows:

*Officially appointed vehicle main dealers* – This is the best source of parts which are peculiar to your vehicle and are otherwise not generally available (eg complete cylinder heads, internal transmission components, badges, interior trim etc). It is also the only place at which you should buy parts if your car is still under warranty. To be sure of obtaining the correct parts it will always be necessary to give the storeman your vehicle's engine and chassis number, and if possible, to take the 'old' part along for positive identification. Remember that many parts are available on a factory exchange scheme – any parts returned should always be clean! It obviously makes good sense to go straight to the specialists on your car for this type of part, for they are best equipped to supply you.

*Other dealers and auto accessory stores* – These are often very good places to buy materials and components needed for the maintenance of your vehicle (eg, oil filters, spark plugs, bulbs, fan belts, oils and greases, touch-up paint, filler paste etc). They also sell general accessories, usually have convenient opening hours, charge lower prices and can often be found not far from home.

*Motor factors* – Good factors will stock all of the more important components which wear out relatively quickly (eg clutch components, pistons, valves, exhaust system, brake cylinder/pipes/hoses/seals/shoes and pads etc). Motor factors will often provide new or reconditioned components on a part exchange basis – this can save a considerable amount of money.

## Vehicle identification numbers

*The vehicle serial number and suffix letters* are stamped on a plate which is fixed to the bonnet lock platform (photo).

The *engine number* will be found on the right-hand side of the cylinder block, immediately above the fuel pump (photo).

Vehicle identification plate, which will be found on the bonnet lock platform

Engine number location, just above the fuel pump

# Tools and working facilities

## Introduction

A selection of good tools is a fundamental requirement for anyone contemplating the maintenance and repair of a motor vehicle. For the owner who does not possess any, their purchase will prove a considerable expense, offsetting some of the savings made by doing-it-yourself. However, provided that the tools purchased are of good quality, they will last for many years and prove an extremely worthwhile investment.

To help the average owner to decide which tools are needed to carry out the various tasks detailed in this manual, we have compiled three lists of tools under the following headings: *Maintenance and minor repair*, *Repair and overhaul*, and *Special*. The newcomer to practical mechanics should start off with the *Maintenance and minor repair* tool kit and confine himself to the simpler jobs around the vehicle. Then, as his confidence and experience grows, he can undertake more difficult tasks, buying extra tools as, and when, they are needed. In this way, a *Maintenance and minor repair* tool kit can be built-up into a *Repair and overhaul* tool kit over a considerable period of time without any major cash outlays. The experienced do-it-yourselfer will have a tool kit good enough for most repair and overhaul procedures and will add tools from the *Special* category when he feels the expense is justified by the amount of use to which these tools will be put.

It is obviously not possible to cover the subject of tools fully here. For those who wish to learn more about tools and their use there is a book entitled *How to Choose and Use Car Tools* available from the publishers of this manual.

## Maintenance and minor repair tool kit

The tools given in this list should be considered as a minimum requirement if routine maintenance, servicing and minor repair operations are to be undertaken. We recommend the purchase of combination spanners (ring one end, open-ended the other); although more expensive than open-ended ones, they do give the advantages of both types of spanner.

> *Combination spanners - $\frac{1}{4}$, $\frac{5}{16}$, $\frac{3}{8}$, $\frac{7}{16}$, $\frac{1}{2}$, $\frac{9}{16}$, $\frac{5}{8}$, $\frac{11}{16}$, $\frac{3}{4}$ in AF*
> *Adjustable spanner - 9 inch*
> *Automatic transmission drain plug key (where applicable)*
> *Spark plug spanner (with rubber insert)*
> *Spark plug gap adjustment tool*
> *Set of feeler gauges*
> *Brake bleed nipple spanner*
> *Screwdriver - 4 in long x $\frac{1}{4}$ in dia (flat blade)*
> *Screwdriver - 4 in long x $\frac{1}{4}$ in dia (cross blade)*
> *Combination pliers - 6 inch*
> *Hacksaw, junior*
> *Tyre pump*
> *Tyre pressure gauge*
> *Oil can*
> *Fine emery cloth (1 sheet)*
> *Wire brush (small)*
> *Funnel (medium size)*

## Repair and overhaul tool kit

These tools are virtually essential for anyone undertaking any major repairs to a motor vehicle, and are additional to those given in the *Maintenance and minor repair* list. Included in this list is a comprehensive set of sockets. Although these are expensive they will be found invaluable as they are so versatile - particularly if various drives are included in the set. We recommend the $\frac{1}{2}$ in square-drive type, as this can be used with most proprietary torque wrenches. If you cannot afford a socket set, even bought piecemeal, then inexpensive tubular box spanners are a useful alternative.

The tools in this list will occasionally need to be supplemented by tools from the *Special* list.

> *Sockets (or box spanners) to cover range in previous list*
> *Reversible ratchet drive (for use with sockets)*
> *Extension piece, 10 inch (for use with sockets)*
> *Universal joint (for use with sockets)*
> *Torque wrench (for use with sockets)*
> *'Mole' wrench - 8 inch*
> *Ball pein hammer*
> *Soft-faced hammer, plastic or rubber*
> *Screwdriver - 6 in long x $\frac{5}{16}$ in dia (flat blade)*
> *Screwdriver - 2 in long x $\frac{5}{16}$ in square (flat blade)*
> *Screwdriver - 1$\frac{1}{2}$ in long x $\frac{1}{4}$ in dia (cross blade)*
> *Screwdriver - 3 in long x $\frac{1}{8}$ in dia (electricians)*
> *Pliers - electricians side cutters*
> *Pliers - needle nosed*
> *Pliers - circlip (internal and external)*
> *Cold chisel - $\frac{1}{2}$ inch*
> *Scriber (this can be made by grinding the end of a broken hacksaw blade)*
> *Scraper (this can be made by flattening and sharpening one end of a piece of copper pipe)*
> *Centre punch*
> *Pin punch*
> *Hacksaw*
> *Valve grinding tool*
> *Steel rule/straight edge*
> *Allen keys*
> *Selection of files*
> *Wire brush (large)*
> *Axle-stands*
> *Jack (strong scissor or hydraulic type)*

## Special tools

The tools in this list are those which are not used regularly, are expensive to buy, or which need to be used in accordance with their manufacturers' instructions. Unless relatively difficult mechanical jobs are undertaken frequently, it will not be economic to buy many of these tools. Where this is the case, you could consider clubbing together with friends (or a motorists' club) to make a joint purchase, or borrowing the tools against a deposit from a local garage or tool hire specialist.

The following list contains only those tools and instruments freely available to the public, and not those special tools produced by the vehicle manufacturer specifically for its dealer network. You will find occasional references to these manufacturers' special tools in the text of this manual. Generally, an alternative method of doing the job without the vehicle manufacturers' special tool is given. However, sometimes, there is no alternative to using them. Where this is the case and the relevant tool cannot be bought or borrowed you will have to entrust the work to a franchised garage.

> *Valve spring compressor (where applicable)*
> *Piston ring compressor*
> *Balljoint separator*
> *Universal hub/bearing puller*
> *Impact screwdriver*
> *Micrometer and/or vernier gauge*
> *Carburettor flow balancing device (where applicable)*
> *Dial gauge*
> *Stroboscopic timing light*
> *Dwell angle meter/tachometer*
> *Universal electrical multi-meter*
> *Cylinder compression gauge*
> *Lifting tackle (photo)*
> *Trolley jack*
> *Light with extension lead*

## Buying tools

For practically all tools, a tool dealer is the best source since he will have a very comprehensive range compared with the average garage or accessory shop. Having said that, accessory shops often offer excellent quality tools at discount prices, so it pays to shop around.

Remember, you don't have to buy the most expensive items on the shelf, but it is always advisable to steer clear of the very cheap tools. There are plenty of good tools around at reasonable prices, so ask the proprietor or manager of the shop for advice before making a purchase.

## Care and maintenance of tools

Having purchased a reasonable tool kit, it is necessary to keep the tools in a clean serviceable condition. After use, always wipe off any dirt, grease and metal particles using a clean, dry cloth, before putting the tools away. Never leave them lying around after they have been used. A simple tool rack on the garage or workshop wall, for items such as screwdrivers and pliers is a good idea. Store all normal spanners and sockets in a metal box. Any measuring instruments, gauges, meters, etc, must be carefully stored where they cannot be damaged or become rusty.

Take a little care when tools are used. Hammer heads inevitably become marked and screwdrivers lose the keen edge on their blades from time to time. A little timely attention with emery cloth or a file will soon restore items like this to a good serviceable finish.

## Working facilities

Not to be forgotten when discussing tools, is the workshop itself. If anything more than routine maintenance is to be carried out, some form of suitable working area becomes essential.

It is appreciated that many an owner mechanic is forced by circumstances to remove an engine or similar item, without the benefit of a garage or workshop. Having done this, any repairs should always be done under the cover of a roof.

Wherever possible, any dismantling should be done on a clean flat workbench or table at a suitable working height.

Any workbench needs a vice: one with a jaw opening of 4 in (100 mm) is suitable for most jobs. As mentioned previously, some clean dry storage space is also required for tools, as well as the lubricants, cleaning fluids, touch-up paints and so on which become necessary.

Another item which may be required, and which has a much more general usage, is an electric drill with a chuck capacity of at least $\frac{5}{16}$ in (8 mm). This, together with a good range of twist drills, is virtually essential for fitting accessories such as wing mirrors and reversing lights.

Last, but not least, always keep a supply of old newspapers and clean, lint-free rags available, and try to keep any working area as clean as possible.

### Spanner jaw gap comparison table

| Jaw gap (in) | Spanner size |
| --- | --- |
| 0.250 | $\frac{1}{4}$ in AF |
| 0.276 | 7 mm |
| 0.313 | $\frac{5}{16}$ in AF |
| 0.315 | 8 mm |
| 0.344 | $\frac{11}{32}$ in AF; $\frac{1}{8}$ in Whitworth |
| 0.354 | 9 mm |
| 0.375 | $\frac{3}{8}$ in AF |
| 0.394 | 10 mm |
| 0.433 | 11 mm |
| 0.438 | $\frac{7}{16}$ in AF |
| 0.445 | $\frac{3}{16}$ in Whitworth; $\frac{1}{4}$ in BSF |
| 0.472 | 12 mm |
| 0.500 | $\frac{1}{2}$ in AF |
| 0.512 | 13 mm |
| 0.525 | $\frac{1}{4}$ in Whitworth; $\frac{5}{16}$ in BSF |
| 0.551 | 14 mm |
| 0.563 | $\frac{9}{16}$ in AF |
| 0.591 | 15 mm |
| 0.600 | $\frac{5}{16}$ in Whitworth; $\frac{3}{8}$ in BSF |
| 0.625 | $\frac{5}{8}$ in AF |
| 0.630 | 16 mm |
| 0.669 | 17 mm |
| 0.686 | $\frac{11}{16}$ in AF |
| 0.709 | 18 mm |
| 0.710 | $\frac{3}{8}$ in Whitworth; $\frac{7}{16}$ in BSF |
| 0.748 | 19 mm |
| 0.750 | $\frac{3}{4}$ in AF |
| 0.813 | $\frac{13}{16}$ in AF |
| 0.820 | $\frac{7}{16}$ in Whitworth; $\frac{1}{2}$ in BSF |
| 0.866 | 22 mm |
| 0.875 | $\frac{7}{8}$ in AF |
| 0.920 | $\frac{1}{2}$ in Whitworth; $\frac{9}{16}$ in BSF |
| 0.938 | $\frac{15}{16}$ in AF |
| 0.945 | 24 mm |
| 1.000 | 1 in AF |
| 1.010 | $\frac{9}{16}$ in Whitworth; $\frac{5}{8}$ in BSF |
| 1.024 | 26 mm |
| 1.063 | $1\frac{1}{16}$ in AF, 27 mm |
| 1.100 | $\frac{5}{8}$ in Whitworth; $\frac{11}{16}$ in BSF |
| 1.125 | $1\frac{1}{8}$ in AF |
| 1.181 | 30 mm |
| 1.200 | $\frac{11}{16}$ in Whitworth; $\frac{3}{4}$ in BSF |
| 1.250 | $1\frac{1}{4}$ in AF |
| 1.260 | 32 mm |
| 1.300 | $\frac{3}{4}$ in Whitworth; $\frac{7}{8}$ in BSF |
| 1.313 | $1\frac{5}{16}$ in AF |
| 1.390 | $\frac{13}{16}$ in Whitworth; $\frac{15}{16}$ in BSF |
| 1.417 | 36 mm |
| 1.438 | $1\frac{7}{16}$ in AF |
| 1.480 | $\frac{7}{8}$ in Whitworth; 1 in BSF |
| 1.500 | $1\frac{1}{2}$ in AF |
| 1.575 | 40 mm; $\frac{15}{16}$ in Whitworth |
| 1.614 | 41 mm |
| 1.625 | $1\frac{5}{8}$ in AF |
| 1.670 | 1 in Whitworth; $1\frac{1}{8}$ in BSF |
| 1.688 | $1\frac{11}{16}$ in AF |
| 1.811 | 46 mm |
| 1.813 | $1\frac{13}{16}$ in AF |
| 1.860 | $1\frac{1}{8}$ in Whitworth; $1\frac{1}{4}$ in BSF |
| 1.875 | $1\frac{7}{8}$ in AF |
| 1.969 | 50 mm |
| 2.000 | 2 in AF |
| 2.050 | $1\frac{1}{4}$ in Whitworth; $1\frac{3}{8}$ in BSF |
| 2.165 | 55 mm |
| 2.362 | 60 mm |

A Haltrac hoist and gantry in use during a typical engine removal sequence

# Jacking and towing

Safety is paramount before venturing underneath a car to carry out any sort of maintenance or overhaul work. Locating a jack on an unsuitable part of the vehicle, placing it upon an unsuitable surface (ie one that is too soft, too slippery or too uneven), or even employing a worn out jack, have been the causes of many severe accidents. As an additional safety measure, all wheels left upon the ground when any form of jacking is carried out should be securely chocked. Extreme care is the watchword of any lifting operation.

The jack supplied with the vehicle is adequate for changing a wheel, but one should never go under the car using this form of support alone. Two forms of jacking design have been employed, the earlier type consisting of slots at the front and rear of the car as shown in the photograph, there being a total of four slots to correspond with the wheel which is to be raised. Ensure the jack is fully home before taking weight upon it.

The alternative design of jacking system is illustrated, and has the lifting slots on the sides of the vehicle. Ensure the jack is fully home in the appropriate slot before taking weight upon it.

For all tasks underneath the car, axle stands should be used. The vehicle should be raised just sufficiently to allow the stands to be placed under the appropriate points, and then jacked higher. The height of the stands is then increased, and the procedure continued until an adequate height is reached. The stands should be employed in pairs, and care should be taken to raise the car either completely evenly or only a little at a time from each side, to obviate the possibility of the car reaching an angle which could cause the stand to topple. For this lifting process a trolley jack, or substantial hydraulic or screw jack is recommended, placed either under the front crossmember or under the rear axle. A suitable wooden packing piece fitted on the jack head will prevent damage to the metalwork of the car. Suitable points for fitting axle stands at the front of the vehicle are shown in the illustration. Stands employed at the rear of the car should be placed under the axle casing, (one on each side of the differential housing),

**Early type jacking system with slots at front and rear of the vehicle**

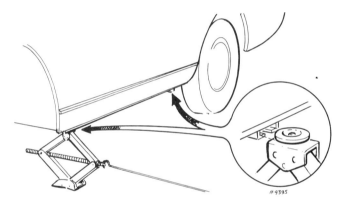

**Later type jacking system**

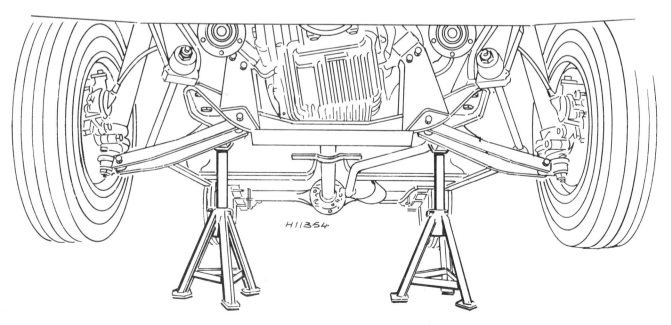

**Use of axle stands at the front of the vehicle**

and as close to the rear spring as possible. Care should be taken not to crush items such as brake pipes when placing the stands against the axle casing.

When the vehicle is being towed, attach the tow rope round the front crossmember, which can be identified from illustrations in Chapter 11. When towing another vehicle, attach the tow rope round the car spring shackle assembly, which can also be identified from illustrations in Chapter 11. The maximum loads which should be towed are given in the table 'General dimensions and weights'.

The manufacturers consider that some models which are fitted with automatic transmissions should not be employed for towing unless certain relatively small modifications are carried out, and owners with this form of transmission are advised to ask the advice of their main dealer in this connection.

Certain precautions are required if it becomes necessary to tow a vehicle with automatic transmission. If the transmission is in running order, the vehicle can be towed with the selector lever at N for a maximum distance of twenty-five miles, at not more than 30 mph. If, however, the transmission is faulty, the vehicle must either be towed with the rear wheels clear of the ground, or alternatively the propeller shaft must be disconnected at the rear and either removed or supported in a sling. If the shaft is removed, seal off the transmission extension housing to prevent both loss of fluid and the entry of foreign matter.

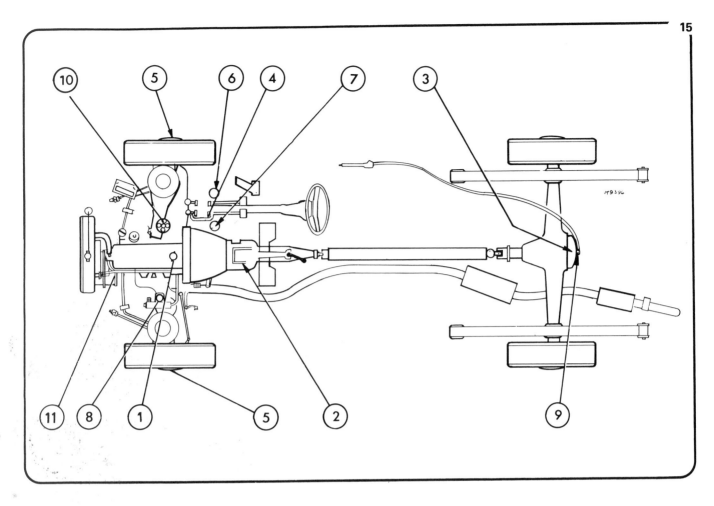

# Recommended lubricants and fluids

| Component or system | Lubricant type or specification | Castrol product |
|---|---|---|
| Engine (1) | 20W/50 multigrade engine oil | Castrol GTX |
| Transmission (2) | | |
| Manual and overdrive | 20W/50 multigrade engine oil | Castrol GTX |
| Automatic | Non-Dexron type automatic transmission fluid | Castrol TQF |
| Rear axle (3) | SAE 90EP hypoid gear oil | Castrol Hypoy |
| Steering box (4) | SAE 90EP hypoid gear oil | Castrol Hypoy |
| Wheel bearings (5) | Multi-purpose grease | Castrol LM Grease |
| Brake fluid reservoir (6) | SAE J1703 hydraulic fluid | Castrol Girling Universal Brake and Clutch Fluid |
| Clutch fluid reservoir (7) | SAE J1703 hydraulic fluid | Castrol Girling Universal Brake and Clutch Fluid |
| Carburettor damper (8) | 20W/50 multigrade engine oil | Castrol GTX |
| Handbrake pull-off springs (9) | Multi-purpose grease | Castrol LM Grease |
| Distributor (10) | 20W/50 multigrade engine oil | Castrol GTX |
| Dynamo (11) | 20W/50 multigrade engine oil | Castrol GTX |
| General lubrication | General-purpose oil | Castrol Everyman |

*The above are general recommendations only. Lubrication requirements vary with different operating requirements. If in doubt, consult the vehicle handbook or your nearest dealer*

# Safety first!

Professional motor mechanics are trained in safe working procedures. However enthusiastic you may be about getting on with the job in hand, do take the time to ensure that your safety is not put at risk. A moment's lack of attention can result in an accident, as can failure to observe certain elementary precautions.

There will always be new ways of having accidents, and the following points do not pretend to be a comprehensive list of all dangers; they are intended rather to make you aware of the risks and to encourage a safety-conscious approach to all work you carry out on your vehicle.

### Essential DOs and DON'Ts

**DON'T** rely on a single jack when working underneath the vehicle. Always use reliable additional means of support, such as axle stands, securely placed under a part of the vehicle that you know will not give way.

**DON'T** attempt to loosen or tighten high-torque nuts (e.g. wheel hub nuts) while the vehicle is on a jack; it may be pulled off.

**DON'T** start the engine without first ascertaining that the transmission is in neutral (or 'Park' where applicable) and the parking brake applied.

**DON'T** suddenly remove the filler cap from a hot cooling system — cover it with a cloth and release the pressure gradually first, or you may get scalded by escaping coolant.

**DON'T** attempt to drain oil until you are sure it has cooled sufficiently to avoid scalding you.

**DON'T** grasp any part of the engine, exhaust or catalytic converter without first ascertaining that it is sufficiently cool to avoid burning you.

**DON'T** syphon toxic liquids such as fuel, brake fluid or antifreeze by mouth, or allow them to remain on your skin.

**DON'T** inhale brake lining dust — it is injurious to health

**DON'T** allow any spilt oil or grease to remain on the floor — wipe it up straight away, before someone slips on it.

**DON'T** use ill-fitting spanners or other tools which may slip and cause injury.

**DON'T** attempt to lift a heavy component which may be beyond your capability — get assistance.

**DON'T** rush to finish a job, or take unverified short cuts.

**DON'T** allow children or animals in or around an unattended vehicle.

**DO** wear eye protection when using power tools such as drill, sander, bench grinder etc, and when working under the vehicle.

**DO** use a barrier cream on your hands prior to undertaking dirty jobs — it will protect your skin from infection as well as making the dirt easier to remove afterwards; but make sure your hands aren't left slippery.

**DO** keep loose clothing (cuffs, tie etc) and long hair well out of the way of moving mechanical parts.

**DO** remove rings, wristwatch etc, before working on the vehicle — especially the electrical system.

**DO** ensure that any lifting tackle used has a safe working load rating adequate for the job.

**DO** keep your work area tidy — it is only too easy to fall over articles left lying around.

**DO** get someone to check periodically that all is well, when working alone on the vehicle.

**DO** carry out work in a logical sequence and check that everything is correctly assembled and tightened afterwards.

**DO** remember that your vehicle's safety affects that of yourself and others. If in doubt on any point, get specialist advice.

**IF,** in spite of following these precautions, you are unfortunate enough to injure yourself, seek medical attention as soon as possible.

### Fire

Remember at all times that petrol (gasoline) is highly flammable. Never smoke, or have any kind of naked flame around, when working on the vehicle. But the risk does not end there — a spark caused by an electrical short-circuit, by two metal surfaces contacting each other, or even by static electricity built up in your body under certain conditions, can ignite petrol vapour, which in a confined space is highly explosive.

Always disconnect the battery earth (ground) terminal before working on any part of the fuel system, and never risk spilling fuel on to a hot engine or exhaust.

It is recommended that a fire extinguisher of a type suitable for fuel and electrical fires is kept handy in the garage or workplace at all times. Never try to extinguish a fuel or electrical fire with water.

### Fumes

Certain fumes are highly toxic and can quickly cause unconsciousness and even death if inhaled to any extent. Petrol (gasoline) vapour comes into this category, as do the vapours from certain solvents such as trichloroethylene. Any draining or pouring of such volatile fluids should be done in a well ventilated area.

When using cleaning fluids and solvents, read the instructions carefully. Never use materials from unmarked containers — they may give off poisonous vapours.

Never run the engine of a motor vehicle in an enclosed space such as a garage. Exhaust fumes contain carbon monoxide which is extremely poisonous; if you need to run the engine, always do so in the open air or at least have the rear of the vehicle outside the workplace.

If you are fortunate enough to have the use of an inspection pit, never drain or pour petrol, and never run the engine, while the vehicle is standing over it; the fumes, being heavier than air, will concentrate in the pit with possibly lethal results.

### The battery

Never cause a spark, or allow a naked light, near the vehicle's battery. It will normally be giving off a certain amount of hydrogen gas, which is highly explosive.

Always disconnect the battery earth (ground) terminal before working on the fuel or electrical systems.

If possible, loosen the filler plugs or cover when charging the battery from an external source. Do not charge at an excessive rate or the battery may burst.

Take care when topping up and when carrying the battery. The acid electrolyte, even when diluted, is very corrosive and should not be allowed to contact the eyes or skin.

If you ever need to prepare electrolyte yourself, always add the acid slowly to the water, and never the other way round. Protect against splashes by wearing rubber gloves and goggles.

### Mains electricity

When using an electric power tool, inspection light etc which works from the mains, always ensure that the appliance is correctly connected to its plug and that, where necessary, it is properly earthed (grounded). Do not use such appliances in damp conditions and, again, beware of creating a spark or applying excessive heat in the vicinity of fuel or fuel vapour.

### Ignition HT voltage

A severe electric shock can result from touching certain parts of the ignition system, such as the HT leads, when the engine is running or being cranked, particularly if components are damp or the insulation is defective. Where an electronic ignition system is fitted, the HT voltage is much higher and could prove fatal.

# Routine maintenance

Maintenance is essential for ensuring safety and desirable for the purpose of getting the best in terms of performance and economy from the car. Over the years the need for periodic lubrication – oiling, greasing and so on – has been drastically reduced if not totally eliminated. This has unfortunately tended to lead some owners to think that because no such action is required the items either no longer exist or will last for ever. This is not the case, and the largest item of maintenance should consist of visual examination, which may in turn reveal a need for repairs.

## Weekly or at 250 miles (400 km) intervals

Check the engine oil level
Check the tyre pressures
Check the radiator coolant level
Check the battery electrolyte level
Check the brake fluid level
Check the carburettor damper level (where relevant)
Check the screen washer reservoir level

## Every 5000 miles (8000 km) or five months

Check specific gravity of the antifreeze

Check valve clearances (aluminium-headed engine only) and adjust if necessary
Clean or renew spark plugs
Lubricate distributor, clean or renew controls, reset gap. Adjust ignition timing (Lucas distributor)
Lubricate distributor, renew contacts if necessary. Reset dwell angle and ignition timing (Delco Remy distributor)
Check idling speed and mixture, and adjust if necessary
Examine front and rear brakes for wear and leaks
Check brake pipes and hoses for damage and leaks
Check fluid level in clutch reservoir
Check that vents in brake and clutch reservoirs are clear
Check balljoints on steering and front suspension for wear
Inspect all steering and suspension dust seals, boots and bushes for deterioration
Check tightness of wheel nuts
Examine tyres for wear or damage
Check tyre tread depth with gauge
Check all units for oil leaks
Change engine oil and filter
Check/top up oil in manual gearbox and rear axle
Check/top up fluid in automatic transmission
Lubricate all pivots, linkages, hinges and catches
Clear door drain holes and heater intake drain
Check cooling system for leaks, when hot

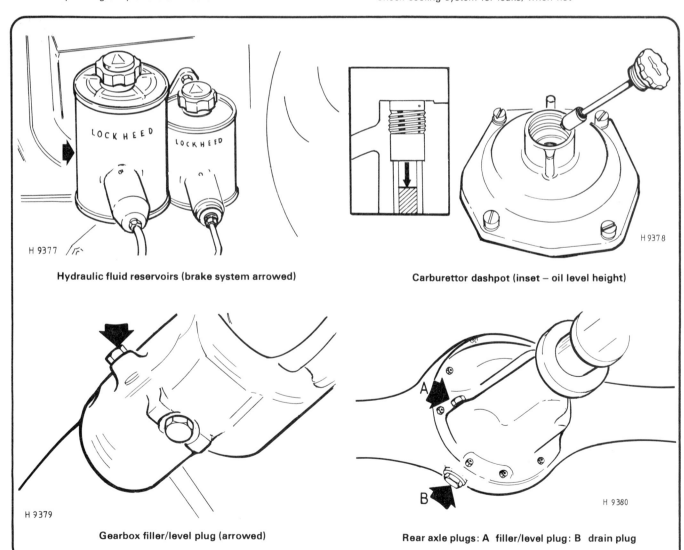

Hydraulic fluid reservoirs (brake system arrowed)

Carburettor dashpot (inset – oil level height)

Gearbox filler/level plug (arrowed)

Rear axle plugs: A filler/level plug: B drain plug

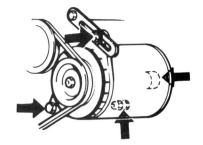

Fanbelt tension adjusting bolts (dynamo fitted)

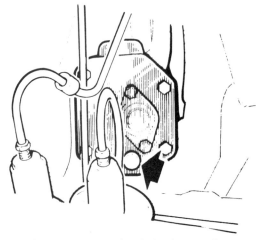

Steering box filler/level plug (arrowed)

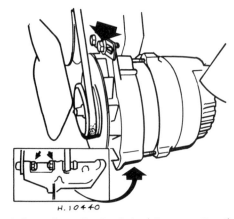

Fanbelt tension adjusting bolts (alternator fitted)

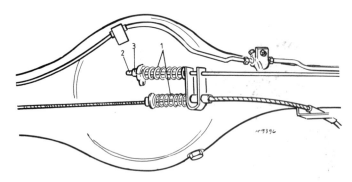

Handbrake pull-off springs (1), rod (2) and bush (3)

Check fuel system for leaks

Check operation of lamps, indicators, windscreen wiper/washer and heated backlight

Check for excess play in steering wheel

Examine safety belts, fittings and anchorages

Check full-throttle upshift speeds on automatic transmission. Adjust downshift cable if necessary

Lubricate generator rear bearing

Clean battery terminals and smear with petroleum jelly

Check exhaust system for leaks

### Every 10 000 miles (16 000 km) or ten months

*Carry out all the items mentioned under the 5000 mile service, plus the following:*

Check fanbelt tension and condition

Clean flame trap

Clean fuel pump filter and sediment chamber

Renew air cleaner element and clean casing

Examine suspension struts and dampers for leakage

Check/top up oil in the steering unit

Check fuel filler to tank connections for leaks

### Every 15 000 miles (24 000 km) or 15 months

*All items mentioned under the 5000 mile service, plus the following:*

Check handbrake ratchet for wear

Examine handbrake cable for defects or corrosion

Check handbrake pivots and pins for security

Lubricate handbrake pull-off springs

### Every 30 000 miles (48 000 km) or 30 months

*All items mentioned under the 5000 mile, 10 000 mile and 15 000 mile services, plus the following:*

Renew brake servo air filter element, if fitted

Check metal brake pipes for corrosion

Clean front hubs, repack bearings with grease, and re-set the endfloat

Examine suspension struts and dampers for security of fixings, and for mounting rubber condition

Clean overdrive sump filter, magnet and pressure filter

# Chapter 1 Engine

## Contents

Big-end bearings – examination and renovation ............................... 25
Camshaft and tappets – refitting .................................................. 42
Camshaft, bearings and tappets – examination and renovation ... 32
Camshaft – removal ...................................................................... 17
Closed crankcase ventilation system – description and
maintenance .................................................................................. 22
Connecting rods, pistons and piston rings – examination and
renovation ...................................................................................... 27
Crankshaft and main bearings – examination and renovation ...... 24
Crankshaft and main bearings – reassembly .............................. 38
Crankshaft, main bearings and thrust washers – removal .............. 19
Crankshaft pulley, timing gear and cover – removal ...................... 12
Crankshaft pulley wheel – refitting ............................................... 44
Cylinder bores – examination and renovation .............................. 26
Cylinder head – examination and renovation ............................... 30
Cylinder head – refitting ............................................................... 50
Cylinder head – removal ............................................................... 10
Decarbonisation ........................................................................... 36
Engine dismantling – ancillaries .................................................. 7
Engine dismantling – general ...................................................... 6
Engine – general examination ..................................................... 23
Engine mountings and damper – removal and refitting ................ 21
Engine reassembly – ancillaries .................................................. 53
Engine reassembly – general ....................................................... 37
Engine – removal .......................................................................... 5
Engine – refitting .......................................................................... 54
Fault diagnosis – engine .............................................................. 55
Flywheel – examination and renovation ....................................... 33
Flywheel – refitting ....................................................................... 47

Flywheel – removal ....................................................................... 15
General description ....................................................................... 1
Gudgeon pins – removal ............................................................... 14
Inlet and exhaust manifolds – inspection ..................................... 35
Inlet and exhaust manifolds – refitting ......................................... 49
Inlet and exhaust manifolds – removal ......................................... 9
Major operations possible with engine in place ........................... 3
Major operations possible with engine removed .......................... 4
Oil filter – removal and refitting .................................................... 20
Oil pump – examination and renovation ....................................... 34
Oil pump – refitting ....................................................................... 45
Oil pump – removal ....................................................................... 16
Pistons, connecting rods and big-end bearings – refitting ........... 41
Pistons, connecting rods and big-end bearings – removal ........... 13
Pistons, gudgeon pins and connecting rods – reassembly .......... 39
Piston rings – refitting .................................................................. 40
Routine maintenance .................................................................... 2
Sump – refitting ............................................................................ 46
Sump – removal ........................................................................... 11
Tappets – removal ........................................................................ 18
Timing chain and sprockets – examination and renovation ......... 31
Timing chain tensioner, sprockets and cover – refitting ............... 43
Valve rocker clearances – checking and adjustment ................... 52
Valve rocker gear – examination and renovation ......................... 28
Valve rocker gear – reassembly and refitting .............................. 51
Valve rocker gear – removal ........................................................ 8
Valves – removal and renovation ................................................. 29
Valves and springs – reassembly to cylinder head ...................... 48

## Specifications

*Covers the 1500 and 1725 cc engines – the latter with either a cast iron or aluminium head. A high or low compression head is available for both size engines in cast iron only.*

### Engine – general

| | |
|---|---|
| Type ..................................................................................... | Four-cylinder in-line ohv pushrod operated |
| Bore: | |
|     Grade A ......................................................................... | 3.2102 to 3.2106 in (81.539 to 81.549 mm) |
|     Grade B ......................................................................... | 3.2106 to 3.2110 in (81.549 to 81.559 mm) |
|     Grade C ......................................................................... | 3.2110 to 3.2114 in (81.559 to 81.569 mm) |
|     Grade D ......................................................................... | 3.2114 to 3.2118 in (81.569 to 81.579 mm) |

| | **1725** | **1500** |
|---|---|---|
| Stroke ................................................................................ | 3.25 in (82.55 mm) | 2.82 in (71.63 mm) |
| Capacity (standard bore) .................................................. | 1724 cc (105.1 in$^3$) | 1496 cc (91.28 in$^3$) |
| Firing order ...................................................................... | 1-3-4-2 | |
| No 1 cylinder position ...................................................... | Front of engine | |

| | |
|---|---|
| Compression ratios: | |
|   Aluminium head, twin carburettors (320 cam) ................ | 9.6:1 |
|   Aluminium head, single and twin carburettors (298 | |
|   and 295 cams) ................................................................. | 9.2:1 |
|   Cast iron head, high compression (HC) ......................... | 8.4:1 |
|   Cast iron head, low compression (LC) ........................... | 7.5:1 |

### Cylinder block

| | |
|---|---|
| Maximum oversize (with or without liners) ........................ | 0.030 in (0.76 mm) |

## Camshaft
Journal diameter ........................................................ 1.7477 to 1.7470 in (44.39 to 44.37 mm)
Bearing internal diameter ......................................... 1.7500 to 1.7490 in (44.45 to 44.51 mm)
Bearing running clearance ........................................ 0.003 to 0.0013 in (0.07 to 0.03 mm)
Endfloat ................................................................... 0.002 to 0.003 in (0.05 to 0.07 mm)

## Crankshaft
Throw:
    1725 engine ......................................................... 1.625 in (41.28 mm)
    1500 engine ......................................................... 1.410 in (35.81 mm)
Journal diameter (A) ................................................ 2.3745 to 2.3740 in (60.312 to 60.299 mm)
Journal diameter (B) ................................................ 2.365 in (60.071 mm)
Maximum regrinding undersize ................................. 0.040 in (1.01 mm)
Crankpin diameter (A) .............................................. 2.1260 to 2.1255 in (54.000 to 53.987 mm)
Crankpin diameter (B) .............................................. 2.115 in (53.721 mm)
Endfloat ................................................................... 0.002 to 0.008 in (0.05 to 0.20 mm)
Main bearing running clearance ............................... 0.0025 to 0.0010 in (0.063 to 0.025 mm)

## Connecting rods
Distance between centres:
    1725 engine ......................................................... 5.625 in (14.28 cms)
    1500 engine ......................................................... 5.845 in (14.84 cms)
Big-end bore (without bearings) ............................... 2.2715 to 2.2710 in (57.69 to 57.68 mm)
Big-end running clearance ........................................ 0.002 to 0.0015 in (0.05 to 0.03 mm)
    Later models ....................................................... 0.0022 to 0.0005 in (0.056 to 0.013 mm)
Big-end endfloat ...................................................... 0.0125 to 0.0075 in (0.317 to 0.190 mm)
Small-end bore (with bush):
    White – High grade .............................................. 0.9378 to 0.9377 in (23.820 to 23.817 mm)
    Green – Med grade .............................................. 0.9377 to 0.9376 in (23.817 to 23.815 mm)
    Yellow – Low grade ............................................. 0.9376 to 0.9375 in (23.815 to 23.812 mm)

## Gudgeon pins
Type ......................................................................... Fully-floating with circlip location
Fit in piston ............................................................. Push fit at 68°F (20°C)
Diameter:
    Service grade (blue) ............................................ 0.9378 to 0.9377 in (23.82 to 23.817 mm)
    High grade (white) ............................................... 0.9377 to 0.9376 in (23.817 to 23.815 mm)
    Med grade (green) ............................................... 0.9376 to 0.9375 in (23.815 to 23.812 mm)
    Low grade (yellow) .............................................. 0.9375 to 0.9374 in (23.812 to 23.809 mm)

## Pistons and piston rings
Piston types:
    All except Holbay engine ..................................... Slotted with split skirt
    Holbay engine ..................................................... Solid skirt
Rings:
    Compression ........................................................ 2
    Scraper ................................................................ 1
Piston diameter:
    All except Holbay engine:
        Grade A (Not available for service use) .......... 3.2096 to 3.2092 in (81.524 to 81.514 mm)
        Grade B (Not available for service use) .......... 3.2100 to 3.2096 in (81.534 to 81.524 mm)
        Grade C ......................................................... 3.2104 to 3.2100 in (81.544 to 81.534 mm)
        Grade D ......................................................... 3.2108 to 3.2104 in (81.555 to 81.544 mm)
        Grade E ......................................................... 3.2112 to 3.2108 in (81.565 to 81.555 mm)
    Oversize available above standard size (C, D or E) ........ 0.030 in (0.76 mm)
    Holbay engine:
        Grade A ......................................................... 3.2080 to 3.2076 in (81.48 to 81.47 mm)
        Grade B ......................................................... 3.2084 to 3.2080 in (81.49 to 81.48 mm)
        Grade C ......................................................... 3.2088 to 3.2084 in (81.50 to 81.49 mm)
        Grade D ......................................................... 3.2092 to 3.2088 in (81.52 to 81.50 mm)
        Grade E (for service use only) ....................... 3.2096 to 3.2092 in (81.52 to 81.51 mm)
Piston skirt clearance measured at right angle to gudgeon pin hole at
bottom of skirt:
    All except Holbay engine ..................................... 0.0006 to 0.0014 in (0.015 to 0.035 mm)
    Holbay engine ..................................................... 0.0022 to 0.003 in (0.05 to 0.07 mm)
Ring gap (Grade A bore) Top ring ............................ 0.032 to 0.024 in (0.81 to 0.60 mm)
Ring gap – Second and scraper ................................ 0.014 to 0.009 in (0.35 to 0.22 mm)
Side clearance, piston ring in groove ....................... 0.0015 to 0.0035 in (0.038 to 0.089 mm)

Piston bowl volume:

| | 1725 | 1500 |
|---|---|---|
| High compression | 6.9 to 7.5 cc | Flat top |
| Low compression | 15.3 to 15.7 cc | 6.9 to 7.5 cc |

Compression identification marks:
   HC .................................................................................... High compression
   △ .................................................................................... High compression 1500 cc
   LC .................................................................................... Low compression
   ○ .................................................................................... Low compression 1725 cc
   ◇ .................................................................................... Low compression 1500 cc/High compression 1725 cc

## Cylinder head
Material .................................................................................... Aluminium (1725 cc); Cast iron (1725 cc and 1500 cc)
Gasket type .................................................................................... Steel, copper, asbestos (aluminium head) or varnished steel pressing (cast iron head)

## Valves
Valve clearances (hot):
  All except Holbay and Arrow engines:
    255, 260 and 298 camshafts .................................................... Inlet – 0.012 in (0.30 mm)
      Exhaust – 0.014 in (0.35 mm)

    295 and 320 camshafts ............................................................ Inlet – 0.013 in (0.33 mm)
      Exhaust – 0.013 in (0.33 mm)

    Holbay engine ..................................................................... Inlet – 0.013 in (0.33 mm)
      Exhaust – 0.013 in (0.33 mm)

    Arrow engine ...................................................................... Inlet – 0.012 in (0.30 mm)
      Exhaust – 0.014 in (0.35 mm)
Valve seat and face angle .............................................................. 45°
Valve stem diameter:
  Inlet ................................................................................... 0.3110 to 0.3105 in (7.90 to 7.89 mm)
  Exhaust ............................................................................... 0.3100 to 0.3095 in (7.87 to 7.86 mm)
Valve stem to guide clearance:
  Inlet:
    Early models ...................................................................... 0.0015 to 0.003 in (0.038 to 0.076 mm)
    Later models ...................................................................... 0.001 to 0.0025 in (0.025 to 0.063 mm)
  Exhaust ............................................................................... 0.0025 to 0.004 in (0.063 to 0.102 mm)
Valve length .............................................................................. 4.66 in (118.3 mm)
Valve guides:
  OD ...................................................................................... 0.5640 to 0.5635 in (14.30 to 14.27 mm)
  Interference fit ....................................................................... 0.0025 to 0.0045 in (0.063 to 0.114 mm)
  Length:
    Inlet ................................................................................ 2.0 in (50.8 mm)
    Exhaust ............................................................................ 2.15 in (54.6 mm)
  Fitted height above head ......................................................... 0.50 in (12.7 mm)

| Valve head diameter: | **Aluminium head** | **Iron head (1725 and 1500)** |
|---|---|---|
| Inlet | 1.503 in (38.17 mm) | 1.434 in (36.42 mm) |
| Exhaust | 1.204 in (30.58 mm) | 1.174 in (29.81 mm) |

Valve springs:

| | **Aluminium head** | | **Iron head (1725 and 1500)** |
|---|---|---|---|
| Type | *Single* | *Dual* | *Single* |
| Length fitted (except Holbay): | | | |
|   Inner | – | 1.28 in (32.5 mm)* | – |
|   Outer | 1.48 in (36.7 mm) | 1.40 in (35.6 mm)* | 1.58 in (40.1 mm) |
| Length fitted (Holbay): | | | |
|   Inner | – | 1.230 in (31.2 mm) | – |
|   Outer | – | 1.400 in (35.5 mm) | – |

*Loading varies according to year of manufacture*

## Lubrication
Engine sump capacity (incl. filter) ................................................... 7.5 pints (9 US pints, 4.2 litres)
Filter capacity ........................................................................... 1 pint (1.2 US pints, 0.56 litres)
Oil pump type ............................................................................ Eccentric lobe
Pump drive ............................................................................... Skew gear from camshaft
Normal pressure (hot engine in new condition) ................................... 41 to 45 lbf/in² (2.9 to 3.2 kgf/cm²)
Oil filter type ............................................................................ Full flow – disposable

## Torque wrench settings

| | lbf ft | Nm |
|---|---|---|
| Cylinder head bolts and nuts (iron and aluminium heads, cold only) ... | 45 | 61 |
|   (Using RG 225A) ........................................ | 39 | 53 |
| Cylinder head studs in cylinder block .................................. | 11 | 15 |
| Valve rocker standard assembly: | | |
|   Nuts and bolts .......................................... | 11 | 15 |
|   Studs .................................................. | 9 | 12 |
| Manifolds to cylinder head: | | |
|   ⅜ in nuts and bolts ..................................... | 33 | 45 |
|   5/16 in nuts and bolts ................................... | 16 | 22 |

| Manifold studs in cylinder head: | lbf ft | Nm |
|---|---|---|
| $\frac{3}{8}$ in | 15 | 20 |
| $\frac{5}{16}$ in | 13 | 18 |
| Connecting rod nuts | 29 | 39 |
| Main bearing cap bolts | 55 | 75 |
| Flywheel to crankshaft bolts | 39 | 53 |
| Clutch to flywheel bolts | 16 | 22 |
| Crankshaft pulley bolt | 50 | 68 |
| Camshaft sprocket bolt | 34 | 46 |
| Sump to cylinder block | 7 | 9 |
| Spark plugs | 12 | 16 |

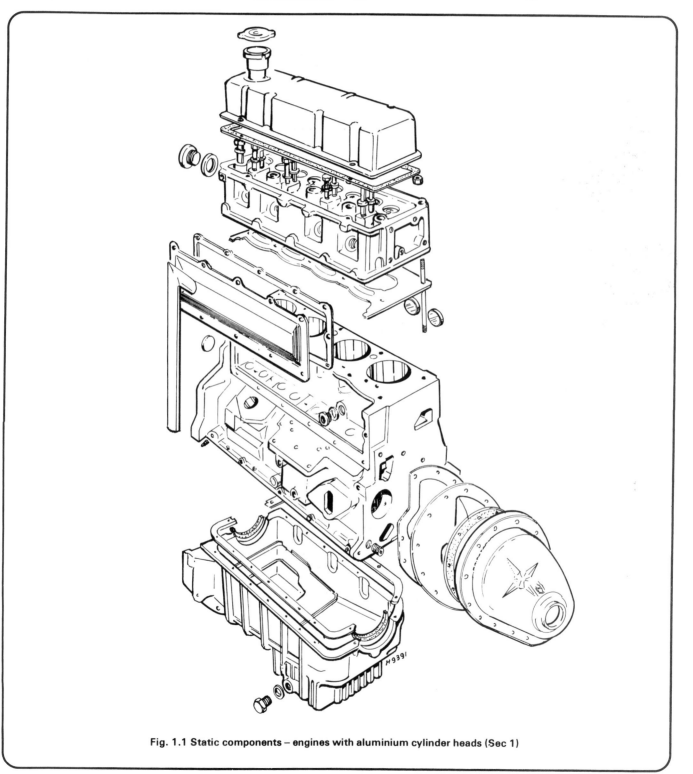

Fig. 1.1 Static components – engines with aluminium cylinder heads (Sec 1)

## 1 General description

The range of cars to which this manual refers is fitted with a 1500cc or 1725cc version of the Hillman Chrysler engine. Both versions are very similar, but whilst some engine parts are interchangeable, others are not. Care is therefore necessary to ensure that parts which look alike are in fact correct.

The 1725cc engine has a cylinder head made of aluminium for the high performance high compression versions of the range. The increase in capacity for the 1725cc engine is achieved by lengthening the stroke which means also that the throw of the crankshaft is different. The 1725cc engine is, in fact, almost exactly a 'square' engine in that the bore and stroke are almost exactly the same, whereas the 1500cc engine is quite noticeably over-square, the stroke being less than that of the larger capacity motor. Engines are all four-cylinder, fitted with two valves per cylinder which are operated by overhead rockers and pushrods from a single camshaft mounted in the right-hand side of the engine block.

The crankshaft runs in five main bearings and the endfloat is controlled by a pair of semi-circular thrust washers located in the upper half of the centre main bearing journal. The camshaft is driven by a duplex chain from a sprocket on the forward end of the crankshaft. This chain is tensioned by a hard rubber slipper supported on a steel leaf pivoting inside the cover. The camshaft, in turn, drives the oil pump through a skew gear and the oil pump driveshaft also drives the distributor.

The pistons are a fully-floating fit to the connecting rods and the gudgeon pins are retained in the piston with circlips. The connecting rod small-end bush is renewable and gudgeon pins are available in different sizes as required for the fit of the piston to the small-end of the connecting rod. The lubrication system is of the forced feed type through a full-flow oil filter to the crankshaft main bearings, connecting rod big-end bearings, camshaft bearings and valve rocker gear. The oil pump is fully submersed and is of the eccentric lobe twin rotor type.

The engine is flexibly mounted into the body frame at three points. There is one mounting bracket fitted to each side of the engine block, centrally, and the third suspension point is onto a crossmember which runs underneath the gearbox. It will be appreciated, therefore, that neither the engine nor the gearbox is fully supported when either one is removed.

The following list summarizes the differences between Holbay

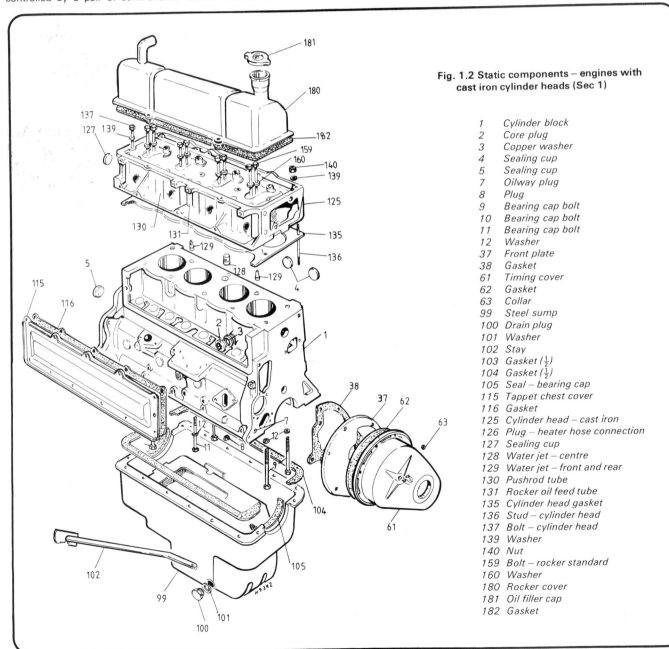

**Fig. 1.2 Static components — engines with cast iron cylinder heads (Sec 1)**

| | |
|---|---|
| 1 | Cylinder block |
| 2 | Core plug |
| 3 | Copper washer |
| 4 | Sealing cup |
| 5 | Sealing cup |
| 7 | Oilway plug |
| 8 | Plug |
| 9 | Bearing cap bolt |
| 10 | Bearing cap bolt |
| 11 | Bearing cap bolt |
| 12 | Washer |
| 37 | Front plate |
| 38 | Gasket |
| 61 | Timing cover |
| 62 | Gasket |
| 63 | Collar |
| 99 | Steel sump |
| 100 | Drain plug |
| 101 | Washer |
| 102 | Stay |
| 103 | Gasket ($\frac{1}{2}$) |
| 104 | Gasket ($\frac{1}{2}$) |
| 105 | Seal – bearing cap |
| 115 | Tappet chest cover |
| 116 | Gasket |
| 125 | Cylinder head – cast iron |
| 126 | Plug – heater hose connection |
| 127 | Sealing cup |
| 128 | Water jet – centre |
| 129 | Water jet – front and rear |
| 130 | Pushrod tube |
| 131 | Rocker oil feed tube |
| 135 | Cylinder head gasket |
| 136 | Stud – cylinder head |
| 137 | Bolt – cylinder head |
| 139 | Washer |
| 140 | Nut |
| 159 | Bolt – rocker standard |
| 160 | Washer |
| 180 | Rocker cover |
| 181 | Oil filler cap |
| 182 | Gasket |

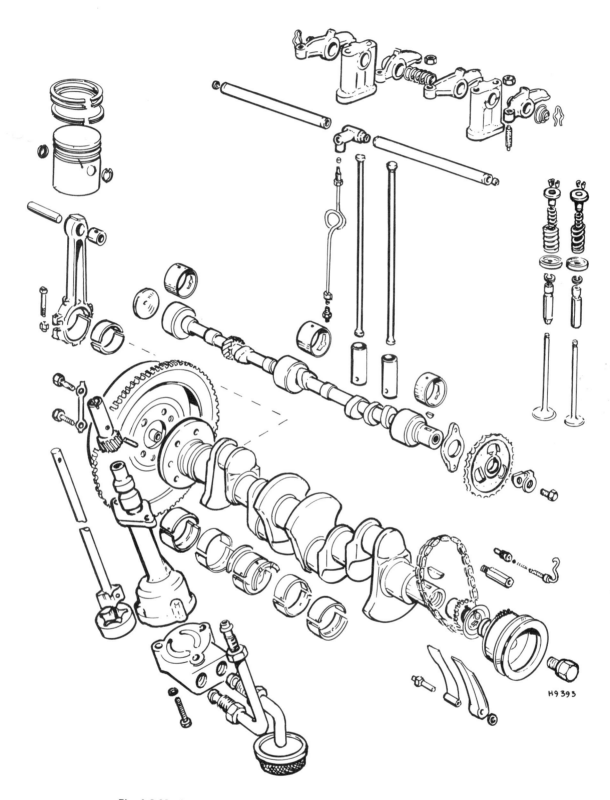

H9393

Fig. 1.3 Moving components – engines with aluminium cylinder heads (Sec 1)

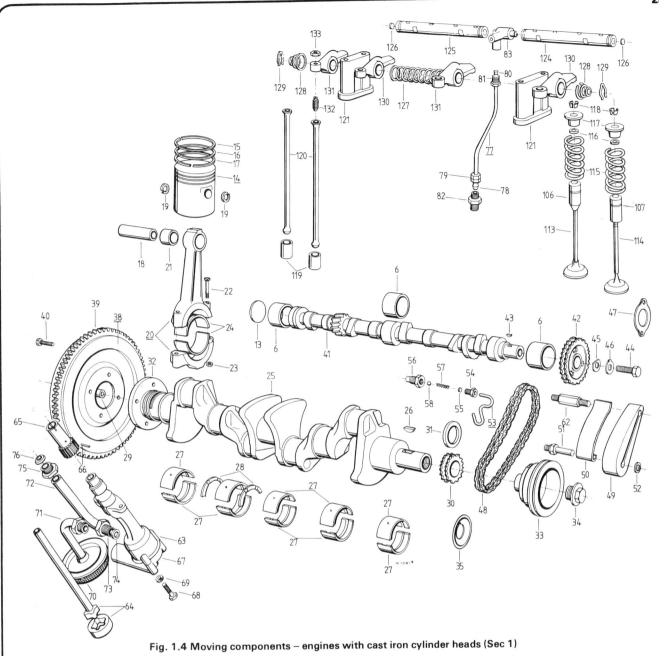

**Fig. 1.4 Moving components – engines with cast iron cylinder heads (Sec 1)**

| | | | |
|---|---|---|---|
| 6 | Bearing – camshaft | 34 | Pulley bolt |
| 13 | Camshaft sealing disc | 35 | Oil thrower |
| 14 | Piston assembly | 38 | Flywheel |
| 15 | Top ring – compression | 39 | Starter ring |
| 16 | Lower ring – compression | 40 | Flywheel bolt |
| 17 | Scraper ring | 41 | Camshaft |
| 18 | Gudgeon pin | 42 | Timing sprocket |
| 19 | Circlip | 43 | Woodruff key |
| 20 | Connecting rod | 44 | Bolt |
| 21 | Small-end bush | 45 | Retaining washer |
| 22 | Connecting rod cap bolt | 46 | Tab washer |
| 23 | Nut | 47 | Thrust plate |
| 24 | Big-end bearing shells | 48 | Timing chain |
| 25 | Crankshaft | 49 | Tensioner pad |
| 26 | Woodruff key | 50 | Tensioner blade |
| 27 | Main bearing shells | 51 | Pivot pin |
| 28 | Endfloat thrust washers | 52 | Washer |
| 29 | Bush – input shaft | 53 | Oil pipe |
| 30 | Timing sprocket | 54 | Nut |
| 31 | Damper ring | 55 | Olive |
| 32 | Flywheel dowel | 56 | Adaptor |
| 33 | Pulley wheel | 57 | Spring |

| | | | |
|---|---|---|---|
| 58 | Ball | 83 | Adaptor |
| 62 | Stud | 100 | Valve guide – inlet |
| 63 | Oil pump body | 107 | Valve guide – exhaust |
| 64 | Oil pump shaft and rotor | 113 | Inlet valve |
| 65 | Drivegear | 114 | Exhaust valve |
| 66 | Dowel pin | 115 | Valve spring |
| 67 | End cover | 116 | Sealing ring |
| 68 | Cover screw | 117 | Cup |
| 69 | Spring washer | 118 | Cotter (collets) |
| 70 | Strainer | 119 | Tappet |
| 71 | Locknut | 120 | Pushrod |
| 72 | Delivery pipe | 121 | Rocker shaft – standard |
| 73 | Nut – pipe to pump | 124 | Rocker shaft – front |
| 74 | Olive | 125 | Rocker shaft – rear |
| 75 | Nut – pipe to block | 126 | Plug |
| 76 | Olive | 127 | Inner spring |
| 77 | Pipe – rocker oil feed | 128 | Outer spring |
| 78 | Olive | 129 | Retaining clip |
| 79 | Nut | 130 | Rocker (Nos 1, 3, 5, & 7) |
| 80 | Olive | 131 | Rocker (Nos 2, 4, 6 & 8) |
| 81 | Nut | 132 | Adjusting screw |
| 82 | Union | 133 | Locknut |

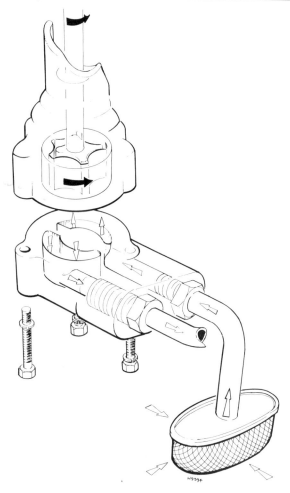

Fig. 1.5 Cutaway drawing of oil pump, showing flow lines (Sec 1)

engines fitted to GLS models and standard 1725cc engines with an aluminium head:

(a) *Cylinder head – modified ports and combustion chambers*
(b) *Exhaust valves – new material specification*
(c) *Valve springs – different rating and improved quality*
(d) *Valve spring cups – hardened*
(e) *Pushrods – tubular*
(f) *Valve/rocker clearances – revised*
(g) *Rocker cover – cast aluminium*
(h) *Inlet manifold – four branch type*
(j) *Exhaust manifold – new design*
(k) *Manifold/head gasket – new design*
(l) *Camshaft – new design (also used on some other models – see Specifications)*
(m) *Piston – flat top, similar to Minx 1500cc piston but 0.4 in (10 mm) shorter in overall height. (For clearance and grading see Specifications)*
(n) *Flywheel – new design for 8½ in (216 mm) diameter clutch*
(p) *Oil filter base – tapping for temperature gauge transmitter*
(q) *Distributor – new model without vacuum advance. Vacuum retard on later models*

## 2  Routine maintenance

1    Once a week, or more often if high mileages are being driven, remove the oil level dipstick and check the level of the oil in the sump, which should be at the full mark. Top-up the level with the recommended grade of oil (see Recommended Lubricants). If an engine appears to be using oil at a rate of more than 1 pint per 500 miles it should be considered as excessive and steps should be taken to discover whether there is a leak in the system or whether the oil is being consumed due to excessive wear in the engine.

2    Every 5000 miles run the engine until it is hot. Then place a container with a minimum capacity of one gallon under the drain plug in the sump, undo the drain plug and allow the old oil to drain out for at least ten minutes. The oil filter cartridge should also be unscrewed and a new one fitted as described in Section 20 of this Chapter.

3    Carefully, clean the drain plug and make sure that the washer is clean and intact. Refit the plug in the sump, tightening it firmly. Then refill the sump with 7½ pints of the recommended oil, run the engine and recheck the level on the dipstick. Examine the point where the new filter cartridge has been screwed in to make sure that there are no oil leaks of any sort.

4    If the car is regularly used in extreme conditions of heat, cold or excessively dusty atmospheres, it is advantageous to change the engine oil more often. In such circumstances a frequency of 3000 miles between changes is recommended.

## 3  Major operations possible with engine in place

1    The following work may be conveniently carried out with the engine in place:

(a) *Removal and refitting of the cylinder head assembly*
(b) *Removal and refitting of the clutch assembly*
(c) *Removal and refitting of the engine front mountings*
(d) *Removal and refitting of the timing chain cover, timing chain and timing chain sprockets*

2    The following work can be carried out with the engine still mounted in the car but it is preferable, if possible, to remove the engine. If the engine is left in position, great care must be taken to ensure that all the parts removed and refitted are kept scrupulously clean. It is very easy for extraneous dirt to find its way where it should not be when the engine is still in place in the car frame:

(a) *Removal and refitting of the sump*
(b) *Removal and refitting of the oil pump*
(c) *Removal and refitting of the connecting rod big-end bearings*
(d) *Removal and refitting of pistons and connecting rods (after the removal of the cylinder head and sump)*
(e) *Removal and refitting of the camshaft*
(f) *Removal and refitting of the flywheel (after removing the gearbox and clutch)*
(g) *Removal and refitting of the crankshaft main bearing shells*

## 4  Major operations possible with engine removed

The following work can only be carried out with the engine removed:

(a) *Removal and refitting of the crankshaft*
(b) *Renewal of the camshaft bearings*

## 5  Engine – removal

1    The description that follows will assume that the engine is being removed from the car by itself, ie with the gearbox left in the car. For occasions when it is required to remove the engine and gearbox together as one unit from the car, and for vehicles with automatic transmission, information is supplied at the end of this Section. It is necessary to disconnect and remove several items from the engine before it can be lifted from the car, and these are listed in the description which follows. Detailed removal procedures for the individual items will be found in the appropriate Chapters. For example, where an instruction to 'remove carburettor' is given, the full implication of this removal will be given in Chapter 3. Before starting work on the actual removal of the engine, it is well worth while to spend some time getting the engine thoroughly cleaned off away from the area where the removal and subsequent dismantling is to take place. If this cleaning can be done at a service station which may be equipped with pressure cleaning equipment, so much the better. Otherwise, use paraffin and stiff brushes and scrapers to remove the bulk of the caked on dirt before removing the engine. The final, thorough cleaning of the exterior of the engine may be left until it is removed from the car.

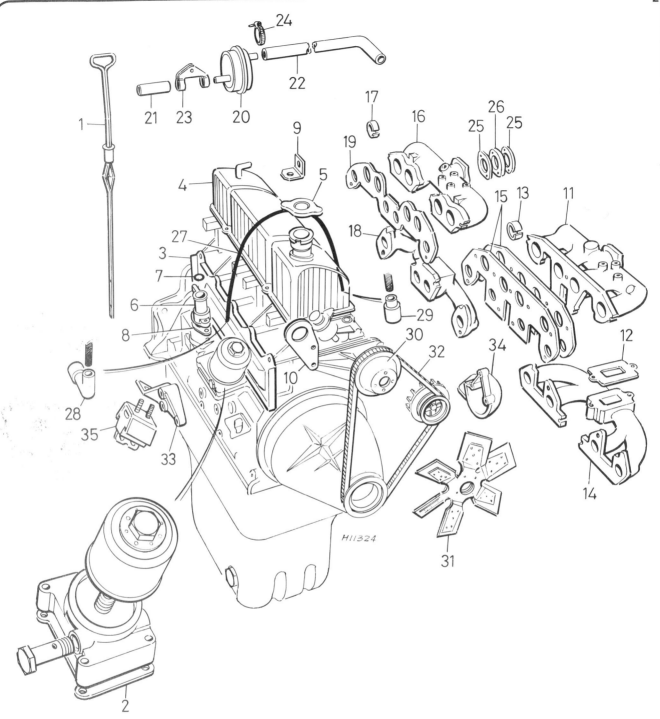

**Fig. 1.6 Engine ancillary attachments – typical (Sec 5)**

| | |
|---|---|
| 1 | Dipstick |
| 2 | Gasket |
| 3 | Tappet cover |
| 4 | Rocker cover |
| 5 | Filler cap (oil) |
| 6 | Distributor drive bracket |
| 7 | Oil seal |
| 8 | Gasket |
| 9 | Lifting bracket |
| 10 | Slinging eye |
| 11 | Inlet manifold aluminium head |
| 12 | Hot spot plate |
| 13 | Locating ring |
| 14 | Exhaust manifold aluminium head |
| 15 | Manifold gaskets aluminium head |
| 16 | Inlet manifold iron head |
| 17 | Locating ring |
| 18 | Exhaust manifold iron head |
| 19 | Manifold gaskets iron head |
| 20 | Flame trap |
| 21 | Breather hose |
| 22 | Breather hose |
| 23 | Support sleeve |
| 24 | Hose clip |
| 25 | Carburettor gaskets |
| 26 | Insulating washer |
| 27 | Suction pipe |
| 28 | Elbow |
| 29 | Sleeve |
| 30 | Fan pulley |
| 31 | Fan |
| 32 | Fanbelt |
| 33 | Right-hand engine mounting bracket |
| 34 | Left-hand engine mounting bracket |
| 35 | Mounting rubber |

Decide whether you are going to jack-up the car and support it on axle stands or raise the front end of the car onto wheel ramps. If the latter method, run the car up now (and chock the rear wheels) whilst you still have engine power available. Remember that with the front wheels supported on ramps, the working height and engine lifting height is going to be increased. If stands are to be used, the front of the car can be jacked up later when ready.

2   Once you are sure that the car is in the correct position, (which should be on level ground or level floor), the work of removing the engine may begin.

3   Open the bonnet and disconnect the battery leads and, having unscrewed the battery clamps, remove the battery from the car.

4   With the bonnet propped open, mark the position of the bonnet hinges before removing the hinge clamping bolts. It is easier if you have somebody to help you at the next stage, to lift the bonnet off. Care is required if damage is to be avoided to the surrounding paintwork as the bonnet is quite heavy and could easily slip and scratch the paint nearby. It can be done single-handed, however, by supporting the rear of the bonnet corners by blocks of wood. Full details can be found in Chapter 12. When the bonnet is removed, place it somewhere where it cannot be damaged and where the edges will not be scratched or chipped by hard surfaces.

5   Drain the oil from the sump of the engine.

6   Drain the liquid from the cooling system.

7   Detach both hose pipes from the top and bottom of the radiator by slackening the hose clips and pulling the pipes carefully from the radiator shell. Detach the heater water hoses from their connections on the water pump body at the front of the engine. Also unclip the two hoses from the top of the cylinder head. When this has been done, both of these hoses may be put to one side, clear of the engine.

8   Undo the four bolts which secure the radiator to the front body panel of the car, holding the radiator vertical to prevent it being damaged on the fan blades, lift it out carefully.

9   Detach the high tension lead from the centre of the coil by simply pulling it out. Then pull all the high tension leads off the spark plugs. After unclipping the distributor cap, the cap and leads may be lifted away. Disconnect the leads from the rear of the dynamo or alternator.

10   Disconnect the low tension lead from one of the coil terminals to the distributor. Ensure that all leads removed are in some way identifiable for refitting purposes. If their original colour coding has become indistinct, strong adhesive tape suitably marked or some other method of identification should be employed.

11   Disconnect the lead wire from the terminal on the thermostat sender unit, mounted in the water pump housing.

12   Disconnect the wire lead attached to the oil pressure gauge sender unit underneath the distributor in the side of the block.

13   Remove the carburettors. Although not essential, this is done for safety's sake. Disconnect the earthing cable strip which is attached to one of the bolts securing the timing cover case to the front of the engine. The other end of the cable is attached to the body frame nearby (photo). Undo the union connecting the fuel pipe to the inlet side of the fuel pump on the right-hand side of the engine.

14   Remove the nut on the terminal of the starter motor securing the lead from the battery.

15   Detach the exhaust pipe from the exhaust manifold by unscrewing the two nuts which hold the flange of the pipe to the manifold.

16   Remove the two bolts and the nuts holding the starter motor to the clutch flywheel bellhousing and remove the starter motor.

17   It is now time to go underneath the car, so if it has not already been put up on wheel ramps, and it is necesary to support it and raise it at the front on stands, do so now. It is best if the stands are placed underneath the side frame members just behind the anti-roll bar clamps. It is most important that the car is properly and firmly supported because there are some bolts to be undone which may be quite stiff and the force required to turn them could well move the car off a shaky form of support.

18   Undo the nuts and bolts securing the clutch hydraulic slave cylinder to the bellhousing and lift it to one side. It is not necessary to disconnect any of the hydraulic lines for this, but ensure that nobody inadvertently puts his foot on the clutch pedal otherwise the piston will blow out of the cylinder and deposit hydraulic fluid either over your floor or somebody underneath the car.

19   Remove the two clamps which hold the centre of the anti-roll bar to the side frame members. Each clamp is held by two bolts which locate into captive nuts in the side frame members. It is necessary to do this in order to enable the torsion bar to drop down a few inches.

This will permit the sump of the engine to clear the torsion bar when the engine is drawn forward eventually, to detach it from the gearbox input shaft (photo).

20   Remove the four bolts which hold the two stays from the sump to the bellhousing. These stays act as stiffeners for the whole engine and gearbox assembly. The forward ends of the stays may next be detached from the side of the sump. Note that each stay is held by a bolt and a nut over a stud at the forward end. Do not lose the specially shaped nut as this is required to line up the stay on assembly (photo). On steel sump models, remove the stay brackets and flywheel coverplate.

21   Where an engine mounting damper is fitted, it should be removed by taking out the $\frac{1}{2}$ in AF nut, spring washer and flat washer from the upper mounting, followed by the $\frac{9}{16}$ in AF bolt and shakeproof washer from the lower mounting. Lift out the damper by moving its upper end over the threaded end of the upper mounting spindle.

22   If everything has been done correctly, the engine is now attached to the car at only three positions, namely, the left and right-hand side engine mountings and by the top bolts onto the gearbox bellhousing. Before proceeding further, it will be necessary to provide support underneath the gearbox so it will not tip forward when the engine is taken away from it. This should now be done either using a jack or supporting the gearbox under the drain plug with a suitable stand or wooden blocks. This must be done before any attempt is made to detach the engine from its mountings. The engine should now be supported by the hoist of whichever type is being used, so that the weight of it may be taken before disconnecting the mounting brackets. On the left-hand side of the cylinder head, at the front and rear, are two holding-down studs each with two nuts. In addition to the hose clips which are attached to them, the rear stud also has a strong lifting bracket fitted to it. It is desirable to obtain another bracket exactly the same as this, which should then be fitted underneath the top nut of the forward stud. A sling between these two brackets is the best means of lifting the engine out. It is possible to use the eye of the large plate bracket attached to the front right-hand side of the engine block, but this would impart a slight twist when the engine is lifted, making it difficult to draw the engine forward off the gearbox input shaft. This twist causes even greater problems when the engine is being refitted.

23   Once the sling has been satisfactorily attached, the strain should be taken on it sufficiently to permit the engine mounting bracket bolts to be removed without undue strain or without allowing the engine to drop.

24   The engine mountings should be undone by using the two bolts which attach the lower part of the flexible mounting to the chassis frame. Do not detach the bracket on the engine from the top of the mounting by undoing the two uppermost nuts. If the latter method is used it may prove very difficult, if not impossible, to lift the engine vertically as the mounting studs will be inclined at an angle of 45° (photo).

25   The remainder of the bolts holding the gearbox bellhousing to the engine should now be removed. It should be noted that one of the long bolts on the lower left-hand side of the bellhousing is, in fact, a dowel pin and once the nut has been removed it is not necessary to attempt to remove it as it will remain in place when the engine is drawn away (photos).

26   With all attachments now removed (other than the connection between the engine and gearbox input shaft) the whole engine should be drawn forward to disengage it from the gearbox. This normally presents no difficulties but in case the two are reluctant to part it will be necessary, perhaps, to rock it to get it to come forward. It is important to remember that the engine should not be raised or lowered at this stage in an attempt to separate it from the gearbox. Until clear of the gearbox input shaft, any upwards or downwards strain could cause severe damage to the clutch or the gearbox (photo).

27   Once the engine has been drawn forward from the gearbox, it may be lifted straight up and clear of the car without any tilting whatsoever (photos).

28   If the engine is removed together with the gearbox, the procedures are exactly the same except that the bolts which join the engine and gearbox together at the bellhousing do not have to be removed. The starter motor may also remain in place.

29   In addition, remove the propeller shaft (see Chapter 7) and then the gearbox supporting crossmember, allowing the rear end of the gearbox to drop down sufficiently for the engine to be tilted up to clear it through the engine compartment on the way out. Details of removal of the crossmember may be found in Chapter 6 under the Section

5.13 Remove the earth cable

5.19 Remove the anti-roll bar clamps

5.20 Remove the stay braces

5.24 Remove the engine mounting bolts

5.25a Remove the bellhousing bolts

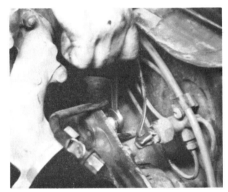

5.25b Remove the bellhousing bolts

5.26 Draw engine forward from gearbox before lifting

5.27a Lifting the engine

5.27b Removing the engine from the car

concerned with gearbox removal. It will also be necessary to remove the gear change lever from inside the car as also described in Chapter 6.

30 The gearbox crossmember should only be removed after the full weight of the engine has been supported at the front and the engine mountings have been unbolted. As soon as this situation is reached, a support in the form of a jack or suitable blocks should be placed under the gearbox and the gearbox crossmember support, detached from the bodywork of the car and then from the bottom of the gearbox itself.

31 Detach the speedometer cable from the side of the gearbox by unscrewing the milled retaining collar. Disconnect the steering centre track rod, the clutch slave cylinder, and the leads from the reversing light switch.

32 Without moving the support immediately from under the gearbox, start to lift the engine forward and up. The gearbox itself will have to be lowered, which will mean gradual or total removal of the support which has been placed underneath it. Prepare to collect any oil which

may drop from the gearbox rear extension cover. Allow the gearbox to come to rest on the floor, but do not let it drop or scrape along the floor. By a gradual process of lifting and moving forward on the hoist, the whole assembly can be drawn up through the engine compartment. The operation is more difficult than lifting the engine out by itself, however, and it is strongly advised that additional help should be on hand to ensure that accidents and damage do not occur.

33 Once the engine is clear of the car, either with or without the gearbox attached, lower it as soon as possible to the ground or area where it is to be externally cleaned. It is better if this place is not close to where the engine is to be dismantled. Further cleaning at this stage is well worth the time spent on it as the risk of filth and grit getting into the engine later on is greatly reduced. Be careful not to let paraffin or cleaning fluids of any kind contaminate the clutch friction disc during this process. Once the engine is cleaned, put it in the position where it is to be dismantled and prop it securely to prevent any damage either to itself or to the person concerned.

## Cars with automatic transmission – Model 35

34 On these vehicles, it is only possible to remove and refit the engine complete with the automatic transmission.

35 Disconnect the battery, then drain sufficient water from the cooling system to permit removal of the top hose.

36 If necessary, remove the air cleaner, rocker cover and distributor cap.

37 Remove the throttle operating shaft from the carburettor and its bearing.

38 If necessary, disconnect the brake servo hose from the manifold.

39 Disconnect the downshift cable clevis from its yoke on the cable end by removing the nut at its attachment position.

40 Disconnect and plug the fuel feed pipe.

41 Disconnect the transmission filler tube at its cylinder head end.

42 Where applicable, remove the body tunnel cover plate and undo the filler tube nut. Pull the tube out of the transmission case.

43 Disconnect the starter motor heavy lead and, where applicable, the oil gauge feed pipe.

44 Using a suitable attachment bracket and lifting tackle, take the weight of the engine at the rear lifting eye.

45 From beneath the car, drain the transmission fluid, but beware of scalding if the fluid is hot.

46 Disconnect the exhaust pipe(s) and remove the exhaust system as necessary for access purposes.

47 Disconnect the starter inhibitor switch wires and the speedometer cable.

48 Remove the propeller shaft (refer to Chapter 7, Sections 3 and 4).

49 Disconnect the transmission selector linkage.

50 Ensure the weight is being taken by the lifting tackle. Undo and remove the transmission rear mounting rubbers and crossmember.

51 Lower the engine to give access to the transmission filler tube nut (where not previously removed), then remove the filler tube. Lift engine again to approximately the normal position. Place a support under the transmission.

52 Remove the engine mountings as described in paragraph 24.

53 Remove the engine and transmission unit, generally as described in paragraphs 29 to 33. References therein to the propeller shaft and crossmember should be ignored.

54 If the torque converter is to be removed, disconnect the two stay bars from the bellhousing to the sump (where applicable).

55 Commencing with the two bottom bolts, remove all six bolts from the transmission to converter housing, using a suitable cranked spanner.

56 With a container beneath the transmission to catch spilt fluid, withdraw the gearbox rearwards and downwards.

57 To remove the converter housing, disconnect and remove the starter motor.

58 Remove the bottom front coverplate and the stay brackets to the cylinder block (where applicable).

59 Remove the retaining bolts and lift away the housing.

60 The converter can be removed, after removal of the housing, by taking out the four special bolts. On engines with aluminium sumps, a special spanner will be required unless the sump is removed (Fig. 1.7).

## Cars with automatic transmission – Model 45

61 On these vehicles, it is only possible to remove and refit the engine complete with the automatic transmission.

62 Disconnect the battery, then drain sufficient water from the cooling system to permit removal of the top hose.

63 Loosen the exhaust manifold flange nuts.

64 Remove the plenum chamber drain hose.

65 Disconnect the inner and outer downshift cables at the carburettor.

66 From beneath the car, remove the propeller shaft (refer to Chapter 7, Sections 3 and 4).

67 Remove the sump stiffener brackets (where applicable) and the dirt shield.

68 On twin carburettor models, loosen the exhaust downpipe/exhaust pipe joint.

69 Remove the transmission guard plate.

70 Using a suitable separator, disconnect the steering tie-rod at the drop arm and idle arm. Lift the ball-pins free and allow the tie-rod to hang from the outer balljoints.

71 Place a suitable container in position, loosen the oil filler tube union nut and drain the oil.

72 Disconnect and plug the oil cooler lines at the transmission.

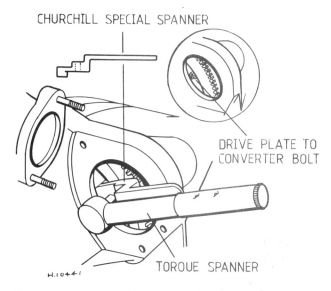

**Fig. 1.7 Using the special spanner and a torque wrench on the converter/driveplate bolts. The tool illustrated is Churchill part No RG523 (Sec 5)**

73 Disconnect the selector lever linkage, noting whether the rod is inside or outside the lever.

74 Disconnect the speedometer cable and inhibitor switch wiring, noting the wire colours.

75 Ensure the weight is being taken by the lifting tackle. Undo and remove the transmission rear mounting rubbers and crossmember.

76 Lower the engine to give access to the transmission filler tube nut, then remove the filler tube. Lift the engine again, to approximately the normal position. Place a support under the transmission.

77 Remove the engine mountings as described in paragraph 24.

78 Remove the engine and transmission unit, generally as described in paragraphs 29 to 33. References therein to the propeller shaft and crossmember should be ignored.

79 To remove the torque converter, turn the crankshaft as necessary and remove the torque converter to driveplate bolts.

80 Remove the bolts and nuts securing the torque converter housing to the engine and starter motor.

81 Move the transmission and torque converter away from the engine, ensuring the torque converter does not separate from the transmission.

## 6 Engine dismantling – general

1 It is necessary to have as much space available as possible, properly cleaned in advance, to facilitate both detailed dismantling and the systematic storage of clean items.

2 If a suitable, strong workbench is not available, it is safer to carry out engine dismantling on the ground. In this case, ensure the unit cannot topple to cause damage or injury.

3 Before starting any dismantling, the exterior of the engine should be cleaned thoroughly with a stiff brush, using either paraffin or one of the proprietary grease solvents which should then be washed off with water.

4 As the engine is dismantled, clean each part and keep related items together. Loosely refit nuts, bolts and washers as far as possible, thus confirming their correct locations. Clean items should be covered, or placed in polythene bags or other suitable containers, to prevent ingress of dust, grit and moisture.

5 Parts which have oilways should not be washed with paraffin, and a petrol-moistened rag should be employed for these items. Taking such parts to an engineering shop, to have the oilways blown out with a high-pressure line, is time well spent.

## 7 Engine dismantling – ancillaries

1 If you are intending to obtain an exchange engine complete, or what is called a short motor (which is basically the cylinder block, crankshaft and pistons), it will be necessary first of all to remove all those parts of the engine which are not included in the exchange. If you are stripping the engine completely yourself, with the likelihood of some outside work to be done by specialists, all these items will be taken off anyway.

2 Check with the suppliers of the complete exchange replacement unit which items should be removed. The following list provides a general guide:

(a) *Dynamo or alternator – Chapter 10*
(b) *Distributor – Chapter 4*
(c) *Thermostat and housing – Chapter 2*
(d) *Oil filter (expendable) – Chapter 1*
(e) *Carburettor(s) – Chapter 3*
(f) *Inlet manifold – Chapter 1*
(g) *Exhaust manifold – Chapter 1*
(h) *Water pump – Chapter 2*
(j) *Fuel pump – Chapter 3*
(k) *Engine mounting brackets – Chapter 1*

3 If an exchange replacement short motor (half-engine) only is being purchased, the following additional items should be removed:

(a) *Cylinder head complete with valve rocker gear*
(b) *Flywheel*
(c) *Sump*
(d) *Oil pump*

## 8 Valve rocker gear – removal

1 The valve rocker gear will need to be removed if it is desired to remove the cylinder head, with the engine either in or out of the car.

2 Remove the four screws which secure the rocker box cover to the cylinder head. It will be necessary to disconnect the breather pipe which goes into the cover and to unclip the high tension plug leads from the rear end of the engine to remove it.

3 The rocker gear may be removed as an assembly complete. The shaft and rocker arms are mounted on four standards, each of which is held to the head by two long bolts. All eight bolts should be undone evenly so as to permit any springs which may be in compression to ease themselves into their free state without unduly distorting the rocker shaft during the process of removal. Undo the small brass union which connects the oil feed pipe to the T-piece in the centre of the rocker shaft assembly. By gripping the assembly with a hand at each end, it may now be lifted straight up off the head. Be careful not to let it separate in the centre as it will come apart quite easily, and the T-piece may drop somewhere difficult to reach.

## 9 Inlet and exhaust manifold – removal

### Single carburettor type

1 If the engine is being dismantled completely or if the cylinder head is being removed, it is not necessary to detach either the inlet or exhaust manifold.

2 Both manifolds must be removed together as they are bolted together and mounted to the engine on a common gasket.

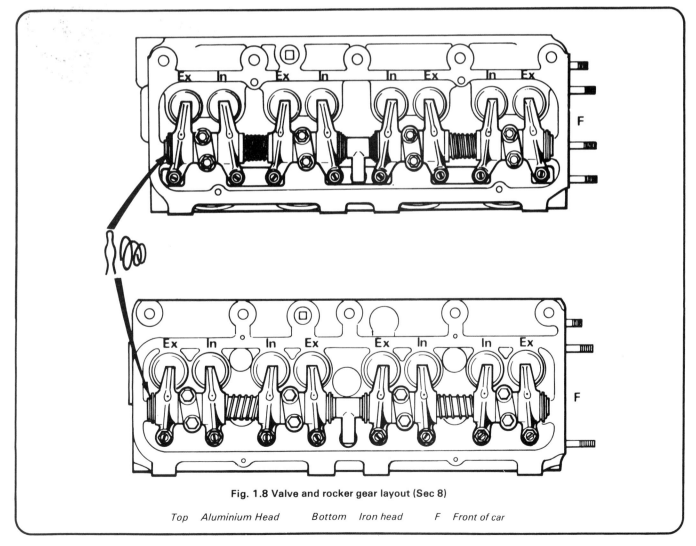

**Fig. 1.8 Valve and rocker gear layout (Sec 8)**

*Top    Aluminium Head        Bottom    Iron head        F    Front of car*

3  First disconnect the carburettor controls and fuel pipe connections to the carburettor. Remove the carburettor, together with its air cleaner from the inlet manifold flange. Details are given in Chapter 3. Disconnect the exhaust pipe from the flange on the exhaust manifold by undoing the two securing nuts. Remove the six nuts and three bolts which hold the manifolds to the cylinder head. Lift off the manifolds.

4  If the two manifolds are to be separated, the two bolts holding them together should be removed. Between the two manifolds there is a heat deflector plate. This has a hole in the centre which is normally positioned centrally above the aperture in the flange on the exhaust manifold.

### Twin carburettor type

5  Partially drain the cooling system to permit removal of the inlet and outlet hoses from their connections on the inlet manifold.

6  Remove the air cleaner (refer to Chapter 3 if necessary).

7  Disconnect the brake servo vacuum pipe from the inlet manifold.

8  Remove the accelerator cable bracket (two $\frac{7}{16}$ in AF nuts), then disconnect the cable from the carburettor throttle lever.

9  Disconnect both choke cables at the carburettors and the fuel feed pipe at the T-piece.

10  Remove one $\frac{9}{16}$ in AF nut, two $\frac{1}{2}$ in AF bolts and two $\frac{9}{16}$ in AF bolts and lift away the inlet manifold complete with the carburettors.

11  Remove the four $\frac{1}{2}$ AF steel nuts and four $\frac{1}{2}$ in AF bolts, and four $\frac{1}{2}$ in AF brass nuts on the exhaust pipe flange and lift away the exhaust manifold.

### Holbay engine

12  The inlet manifold is basically identical to the twin carburettor version described earlier in this Section, but there are two fixing nuts in the centre, and a $\frac{5}{16}$ in Allen key is required to remove the manifold end screws. There is no need to remove the carburettors.

13  Remove the exhaust manifold by following the procedure described for twin carburettor versions earlier in this Section. Note the clip which secures the manifold to the exhaust pipe after the Y-junction.

14  Note that both manifolds must be removed in order to remove the cylinder head on the Holbay engine.

## 10  Cylinder head – removal

1  The cylinder head may be removed with the engine either in or out of the car.

2  If the engine is to remain in the car, the following must be done first.

3  Drain the cooling system.

4  Remove the air cleaner from the carburettor, and preferably remove the carburettor also as a safety precaution.

5  Disconnect the top radiator hose from either the radiator or the cylinder head.

6  Remove the electrical lead from the water temperature gauge sender unit at the front of the cylinder head.

7  Disconnect all the leads from the spark plugs.

8  Disconnect the heater water pipes from the water pump housing at the front of the cylinder head and also unclip them from the two clips mounted onto the cylinder head studs (photos).

9  Disconnect the fuel feed pipe and detach it from its clip, bolted to the front of the cylinder head (photo).

10  Disconnect the exhaust pipe from the exhaust manifold by unscrewing the nuts underneath the flange.

11  With the foregoing completed, removal of the cylinder head is now the same whether the engine is in or out of the car. Remove the screws which hold the top edge of the tappet cover to the cylinder head and *slacken* the other screws which hold the bottom edge of the tappet cover to the cylinder block. Remove the rocker cover and valve rocker gear assembly.

12  Next, carefully remove all the pushrods. When lifting them out, make sure they are not still attached to the tappets. If the tappets are inadvertently lifted up, they could become dislodged inside the tappet chest, involving a lot of extra work when the head is refitted. This, of course, applies only when the engine is in the car. Keep the pushrods in the same order by putting them through a numbered piece of pierced cardboard. The head is held in position by eight bolts and two nuts on studs, one at the front and one at the rear on the left-hand side of the head. These bolts and nuts should be slackened off in reverse

order of the tightening sequence, as indicated in Fig. 1.23.

13  It should now be possible to lift the head straight off the top of the cylinder block, complete with the manifolds which provide a useful hand-hold. Take care not to damage the rocker oil supply pipe. Should there be any difficulty in removing the head, no attempt should be made to force any form of lever into the space between the head and cylinder block. This could cause damage to the finely machined surfaces of the two parts. With the engine still in the car, it is possible to use the piston compression to help lift the head and break the tight joint. The engine can be turned either by putting the car in gear and moving it forwards or backwards, or re-connecting the battery, and giving the engine a quick turn on the starter motor. With the engine out of the car, it may be necessary to strike against the side of the head with a wooden block or soft-faced mallet. After removing the head, remove the cylinder head gasket.

### Holbay engine

14  The procedure for cylinder head removal is similar to that for standard versions. It is necessary, however, to remove the inlet manifold and disconnect the exhaust manifold, before removal of the head.

## 11  Sump – removal

1  Removal of the sump with the engine in the car is possible, but not easy. The engine must be removed from its forward mountings, and for those engines fitted with an aluminium cylinder head (and therefore an aluminium sump) it will be necessary to drop the front axle crossmember away from the bodywork side frame.

2  Disconnect the battery. Drain the engine oil.

3  On steel sump engines only, drain the cooling system and remove the top and bottom hoses to prevent strain on radiator stubs.

4  Raise the car sufficiently high so it is possible to work underneath it comfortably. If working with the car over a pit or on a ramp, it should also be raised sufficiently to allow the wheels to clear the ground. The car must then be supported on proper body stands.

5  The weight of the engine must be supported during the sump removal operation, and this can be done by using a conventional hoist and supporting the engine as would be done for removing it.

6  Remove the sump to bellhousing stay brackets (see Section 5, paragraph 20).

### Steel sump

7  Take the weight of the engine on the hoist and disconnect the engine mountings (see Section 5, paragraph 22).

8  Remove the anti-roll bar (see Chapter 11).

9  Raise the engine, taking care that wiring and controls which remain connected are not damaged.

10  Remove sump bolts and the sump by drawing it forward and lowering it to clear the internal oil pump screen filler.

### Aluminium sump

11  Loosen the sump bolts and remove most of them, leaving enough to prevent the sump from falling.

12  Disconnect the engine mountings and remove the anti-roll bar. Remove the four $\frac{5}{8}$ in AF bolts securing the front crossmember to the underframe. Pull down the crossmember against the springs, and keep down by placing wooden blocks between the ends of the crossmember and the sideframes. Take great care that the front brake flexible hoses are not strained during this operation, illustrated in Fig. 1.9.

13  Complete removal of the sump.

14  With the engine on the bench, sump removal is straightforward, although it is much better if the cylinder head is also removed so the engine can be stood inverted. Before the engine is inverted, see precautions under the Section headed 'Tappets – removal', and also remove the rocker oil supply pipe.

## 12  Crankshaft pulley, timing gear and cover – removal

1  Removal of the crankshaft pulley, timing gear cover and timing gear will be necessary if the timing chain should be slack and noisy, or the tensioner needs attention. It is possible to carry out this work with

10.8a Disconnect the heater hoses ...

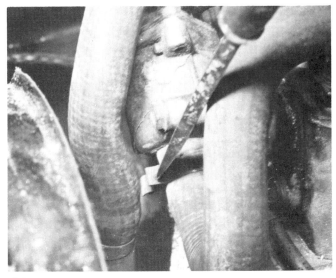

10.8b ... from the water pump ...

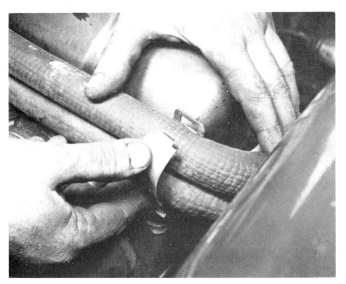

10.8c ... and unclip them

10.9 Detach the fuel pipe clip

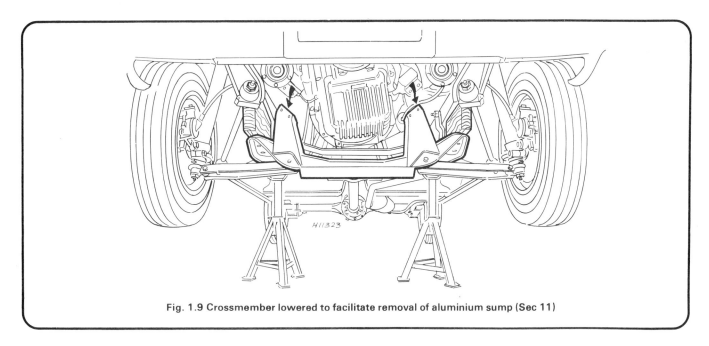

Fig. 1.9 Crossmember lowered to facilitate removal of aluminium sump (Sec 11)

the engine in the car. If the engine *is* in the car, first remove the radiator completely as described in Chapter 2.

2    Slacken the generator or alternator mounting bolts so as to slacken the fan belt and then remove the fan belt. For details see Chapter 2. The crankshaft pulley is held into position by a large bolt through the centre boss, and this must be undone using a suitable socket wrench. With the engine in the car a gear should be engaged to prevent the engine from turning when the bolt is being undone. If the engine is out of the car it will be necessary to hold the flywheel ring with a suitable lever engaged in the ring gear teeth.

3    The crankshaft pulley is keyed onto the end of the crankshaft and under normal circumstances it should be possible to pull it straight off. If some resistance is met, it is in order to lever it from behind equally on each side simultaneously, but great care should be taken to avoid distorting the timing cover during this operation. If reasonable pressure fails to dislodge the cover, it may be necessary to obtain the services of a puller in order to draw it off properly without damaging anything.

4    Once the crankshaft pulley wheel has been removed, the bolts which hold the timing case cover to the front of the engine block should be taken out. The cover can then be removed and when this is done the timing chain tensioner, which is held in position by the cover, will fall down and hang on its pivot.

5    To remove the timing chain and sprockets, first remove the split pin and washer from the tensioner pivot. Withdraw the tensioner.

6    The timing chain and the two sprockets on which it runs have all to be removed together. First remove the screw, tab washer and plain washer from the front of the camshaft. Take off the oil thrower which is mounted on the crankshaft in front of the crankshaft sprocket. Align the sprocket timing marks to aid refitting.

7    The crankshaft sprocket is a tight fit onto the keyed end of the crankshaft and will most probably require the services of a puller in order to draw it off. Once the puller is in position and ready to move the sprocket, the camshaft sprocket should also be moved forward with the aid of suitable levers at the same time as the other sprocket is being moved forward. Both sprockets and the chain can then be drawn off together.

8    Remove the chain oil feed pipe, spring and ball. Note the discharge angle for refitting (photo).

## 13 Pistons, connecting rods and big-end bearings – removal

1    It is possible to remove the pistons, connecting rods and big-end bearings from the engine with the engine still in the car, provided that the cylinder head and sump are also removed first. With the engine removed from the car, the task is much easier and generally cleaner, but, of course, it is understood that if a quick emergency repair job is to be done and speed is of the essence, it would be in order to do any work with the engine still in the car. With the sump removed and the crankshaft exposed, each of the big-end bearing caps can be detached after removing the two self-locking nuts which hold each cap to the connecting rod stud. Rotate the engine to bring each connecting rod cap suitably into position for unscrewing the nuts.

2    With the nuts removed, each big-end bearing cap can be pulled off. It must be noted that the connecting rods and big-end caps are not marked in any way, other than a small forging flash on the side of the connecting rod and cap, which matches up on each one. It is nevertheless, wise to make a mark of your own if the same connecting rod and caps are to be re-used, as they must be refitted exactly as they came out. The same applies to the big-end bearing shells which will be released as soon as the connecting rods are detached from the crankshaft. It is inadvisable to re-use these shells anyway, but if they are not renewed they must be put back in exactly the same location from which they came.

3    If any difficulty is experienced in removing the big-end bearing caps from the studs of the connecting rods, it will help if the crankshaft is revolved to dislodge them. If this is done, however, care must be taken to ensure that nothing gets jammed when the connecting rod comes away from the crankshaft at the top of its stroke. Once released, the connecting rods and pistons can be pushed up through the cylinder bores and out of the top of the block. Make sure the pistons are kept in such a way that they can easily be identified and refitted into the same bore, if necessary.

4    The self-locking nuts securing the big-end bearing caps must *not* be reused. The bolts may only be reused if they have not been subject to abnormal strain imposed by a run big-end or a seizure.

12.8 Remove the chain oil feed pipe

## 14 Gudgeon pins – removal

The gudgeon pins will be removed if it is desired to fit new pistons to the existing connecting rods or vice versa. The gudgeon pins are held in position by a circlip in each side of the piston and after this is removed any carbon should be cleaned away. Warm the piston and connecting rod assemblies, preferably in warm oil, when the gudgeon pin can be pushed out with the finger. If the piston is cold and the gudgeon pin is tight, it should not be forced out.

## 15 Flywheel – removal

1    The flywheel may be removed with the engine in the car provided that the gearbox and clutch assemblies are both removed first. The flywheel would normally be removed in these circumstances for purposes of renewing the starter ring, which may have damaged teeth, or because of a badly scored face due to a badly worn clutch friction disc.

2    With the gearbox and clutch removed as described in Chapters 6 and 5 respectively, the five bolt heads which secure the flywheel to the crankshaft flange will come into view. These bolts are locked into position by tab washers. Knock back the tabs and then undo and remove the five securing bolts. The flywheel is located to the crankshaft flange on a register and is positioned by a dowel pin. It will be necessary to use a little leverage to draw the flywheel off and great care should be taken that it does not come off with a sudden jerk and fall down. One way of preventing this is to put a stud (a longer bolt with the head sawn off) into one of the bolt holes so that when the flywheel comes free, the end of the stud will support it. If the dowel comes out together with the flywheel it should be remembered that the dowel should be removed from the flywheel and refitted in the crankshaft flange before the flywheel is itself refitted.

## 16 Oil pump – removal

1    The oil pump may be removed from the engine whilst the engine is still in the car. It is first necessary to remove the sump. As the oil pump drive spindle also drives the distributor, care must be taken to ensure that the ignition timing is not lost when the oil pump is removed and eventually refitted. It is, therefore, necessary also to remove the distributor cap and turn the engine until the rotor is in line with the number four plug high tension lead segment. The timing marker on the crankshaft pulley wheel must then also be set against the top dead centre position. For full details of engine timing refer to Chapter 4.

2    Once the crankshaft has been set to the correct position the distributor should be removed. By looking down into the distributor mounting opening it will be possible to see the top of the oil pump

spindle and the position of the offset slot. Take a careful note of this position. (see Fig. 1.11).

3   Disconnect the oil delivery pipe union from the pump and also at the other end from inside the crankcase. The two bolts holding the pump to the crankcase can then be removed and the pump drawn out.

## 17  Camshaft – removal

1   Although it is possible to remove the camshaft with the engine still in the car, this is not recommended. Where it is essential to do so however, the following procedure is suggested.
2   Disconnect the battery.
3   Drain the cooling system and remove the radiator.
4   Remove the distributor complete with mounting base.
5   Remove the fuel pump.
6   Unbolt and remove the tappet chest cover. Slacken the rocker arm adjuster screws having first removed the rocker cover. Remove the pushrods and tappets, and keep in order to provide for refitting in their original positions.
7   Remove the crankshaft pulley, timing cover, and oil thrower.
8   Temporarily, refit the crankshaft pulley. Turn the crankshaft until the timing marks on the two sprockets are aligned, as shown in Fig. 1.10. No 4 piston will now be at top dead centre (TDC) on compression stroke. The oil pump distributor drive slots will be in the position shown in Fig. 1.11.
9   Remove the crankshaft pulley again. Withdraw the timing chain and sprockets as an assembly.
10  Unbolt and remove the camshaft thrust plate.
11  Support the weight of the engine using a hoist, or alternatively a jack and a block of wood under the sump.
12  Release the engine mountings (see Section 5, paragraphs 21 to 24).
13  Disconnect the oil gauge pipe or oil pressure warning lamp switch leads at the cylinder block end.
14  Lower the engine just enough to be able to withdraw the camshaft through the aperture below the front grille. Take care not to allow the engine or transmission to damage any steering or chassis items. If the engine cannot be lowered enough to permit withdrawal of the camshaft, remove the grille and raise the engine.
15  Withdraw the camshaft carefully. As this is done, the oil pump drive for the distributor will turn to the position shown in Fig. 1.12. Avoid rotating the camshaft as this is withdrawn. When withdrawing the camshaft from the block, care should be taken to avoid chipping the camshaft bearings with the sharp hardened edges of the cam lobes. It is quite easy to gouge a deep line out of the bearing with one of the cam lobes, and if this is done, the bearing will possibly be damaged seriously enough to warrant renewal, and this is a specialist task. When taken out, put the camshaft where it cannot drop or be damaged as it is of a hard and brittle nature and could easily be cracked or chipped.
16  When the engine is being dismantled away from the vehicle, it should first be inverted to stand on the cylinder head face. (Take the

precaution detailed in Section 18). With the timing sprockets and chain removed, undo the two bolts holding the camshaft thrust plate to the front of the block. Remove the thrust plate and withdraw the camshaft, ensuring that all tappets are clear of the cam lobes, and observing precautions concerning damage to bearings given in paragraph 15.

17  It should be noted that camshafts are not interchangeable between engines fitted with cast iron and those with aluminium cylinder heads. This is due to the different valve arrangements possessed by each engine.

## 18  Tappets – removal

It should always be remembered when the engine is removed from the car and the valve rocker gear detached, that if the engine is inverted, the tappets are liable to fall out of their bores. If it is not intended to remove the tappets, then this can be a nuisance as they should normally be refitted only into the bores from which they have come. It is therefore desirable to remove the tappet chest coverplate

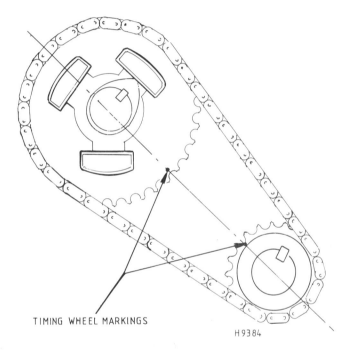

TIMING WHEEL MARKINGS

H9384

**Fig. 1.10 Correct relationship of timing chain sprocket marks and shaft keyways, with No 4 piston at TDC on compression stroke (Sec 17)**

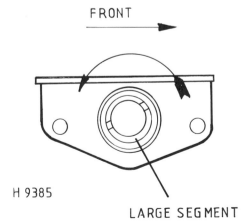

FRONT

H 9385

LARGE SEGMENT

**Fig. 1.11 Oil pump offset driving slot position at TDC on compression stroke and camshaft in position (Sec 17)**

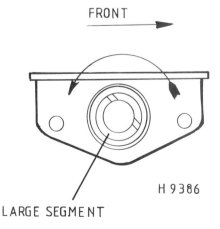

FRONT

LARGE SEGMENT

H 9386

**Fig. 1.12 Oil pump offset driving slot position – No 4 piston at TDC on compression stroke and camshaft withdrawn from engine (Sec 17)**

at an early stage in engine dismantling, lift the tappets from their bores and mark them with a pencil accordingly so they can be returned to the same bore. Normally it is not necessary to renew tappets unless they are severely scored or badly worn, and this is a feature which is normally associated with a damaged camshaft. Certainly, if one or the other is badly damaged it is advisable to renew both. If it is wished to invert the engine, yet retain the tappets in position, (for example, when removing the camshaft for examination) it is simple enough to remove the tappet chest cover, and stuff rags inside sufficient to prevent the tappets from dropping down. Remember, however, that they must be permitted to drop down far enough to clear the lobes of the camshaft when it is withdrawn from the engine block.

## 19 Crankshaft, main bearings and thrust washers – removal

1 If required, the crankshaft main bearing shells can be removed with the engine still in the car. This is not considered advisable, however, insofar that if the bearings are worn sufficiently to necessitate renewal there is every likelihood that the journals will be similarly worn, and that the crankshaft itself will need regrinding. Both methods of dismantling are here described, however.

### Main bearing removal – engine in car

2 Drain the engine oil.
3 Remove the sump, the oil pump, and the distributor.
4 Remove the timing cover, chain tensioner and support pin (this last item unscrews from the front main bearing cap).
5 Slacken each main bearing bolt two turns. Remove any one main bearing cap. Employing a thin strip of soft metal, push the corresponding top half bearing round the crankshaft and remove. Refit the bottom half bearing with cap and bolts, simply to act as a support for the shaft. Do not screw the bolts up tightly.
6 Treat the remaining bearings in like manner, until all the top half shells have been removed.

### Removal of crankshaft and main bearings – engine out of car

7 Remove the sump.
8 Remove the oil pump and distributor.
9 Remove the timing chain and sprockets.
10 Remove the flywheel.
11 Remove the cylinder head and invert the engine. (Note the precautions advised in Section 18).
12 Remove the front plate, by first removing the two bolts adjacent to the camshaft thrust plate. Remove the timing cover mounting stud.
13 Remove the connecting rod bearing cap bolts and caps.
14 At this stage it is opportune to check the crankshaft endfloat, and this should be done by checking the clearance between one thrust bearing surface and the adjacent face on the crankshaft. Ensure the shaft is held firmly against the faces not being measured, thus giving the maximum clearance for measurement purposes between the remaining two faces. Check the clearance with feeler gauges and compare this with the figures given in the Specifications.
15 Remove the main bearing caps.
16 Remove the crankshaft and put it in a safe place.
17 Remove the upper half main bearing shells.
18 Remove the thrust washers by pushing them round the centre crankshaft bearing journal, after first removing the centre main bearing cap.
19 With the engine out of the car and with the crankshaft removed, the thrust bearings are automatically accessible.

## 20 Oil filter – removal and refitting

1 The oil filter element is a throw-away disposable cartridge which is screwed into an adaptor casting bolted to the right-hand side of the engine block. This casting comprises the inlet and outlet passages from the filter and also the oil pressure release valve, and can be detached for further investigation if necessary.
2 The rubber jointing ring on the base of the filter cartridge has a tendency to stick and the cartridge therefore can be very difficult to turn. In such cases it will be necessary to fit some form of strap around the cartridge with a suitable lever to apply sufficient pressure to turn

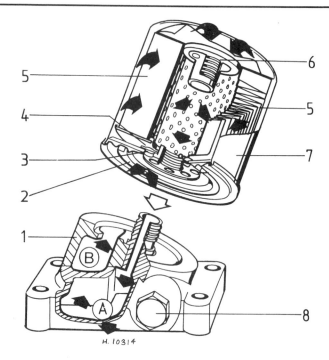

Fig. 1.13 Oil filter – internal flow lines (Sec 20)

1　Adaptor plate
2　Cartridge sealing ring
3,4　Anti-drain valve
5　Filter media

6　Bypass valve
7　Cartridge case
8　Pressure relief valve

*The oil passes through compartment 'B' into the filter and returns to the engine oil galleries via compartment 'A'*

20.2 Removing and refitting the oil cartridge

it. Some versions have a hexagon on the top face and with these, of course, a spanner can be used. When refitting a new element first make sure the jointing faces of the element and the casting are perfectly clean and lightly smeared with engine oil. Then screw the cartridge in by hand, making sure the screw threads are running true until the mating faces just touch. Then screw the cartridge by hand another two-thirds of a revolution only. Do not overtighten otherwise it will be difficult to unscrew later. After fitting a new element, the engine should always be run and a check made for signs of any leakage. Filters with a hexagon on their top face must not be tightened with a spanner (photo).

## 21 Engine mountings and damper – removal and refitting

1   To remove a front mounting initially remove the lifting eye from the rear left-hand side. Next, take the weight of the engine on the lifting eye and remove the front mounting fixing bolts and nuts.
2   Removal and refitting of the engine mounting damper is as described in Section 5, paragraph 21.

## 22 Closed crankshaft ventilation system – description and maintenance

1   The system 'when fitted' comprises a regulating valve fitted to the inlet manifold, a flame trap and three connecting hoses. The regulator valve outer end connects to the tappet chamber coverplate, or the oil filler tube on the rocker cover. The flame trap connects via hoses between the carburettor and the rocker cover.
2   When the engine is idling, manifold depression draws the poppet valve onto its seat to restrict the amount of air passing through the unit. When the throttle opens, the decrease in manifold depression permits the spring to lift the poppet valve from its seat and allows fumes and air to pass into the inlet manifold. Clean ventilating air can then pass from the carburettor through the flame trap and into the engine.
3   Note: Incorrect operation of the valve will result in unsatisfactory idling.
4   To examine and service the system, pull off the hoses to the valve and flame trap. Remove the valve from the manifold.
5   Dismantle the valve and clean all the parts carefully in petrol or paraffin. Do not stretch or fully compress the spring.
6   Check the condition of the spring, valve seat and poppet valve. If unsatisfactory from the point of view of wear, corrosion or damage, the spring must be renewed; poppet valve or valve seat deterioration will entail renewal of the complete valve.
7   Clean the rubber hoses and flame trap by swilling them in petrol or paraffin then shaking dry.
8   Reassemble the valve unit, ensuring that the spring and poppet valve are correctly located, then refit the valve to the manifold.
9   Refit the flame trap with the rocker cover connection at its lowest point to allow any surplus oil to drain back into the engine.
10  Refit the hoses.
11  To test the regulating valve, remove the hose connection. With the engine switched off, use a short rod to check the poppet valve is free to move and will return under spring action.
12  Run the engine at idling speed and check it is unaffected by pressing the poppet valve onto its seat.
13  Increase the engine speed to around 3000 rpm, and then release the throttle and check the engine returns to the idle condition. If this does not occur, a fault in the valve unit is indicated.

## 23 Engine – general examination

1   Examination of an engine runs in two phases. The first is a visual and aural examination when it is running and in the car, and the second is when it is out of the car, having decided that something is wrong and needs repairing. It is not difficult for any owner to find garages, friends and relatives all willing to tell him precisely what is wrong with his engine as they listen to it turning in his car! It is a different matter altogether to decide when to take the car off the road, and do something about putting right whatever faults there may be. In general, if the oil and fuel consumption are reasonable, the performance is satisfactory, and it is not suffering from overheating, underheating, or any other fault which causes aggravation and irritation on the road to a large degree, it is best left alone. Provided the regular maintenance requirements are carried out there is no need to take it to pieces.
2   The first indications of an engine becoming worn (if one has not been able to get the exact mileage the engine has travelled) are an increase in oil consumption and possibly a corresponding increase in fuel consumption. This may also be accompanied by a falling off in performance. On an average family saloon car this is not always easy to detect, and it is a good idea to drive another car of the same type, known to be in very good condition, to make a comparison. If the signs are that the engine is performing poorly, using too much petrol and

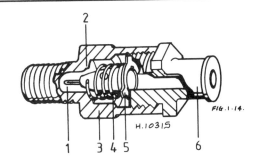

**Fig. 1.14 Crankcase ventilation regulation valve (Sec 22)**

1   Bleed                          4   Spring
2   Valve seat                     5   Valve poppet
3   Valve body                     6   Outer end (inlet)

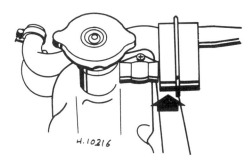

**Fig. 1.15 Flame trap – crankcase ventilation system (Sec 22)**

beginning to burn oil, then one of the first things to do is to test the compression in each cylinder with a proper compression testing gauge. This will indicate whether the pistons are leaking in the cylinders, or the valves are leaking in the head. Depending on the results, the cylinder head may be removed and further examinations carried out to the bores and head as described in subsequent sections. Early action at this stage could well restore the engine to a satisfactory condition. Furthermore, such action would call for proportionately smaller expenditure of money and time. If the condition is left, however, it will get progressively worse until the simple repairs which would have been needed earlier have become major operations. This will be much more expensive and time consuming.

## 24 Crankshaft and main bearings – examination and renovation

1   With the crankshaft removed, examine all the crankpins and main bearing journals for signs of scoring or scratches. If all the surfaces of the bearing journals are obviously undamaged, check next that all the journals are round. This can be done with a micrometer or caliper gauge, taking readings across the diameter of each journal at six or seven points. If you do not own a micrometer or know how to use one, you should have little difficulty at any garage that has good mechanics to get someone to measure it for you.
2   If the crankshaft has ridges or severe score marks in it, it must be reground. Official dealers of the Minx/Hunter series go further and say that a crankshaft in this condition should be renewed, but as this can be a very expensive procedure, it is felt that regrinding should suffice in all but the most extraordinary situations. If there are no signs of ridging or severe scoring of the journals, it may be that the measurements indicate the journals are not round. If the amount of ovality exceeds 0.002 in it is possible that regrinding may be necessary. Certainly, if it is more than this figure it is necessary. Here again, it is best to get the advice of someone who is experienced and familiar with crankshafts and regrinding crankshafts to give an opinion.
3   The main bearing shells themselves are normally matt grey in colour all over and should have no signs of pitting or ridging. Discoloration usually indicates that the surface bearing metal has worn away and the backing material is showing through. It is worthwhile renewing the main bearing shells anyway if you have gone to the

trouble of removing the crankshaft, but they must, of course, be renewed if there is any sign of damage to them or if the crankshaft has been reground. When the crankshaft is reground, the diameter is reduced and consequently one must obtain the proper sized bearing shells to fit. These will normally be supplied by the firm which has reground the crankshaft. Regrinding is normally done in multiples of 0.010 in as necessary and bearing shells are obtainable to suit these standard regrinding sizes. If the crankshaft is not being reground, yet bearing shells are being renewed, make sure you check whether or not the crankshaft has been reground once before. This will be indicated at the back of the bearing shell and will indicate whether or not it is minus 0.010 in or more. The same version of shell bearing must be used when they are renewed.

4    The crankshaft endfoat will already have been checked as described in Section 19, paragraph 15. If this is outside the permissible limit, the thrust faces on the shaft should be reground and oversize washers fitted. If the thrust faces are scored, regrinding and the fitting of new bearings is essential. Should the endfloat be within the permissible limits, it is felt that the thrust washers should still be renewed in view of the very small cost involved.

5    The crankshaft spigot bearing should be examined visually at this stage, and if it appears scored or otherwise worn, should be renewed. The bearing fitted to later cars is of the needle roller bearing type. Previously, a plain sintered bush was used and when it becomes necessary to renew either type, the needle roller bearing must be used.

### Manual gearbox

6    To remove the bush, a special tool is available, or an alternative method would be to use grease. Fill the recess behind the bush and then insert a close fitting bar. Strike the end of the bar with a hammer and, by hydraulic pressure, the bush will eventually be forced out. A special tool, No. CB 0005 with adaptor CB 0005-2, must be used to insert the needle roller bearing, to ensure that it is correctly positioned.

7    Place the adaptor on the main tool spigot, with the boss away from the handle.

8    Place the new crankshaft bearing over the spigot with the internal oil seal facing toward the adaptor, so that, when fitted, the seal is nearest the flywheel end of the crank.

9    Tap the bearing into the crank recess as far as possible.

10 The bearings are pre-packed with lubricant and no extra lubrication is recommended.

### Automatic transmission

11 The spigot bearing fitted to models with an automatic transmission is made of steel and is also specified when a renewal is necessary. The purpose of this bush is only to centralise the torque converter. The removal and refitting procedures follow the same lines as for the manual gearbox.

### 25 Big-end bearings – examination and renovation

The connecting rod bearings, or big-end bearings as they are more commonly known, are subject to wear at a greater rate than those for the crankshaft. Signs that one or more big-end bearings are getting badly worn are a pronounced knocking noise from the engine accompanied by a significant drop in oil pressure, due to the increased clearance between the bearing and the journal permitting oil to flow more freely through the resultantly larger space. If this should happen quite suddenly and action is taken immediately, (and by 'immediately' is meant 'within a few miles'), it is possible the bearing shell may be renewed without any further work needing to be done. If this happens in an engine which has been neglected and in which oil and oil filter changes have not been carried out as they should have been, it is most likely that the rest of the engine is in a pretty terrible state anyway. If it occurs in an engine which has been recently overhauled, it is almost certainly due to a piece of grit or swarf which has got into the oil circulation system and finally come to rest in the bearing shell and scored it. It is in these instances where a renewal of the shell alone accompanied by a thorough flush out of the lubrication system may be all that is required.

It is also felt that, once the work to remove big-end shells has been carried out, one would be unlikely to refit the old parts, bearing in mind the moderate cost of replacement parts.

### 26 Cylinder bores – examination and renovation

1    Worn cylinder bores and piston rings are indicated by loss of power, high oil consumption and blue smoke from the exhaust.

2    Bore wear can be overcome by fitting replacement standard size piston rings, special oil control rings, or by reboring the cylinders and fitting new pistons. The method chosen will depend upon the bore

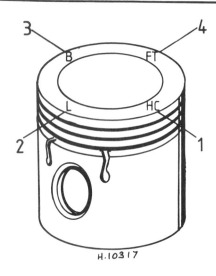

H.10317

**Fig. 1.16 Piston crown markings (Sec 26)**

| 1 HC or LC | Compression ratio indication: HC–high compression; LC–low compression |
| 2 L, M or H | Gudgeon pin bore diameter grading letter: L–low; M–medium; H–high |
| 3 A, B, C, D or E | Piston diameter grading letter |
| 4 FT | Front – mark showing fitting position in engine |

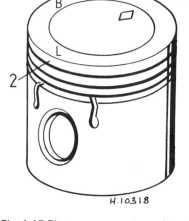

H.10318

**Fig. 1.17 Piston crown markings (Sec 26)**

| 1 Indentation | Front indication and compression identification mark: High compression, 1500cc; Low compression, 1500cc; High compression 1725cc; Low compression 1725cc |
| 2 L, M or H | Gudgeon pin bore diameter grading letter: L–low; M–medium; H–high |
| 3 A, B, C, D or E | Piston diameter grading letter |

condition and the anticipated mileage before further work becomes necessary.

3   If there is scoring of the bores present, or if a noticeable step is present at the top of the bore, reboring will certainly be required. There is, however, no real substitute for experience in this matter, and where doubt exists, specialist advice should be sought.

4   If a decision is taken not to rebore but to fit a replacement ring set to the old pistons, it will be necessary to de-glaze the bores to ensure proper bedding-down of the new rings. To de-glaze, employ a fairly close-fitting wooden dummy piston wrapped with emery cloth (No 1 or 1½ grade). Insert this into each cylinder in turn. Take it up and down the cylinder, at the same time imparting a semi-rotary movement for two or three minutes, till the wall is sufficiently abraided. Remove any foreign matter.

5   Upon completion of work on the cylinder block, it should be cleaned thoroughly. Ensure all the oilways are clear, preferably by blowing through them with compressed air, and cover the cleaned block to prevent contamination.

## 27  Connecting rods, pistons and piston rings – examination and renovation

1   The examination of pistons should first be related to the examination of the cylinder bores as described in Section 26. If the condition of the cylinders is felt to be unsatisfactory, no further action need be taken over the pistons; it is obvious that when the cylinders are rebored a new set of pistons must be purchased to suit the new size.

2   If it is decided that the condition of the cylinders is acceptable, the pistons should then be examined for signs of wear or damage. If, for instance, it has been decided that there appears to be considerable clearance between piston and cylinder walls, but examination of the cylinders shows very little wear, then the clearance is a result of piston wear. It is advised that, in any instance where a new piston set is required, it is much wiser to have the cylinders rebored also, thus returning the complete cylinder assemblies to new condition. A visual examination should be carried out for scoring, cracks and breakage of the pistons. If the piston set appears generally satisfactory, the side clearance between the piston rings and their grooves should be checked with feeler gauges, and compared with the specification. If this clearance is excessive, the piston is normally the worn item and must be renewed. This can be confirmed by remeasuring, using a new piston ring.

3   To check ring gaps, the rings must be removed from the pistons. This must be done with great care because of the extremely brittle material from which they are made. Spread the gap of the ring with the thumbs, very gently, whilst supporting the remainder of the ring with the fingers, until it is just large enough to lift over the piston top. Do not twist or jerk, or it will break. Carefully, place the piston ring in the cylinder bore, about two inches from the top, pressing it down with the piston base, to ensure it is horizontal. The gap can then be tested with a feeler gauge, and compared with the Specifications. If one ring is worn, the others are almost certain to be in a similar condition, and a new set should be employed.

4   The connecting rods are normally re-usable. If, however, serious damage has occurred, such as engine seizure, the rods should be checked for straightness. This must be done on equipment normally only possessed by a specialist engineer.

5   The fit obtained between the gudgeon pin, and its related holes in the small-end bush and in the piston, is critical. At 70°F (21°C) the pin should be a push fit in the piston (employing finger-pressure) and a close free fit in the small-end bush. A further check: if the connecting rod is held horizontally, it should be possible for the connecting rod to fall under its own weight when the piston is held. If the gudgeon pin is too free a fit in the small-end, the bore of the bush (together with the relevant bores in the piston), must be enlarged by a honing process. Oversize gudgeon pins should then be employed. The honing must be carried out by specialist engineers.

## 28  Valve rocker gear – examination and renovation

1   The rockers should move freely on their shaft without excessive slackness.

2   To dismantle, remove the spring clip from one end of each half of the complete assembly and remove the rockers, spacers, standards

and springs, one at a time, laying them out carefully and noting the order in which they were removed. If either the rocker bushes or the rocker shaft are obviously scored and worn at those points where the rockers are pivoting, they should be renewed. The rockers themselves should also be examined on the faces where they bear onto the top of the valve stems. If signs of wear are excessive, they too should be renewed.

## 29  Valves – removal and renovation

1   Place the cylinder head on a work bench.

2   Remove the valves. These are located by a collar which retains two collets (or a split collar) in a groove in the valve stem. The spring must be compressed, using a suitable G-clamp to release the collets and hence the valve. Place the clamp end over the spring collar, with the screw end squarely on the face of the valve head. Screw the clamp up to compress the valve spring, and thus expose the collets. If the spring collar sticks and the screw cannot be turned, give the head of the clamp (over the spring) a tap with a hammer, at the same time ensuring the clamp does not slip off at either end.

3   Take the collets off and release the clamp. Lift off the collar and spring(s). If the end of the valve has become burred, this should be removed with a fine file, to prevent damage to the guide as the valve is withdrawn. Keep springs, collars and collets with their respective valves, and identify each valve with a label or by some other means, to ensure its correct refitting in the cylinder head.

4   Clean each valve, using a wire brush and scraper. Do not, however, allow the wire brush to operate on the stem of the valve where it runs in the guide.

5   Remove dirt from each valve and its guide in turn, and refit the valve in the guide. Check for a sideways movement to ensure that only a small amount of play exists. If considerable play exists, a new valve may be tried and if sufficient improvement is effected, renewal of the worn valves may be all that is required. Insufficient improvement means that the guides require attention. The seating surface of the valves should next be examined, and any with excessive pitting or burning should be discarded. Those with light pitting can be recut cheaply by most garages or motor trade engineers. Valve springs should be examined visually for defects, and the lengths of each checked for comparison. Renew as a set if there is any marked variation. If the engine has covered a high mileage, it is best to renew them as a matter of course.

## 30  Cylinder head – examination and renovation

1   If the test carried out in Section 29, paragraph 4, indicates that unacceptable wear is present in the valve guides, these should be refitted by a specialist who has the necessary equipment for pressing the guides in and out, and for reaming the guides to size.

2   A careful examination of the valve seats should be made. If anything more than minor pitting or burning is present, the surfaces should be recut, using suitable equipment. If any cracks are present (or the surfaces have previously been recut to the extent that the seats have become pocketed) the advice of a specialist engineer should be sought with a view to having inserts fitted.

3   All traces of carbon should now be removed from the head. A wire cap brush and an electric drill are very useful for this purpose, but should not be allowed to touch the valve seats when in use. Additionally, a wire brush should not be employed on an aluminium head. Remove accumulated deposits from the cylinder head surface, taking care not to damage the surface. Wipe the surface clean, and check it for flatness by placing a straight edge across it. If there is any suspicion of distortion, a specialist should be consulted, with a view to the surface being machined flat. Care should be taken to ensure that the engineers consulted are able to advise competently in this matter.

4   Pass a clean rag through each of the valve guides to remove debris. Take each valve in turn, and smear the seating face with a small amount of fine grinding paste. Obtain a suction grinding tool, which can be purchased cheaply at any motorists shop. Pass the valve through the correct valve guide and rotate it on the seating only a short distance in each direction. Lift and revolve frequently to a new position, then continue grinding. The valve must not be revolved in complete rings whilst grinding. If a light spring is placed over the valve stem, behind the head, this can be of assistance in raising the valve

before partially revolving it for further grinding. The width of the line produced by grinding should not be more than 0.07 in (1.8 mm), and specialist engineering advice regarding the fitting of inserts should be sought if this figure is exceeded.

5   Clean the head thoroughly. Either wash in paraffin and dry off, or employ a proprietary solvent cleaner which can then be hosed off with water. Every trace of carborundum paste must be removed, and if possible a high pressure air line should be employed to blow through all orifices and oilways. Functional surfaces (such as the valve guide bores and valve seats) should be oiled to prevent the onset of corrosion, and the head then placed in a plastic bag or other dust-proof container.

## 31  Timing chain and sprockets – examination and renovation

1   Examine the sprocket teeth for damage. Examine the teeth for wear on one side, indicated by lack of symmetry of the tooth as a whole. Renew the sprockets if necessary.

2   It is advised that a new timing chain should always be fitted at a major overhaul, thus eliminating a common source of engine noise.

3   Examine the condition of the chain tensioner pad, and renew if any grooving is present. Examine the tensioner pivot for wear. This can be a source of noise, and it should be renewed if necessary.

4   On engines with cast iron cylinder heads, renew the damper ring fitted to the crankshaft sprocket, shown in Fig. 1.4.

## 32  Camshaft, bearings and tappets – examination and renovation

1   The camshaft lobes should be examined for signs of flats, scoring or other wear and damage. The tappets should also be examined, particularly where they bear against the camshaft, for signs of wear. If the case hardened surfaces of the cam lobes or tappet faces have been penetrated, there will be a darker, more roughly pitted appearance to the surface. In such cases, the tappet or the camshaft will need renewal. Where the camshaft or tappet surface is still bright and clean and showing slight signs of wear, it is best left alone. Any attempt to re-face either will only result in the case hardened surface being reduced in thickness with the possibility of extreme and rapid wear later on. The skew gear in the camshaft (which drives the oil pump shaft and indirectly the distributor) also should be examined for signs of extreme wear on the teeth. Here again, if the skew gear teeth are very badly worn and ridged, it will mean renewal of the complete camshaft. Examine also the teeth on the driven gear. The camshaft bearing journals should be perfectly smooth and show no signs of pitting or scoring, as should the camshaft bearing shells. Refitting the camshaft bearing shells is a specialist task, but it is rare for the journals and bearings to wear out at anything like the same rate as the rest of the engine. Having ascertained that the faces of the tappets are satisfactory, check also that they are not a loose fit in their respective bores. If so, they should be renewed.

2   The camshaft thrust plate (which retains the camshaft into the cylinder block) should also be examined for any signs of ridging or scoring on its thrust face. Renew if necessary.

## 33  Flywheel – examination and renovation

1   There are two areas in which the flywheel may be worn or damaged. The first is the driving face where the clutch friction plate bears against it. Should the clutch plate have been permitted to wear down beyond the level of the rivets, it is possible that the flywheel has been scored. If so, it must be renewed.

2   Examine the teeth of the starter ring gear around the periphery of the flywheel. The edge of the teeth towards the clutch side of the flywheel are designed with a bevel on them. Do not confuse this bevel with wear. If, however, one or more teeth are damaged or worn to any extent, a new ring gear must be fitted.

3   To remove the old ring gear, drill a small hole through the ring between the bases of two gear teeth. Do not drill into the flywheel. Also make a slot with a hacksaw down towards the hole which has been drilled, but again do not cut the flywheel. The gear may then be split with a cold chisel and hammer blow, and removed. Wear eye-protectors whilst splitting the gear.

4   To fit a new ring gear, heat it to a temperature of 220°C (428°F),

not more. This is done in an oven or in a bath of oil, *not* with a naked flame which causes uneven heating and distortion. Place the hot ring gear onto the flywheel, making certain that it beds down completely on to the register. Ensure the bevelled edges of the teeth are facing toward the clutch side of the flywheel. Allow it to cool naturally. If the ring gear is overheated, it should not be used. The temper will have been lost, thereby softening it, and it will wear out in a very short time.

## 34  Oil pump – examination and renovation

1   With the oil pump removed from the engine, it should be inverted and the hexagon-headed screws securing the baseplate to the pump body removed. The outer rotor ring may then be lifted out and this should be done carefully. If dropped, it could easily crack and therefore become unserviceable.

2   The interior of the pump body may then be cleaned thoroughly with petrol or paraffin to remove all traces of oil.

3   The efficiency of any oil pump depends on the clearances between the inner rotor tips and outer rotor and the outer rotor fit in the pump body. These are set to very fine tolerances on manufacture and if any excessive wear occurs, the oil which is normally forced round by the increasing and decreasing size of the apertures between the inner and outer rotors will escape in the increased clearances between them. Thus the pumping efficiency and pressure will be reduced at the output side of the pump.

4   The main feature of checking the pump is to measure the clearances. This is shown in Figs. 1.18 and 1.19. Measure between the ends of the rotors and the face of the body of the pump, by putting a steel straight-edge across the pump body and measuring the gap between it and the faces of both rotors with a feeler blade. The gap should be between 0.001 and 0.003 in (0.025 mm and 0.075 mm). The next clearance to be measured is that between the tip of the inner rotor and the high point of the convex section of the outer rotor, also with a feeler blade. The gap here should be between 0.001 and 0.006 in (0.025 mm and 0.15 mm).

5   The third clearance is that between the outside of the outer rotor and the pump body. This should be between 0.005 and 0.008 in (0.125 and 0.20 mm).

6   If any of the clearances exceed the limits specified, or if the centre rotor spindle should be slack in its bush then a replacement oil pump should be fitted.

7   Whilst the pump is dismantled, the opportunity should be taken to examine and clean the inlet filter gauze screen. Clean it thoroughly in petrol or paraffin and blow it dry. Do not dry it off on any material or cloth which could leave particles remaining hooked up in the gauze.

## 35  Inlet and exhaust manifolds – inspection

Exhaust and inlet manifolds should be examined for signs of cracks or other breakages, particularly on the mounting lugs. The mating faces of both manifolds where they join the cylinder head should be examined to make sure that they are completely flat and free from pitting or burrs. Use a straight edge to check the faces for distortion. If there is distortion or severe pitting or burning, the manifold should be renewed. Examine the exhaust manifold to exhaust pipe flange mounting studs. In time these tend to corrode away and are consequently weakened, and in this case it is good policy to fit replacements. Accumulations of carbon within the ports may be removed with a wire brush or scraper.

## 36  Decarbonisation

1   Modern engines have greatly reduced the need for decarbonising in its old sense. There will always be a certain amount of carbon deposit however, and this should be removed when dismantling is undertaken for overhaul purposes. Carbon deposits in the cylinder head are dealt with in Section 30.

2   In the case of major overhaul, the pistons will be dealt with on the bench and indeed, may be discarded. If they are to be re-used, carbon deposits should be removed from the crown with a soft scraper. It is important also that deposits should be removed from the piston ring grooves. If this is not done, and a new piston ring set is subsequently

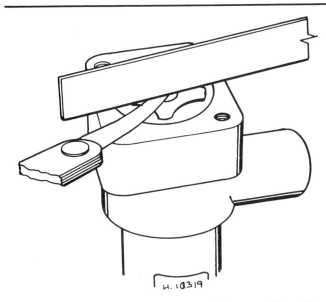

**Fig. 1.18 Checking oil pump rotor end clearance (Sec 34)**

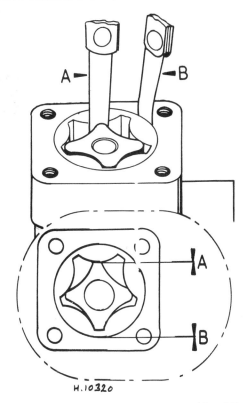

**Fig. 1.19 Checking oil pump clearances (Sec 34)**

*A Rotor tip clearance     B Outer rotor clearance*

employed, it is frequently found impossible to refit the pistons into the cylinders because of the increase of size across the piston rings brought about by the underlying layer of carbon. Other occurrences with this condition include ring breakage when fitting or engine seizure in service. An effective way to clean the ring grooves is to employ a piece of an old piston ring as a scraper, this automatically being an ideal size. Very great care is necessary to prevent the scraper digging into the soft piston material, however, and care also should be taken to avoid personal injury from the sharp edges and corners frequently found on pieces of piston ring.

3    It is quite possible that the piston crowns may be dealt with in the car, but great care must be taken to ensure no particles of dislodged carbon fall either into the cylinder bores and down past the piston

rings or into the water jacket orifices in the cylinder block. Bring the first piston to the top of its stroke. Using a sheet of strong paper and some self adhesive tape, mask off the other three cylinders and surrounding block to prevent any particles falling into the open orifices in the block. To prevent small particles of dislodged carbon from finding their way down the side of the piston which is being decarbonised, press grease into the gap between the piston and cylinder wall. Carbon deposits should be scraped away carefully, leaving a ring of carbon adjacent to the cylinder bore, to preserve a seal and assist with oil conservation. If the piston is dropped to just below top dead centre (TDC), and an old piston ring is pressed down on to it before cleaning begins, a good guide is thus provided of the area which should be cleaned.

4    A wire brush, operated either by hand or by a power drill, should not be used if decarbonising is being done with the engine still in the car. It is virtually impossible to prevent particles being distributed over a large area and the time saved by this method is very little.

5    In addition to the removal of carbon deposits on the pistons, it is a good time also to make sure that traces of gasket or any sealing compound are removed from the mating face of the cylinder block top face.

6    After each piston has been attended to, clean out the grease and carbon. As the engine is revolved to bring the next piston to the top of its stroke for attention, check the bore of the cylinder which has just been decarbonised and make sure that no traces of carbon or grease are adhering to the inside of the bore.

## 37 Engine reassembly – general

1    To ensure maximum life and minimum trouble from the rebuilt engine, cleanliness of every aspect of the reassembly is of prime importance.
2    Ensure all oilways are clear.
3    Oil all moving surfaces on assembly.
4    Have available all the necessary spare parts, gaskets, nuts, bolts, washers, tab washers and lock washers, together with a supply of suitable jointing compound, clean cotton rags, clean engine oil, a torque wrench, and all normal hand tools.

## 38 Crankshaft and main bearings – reassembly

1    If the crankshaft has been reground, it is suggested that this is a suitable time to check the fit of each big-end bearing onto the crankshaft before actually inserting the piston into the cylinder block. If any high spots are apparent when the bearing is turned on the crankshaft, suitable action can be taken. Defects of this nature are rare but can be caused by poor quality workmanship on the regrinding of the crankshaft or damage to the mating faces of the big-end bearing caps, where some previous owner has misguidedly filed them down in an attempt to take up any bearing slackness.
2    To fit the crankshaft and main bearings, stand the cylinder block inverted on the bench and gather together the bearing caps, new bearing shells and the crankshaft. Make sure that the oilways in the crankshaft are all quite clear.
3    Make sure that the bearing housings in the cylinder block are perfectly clean. The centre and two end bearing shells have a central groove running through them, whilst the other two are plain. Each bearing shell has an oil hole in it and this must line up with the corresponding hole in the cylinder block. Each shell is notched, and must line up with the corresponding notch in the cylinder block. Carefully, fit each shell into position taking care not to bend, distort or scratch it. Lubricate the shells with a liberal quantity of clean engine oil (photo).
4    Make sure the crankshaft is the right way round. Carefully, lower it square and straight into position on the shell bearings in the crankcase (photo).
5    Slide the semi-circular thrust washers round the crankshaft, one on each side of the centre main bearing journal, ensuring that the grooves on the washers face away from the journal. Recheck the crankshaft endfloat (see Section 19). Run some engine oil between the bearing surfaces (photos).
6    The centre and end bearing shell lower halves are also grooved and the other two plain. Make sure the bearing caps are clean. Fit the shells into the caps. There are no oilways in the bearing caps so that

38.3 Placing main bearing shells in crankcase housings

38.4 Refitting the crankshaft

38.5a Fitting the thrust washers

38.5b Sliding the thrust washers into position

38.5c Checking crankshaft endfloat

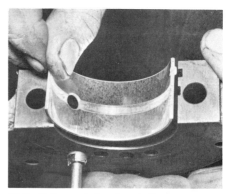
38.6a Fitting main bearing shell to its cap

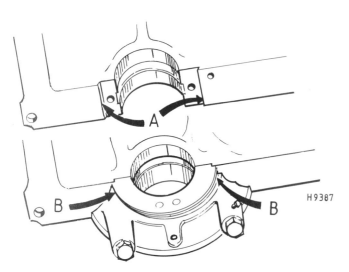

Fig. 1.20 Front main bearing cap – at A employ a non-setting jointing compound to prevent oil leaks, and at B a quick-setting jointing compound to retain the sump cork gaskets during fitting (see also Section 46) (Sec 38)

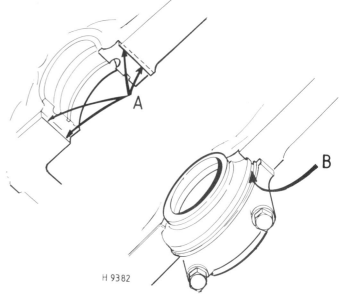

Fig. 1.21 Rear main bearing cap – at A employ a non-setting jointing compound to prevent oil leaks and at B a quick-setting jointing compound to retain the sump cork gaskets during fitting (see also Section 46) (Sec 38)

the holes in the bearing shells will not line up with anything (photo). The front and rear caps are easily identifiable by their particular shape as is the centre one. The others, two and four, are numbered and should be arranged accordingly. As there is the possibility of a seepage of oil through the end main bearing cap mating faces one is advised to put a very thin smear of non-setting jointing compound onto the outside edge of the vertical face where the bearing cap locates into the crankcase. This is shown in Figs. 1.20 and 1.21. Lubricate the main journals of the crankshaft liberally with clean engine oil, place all the bearing caps in position and fit the bolts. The front main bearing cap has a machined front face and this must line up with the front surface

of the cylinder block. Do this with a straight-edge before finally tightening down the bolts. When all the caps are settled correctly in position, tighten the bolts down evenly, using a torque wrench, to the correct torque as given under the specifications. When this has been done revolve the crankshaft to make sure there are no intermittent tight spots. Any signs that something is binding whilst the crankshaft is being revolved indicates something is wrong and there may be a

38.6b Fitting a main bearing cap

38.6c Main bearing cap in position

38.6d Tightening the main bearing cap bolts

high spot on one of the bearings or on the crankshaft itself. This must be investigated or a damaged bearing could result (photos). Note, however, that when a new or reground crankshaft is being fitted, it should only be rotated in the normal direction of rotation, this being clockwise (when viewed from the front). Rotating the shaft in the wrong direction will damage the bearing surfaces.

7    If the main bearings have been removed as described in Section 19, paragraphs 2 to 6 inclusive, refitting is a reversal of the removal procedure with reference where necessary to the earlier paragraphs in this Section.

### 39 Pistons, gudgeon pins and connecting rods – reassembly

1    Refer to Section 27, paragraph 5, which discusses the correct size relationships necessary between small-end bush, gudgeon pin and piston bores.

2    There is an oil squirt hole on one side of each connecting rod and this faces the right-hand side of the cylinder bores. Each piston also

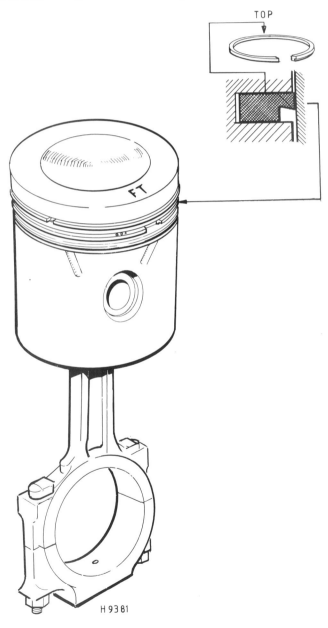

Fig. 1.22 Piston and connecting rod assembly showing relationship of oil squirt hole to FT (front mark) on piston crown and correct fitting of lower compression ring (Sec 39)

has an indication on its top surface, showing which is the front, so therefore, the piston and connecting rod can be assembled properly to ensure that the offset in the piston is in the correct direction. Make sure the piston is sufficiently warm to enable the gudgeon pin to slide easily through the bosses and then place the gudgeon pin half way into the piston. Insert the connecting rod the correct way round, and push the gudgeon pin completely home into position. Fit the circlips into the groove on each end of the piston to locate the gudgeon pin in position. (photos). If the old pistons are being re-used, new gudgeon pin circlips should be purchased.

## 40 Piston rings – refitting

1    Before fitting the rings to the piston, check the end gaps. Push the rings down the bores using the piston until they are about $2\frac{1}{2}$ in below the top. Measure the gap. If the gap is too large you either have the wrong piston rings or the bores are worn more than anticipated. If the gap is too small, it will be necessary to remove material from the end of the ring. Clamp the end of the ring in a vice so that a very small portion of the end projects above the top of the vice. Use a fine file to take off material in very small quantities at a time. Do not clamp the ring so that the end being filed projects too far above the vice jaws or it may easily be snapped off. When every ring has been checked, they should be assembled to the piston to prevent them being mixed up with other rings which will be fitted to other bores.

2    All rings must be fitted from the top of the piston (a possible exception to this is the bottom oil control ring fitted into the skirt of some pistons). To get the new rings into position involves spreading them sufficiently to clear the diameter of the piston and then moving them down over the existing grooves into their appropriate positions. Care must be taken to avoid straining them to a point where they could break. A piece of thin shim steel or an old feeler gauge blade is a useful means of guiding the ends of the rings over the grooves to prevent them inadvertently dropping in.

3    Fit the bottom scraper ring. Move it down the piston a little at a time, taking care to prevent it from snagging in the grooves over which it will pass. Next, fit the lower compression ring. The top edge of the ring will be marked 'top' and this must go uppermost. Do not be misled into thinking that this means that the ring is the top one on the piston. The top compression ring, the last one to go on, can be fitted either way up. When all the rings are in position, try to arrange the gaps to be equally spaced around the piston. Obviously, if the gaps are in a straight line, there will be a much greater tendency for compression loss at that point.

## 41 Pistons, connecting rods and big-end bearings – refitting

1    Place a piston and connecting rod assembly into the top of the block, making sure the front of the piston is toward the front of the engine block. Obtain a suitable piston ring clamp, such as is sold by most motor accessory stores. Place it over the piston and rings, and close it gently until it is firmly (but not too tightly) round the piston. Ensure the clamp is held firmly down against the face of the cylinder block, to prevent a ring coming out underneath it. Tap the piston crown with a hammer handle, to persuade it through the compressor and thence into the bore. Take care not to drive it down, causing the bottom end of the connecting rod to strike the crankshaft, with the possibility of damage to the bearing surface. Fit the remaining pistons in like manner (photos).

2    Invert the cylinder block. Fit a shell bearing into the connecting rod half of the big-end, making sure that the oil hole and notch in the end of the shell line up with the corresponding hole and notch in the connecting rod. Lubricate the big-end journal on the crankshaft with clean engine oil and push the connecting rod down onto the journal. Fit a new shell bearing into the cap, lining up the notch accordingly (there is no oil hole in the cap). Refit it onto the big-end studs. The big-end bearing caps will have been marked on removal as noted in the appropriate section, so there should be no difficulty in identification. Fit new self-locking nuts and tighten evenly to the correct torque (photos).

## 42 Camshaft and tappets – refitting

1    If the tappets have been removed from the cylinder block, they should not be refitted until the camshaft has itself been refitted. If they are still in position in the cylinder block and the engine is out of the car, it is best to lie it on its side, pushing the tappets up in their bores so they will not foul the lobes of the camshaft as it is being inserted. Note that if the engine has been completely dismantled, the camshaft should always be refitted before the oil pump.

2    Make sure that the camshaft bearings are in good condition and clean. Lubricate them with clean engine oil and refit the camshaft in the cylinder block. The main requirement in doing this is to make sure the hardened steel lobes of the camshaft do not damage the soft metal bearing surfaces through which they pass. When the camshaft is fully home, the thrust plate should be refitted and secured by the two bolts. If for any reason the front engine plate has been detached from the block it should be refitted now, using a new gasket (photos).

3    To avoid the tappets falling out of their locations (due to gravity with the engine inverted), it is best to wait until the oil pump and sump has been refitted on the engine and it is once again upright, before fitting them. They should be cleaned and lubricated with engine oil, before refitting them in their appropriate bores (photo).

4    If it was necessary to remove the camshaft with engine still in the vehicle, the following procedure should be employed.

5    Oil the camshaft bearings and cam faces.

6    Ensure the oil pump driving slots are as shown in Fig. 1.12.

7    Hold the camshaft with the keyway as shown in Fig. 1.10 and whilst keeping it at this angle, feed it back into position very gently. When fully home, the oil pump driving slots should be as shown in Fig. 1.11 If the correct slot position does not materialise, withdraw the shaft sufficiently to allow the initial slot position to be moved. Refit the shaft.

8    Refit the camshaft thrust plate.

9    Refit the timing chain and sprockets as an assembly, orientated as shown in Fig. 1.10.

10    Refit all the other parts in reverse order as described in Section 17, paragraphs 1 to 15, where relevant.

11    Check valve clearances and ignition timing.

## 43 Timing chain tensioner, sprockets and cover – refitting

1    Turn the crankshaft to bring the key to the top (No 1 and 4 pistons at TDC).

2    If a chain with a detachable link is being used, refit the link with the open end trailing (the chain revolves in a clockwise direction, when viewed from the front). Note also that the thicker of the two keep plates is located in the centre of the chain.

3    Place the sprockets inside the chain. A straight line through the centres of the sprockets should also pass through the dimple marks, one on the edge of each sprocket, as shown in Fig. 1.10.

4    Turn the camshaft until the key is in approximately the correct position. Offer up the chain and sprocket assembly, readjust the camshaft position if necessary, and place the sprocket on the shafts. Push them on until location on the keys is achieved. Do not strike the camshaft sprocket, or the seal plug at the other end of the shaft may become displaced. The crankshaft sprocket may be tapped on lightly, but that on the camshaft should be pulled on using a washer and bolt.

5    Refit the cover mounting stud between the two sprockets if removed. Check the timing marks are still correctly lined up. Refit the two lockwashers onto the camshaft sprocket mounting bolt, tighten the bolt, and bend the top lockwasher into a flat on the bolt head (photos). Refit the chain oil feed pipe, with spring and ball (see Section 12, paragraph 8). The endfloat of the camshaft should be checked by employing a dial gauge. Excessive endfloat should be rectified by employing an oversize thrust plate of the correct dimension. If the oil pump has been removed it is now opportune to refit it before refitting the timing cover, thus making it possible to keep an easy check on the proper position of the timing wheels (see Section 45).

6    Refit the tensioner arm onto the spindle, and refit the washer and a new split pin to retain the tensioner arm (photos).

7    Refit the oil slinger disc over the crankshaft with the concave side facing outwards. Refit the cover using a new gasket. The tensioner device should be tucked inside the cover and then the cover put on, holding the tensioner in position against the chain. Refit all the securing bolts but do not tighten them up at this juncture, so the cover may be centralised properly as described in Section 44 (photos).

39.2a Assembling gudgeon pin to piston

39.2b Fitting circlips to piston

41.1a Insert the connecting rod carefully into the bore ...

41.1b ... followed by the piston. Fit a ring clamp ...

41.1c ... and carefully tap the piston fully home

41.2a Fitting a big-end bearing cap ...

41.2b ... and tightening the nuts to the correct torque

42.2a Assembling camshaft into cylinder block

42.2b Fitting the thrust plate

42.2c Refitting gasket and front engine plate ...

42.2d ... and securing with the bolts

42.3 Refitting the tappets

43.5a Refitting the cover mounting stud

43.5b Refit the camshaft sprocket bolt and lock into position

43.6a Refitting the tensioner arm

43.6b Refitting the tensioner split pin

43.7a Refitting the oil slinger disc

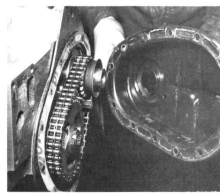

43.7b Refitting the timing cover

44.2 Refitting the crankshaft pulley ...

44.3 ... driving it on if necessary using a wood block

45.6a Refitting the oil pump ...

45.6b ... and suction pipe

46.2a Refitting the sump ...

46.2b ... and tightening the securing bolts

## 44 Crankshaft pulley wheel – refitting

1   The crankshaft pulley wheel is a straight fit onto the end of the crankshaft, the key in the crankshaft engaging in the keyway of the pulley wheel. There is no oil seal built into the timing cover round the crankshaft pulley wheel, the latter having a scroll groove machined into the boss to return any oil which may try to seep through.

2   The timing cover bolts should always be loose when the crankshaft pulley wheel is first refitted to the crankshaft, to enable the pulley boss to centralise in the aperture of the cover. However, there is a bolt adjacent to the aperture which must be tightened before the pulley is driven completely on. In the first instance, therefore, push the pulley wheel partly on ensuring the cover hole is properly centralised about the pulley boss. Check, by turning the engine over, that the boss does not touch on the edge of the hole in the cover. Nip up two or three of the cover bolts, remove the pulley, and tighten the otherwise inaccessible bolt. Tighten all other bolts (photo).

3   If the pulley wheel is a tight fit, it may be necessary to drive it on using a block of wood (photo). The bolt which secures the crankshaft pulley wheel into position may be refitted, but it is easier if left until the engine is reconnected to the gearbox in the car, before it is fully tightened. It is easier to lock the engine, so the necessary torque can be applied. Alternatively, place a block of wood between a crankshaft web and the crankcase.

## 45 Oil pump – refitting

1   The oil pump should not be refitted until the camshaft, crankshaft, pistons, connecting rods and timing chain (but not the cover) have all been reassembled into the block.

2   It is important that the teeth of the oil pump driving spindle are properly meshed with the skew gear on the camshaft to enable the distributor drive (which comes from the oil pump driveshaft also) to be correctly timed. The upper end of the oil pump drive spindle has an offset slot in it which engages the bottom of the distributor drive spindle, and this slot must be put in the right position when refitting the oil pump.

3   First put No 4 piston at top dead centre (TDC) on the compression stroke. If you have just finished assembling the camshaft timing chain and sprockets, the crankshaft will be in the correct position as shown in Fig. 1.10.

4   Refit the oil pump. As the pump is put into position, the spindle will turn due to the curved nature of the gears which mesh together. Initially, therefore, the slot in the spindle must be set so that when it turns it will finish up in the position as shown in Fig. 1.11.

5   The mating faces of the pump, and the crankcase where it fits, must be perfectly clean and free from any scratches or burrs. The oil suction pipe, complete with unions, should also be lightly assembled to the oil pump body, as it will not be possible to fit this after the oil pump has ben bolted down.

6   It is best for the engine to be lying on its side when refitting the oil pump, as in this way it will be easy to look at the position of the driving slot in the top of the spindle. Tighten the pump mounting bolts and the oil suction pipe unions (photos).

7   After the oil pump has been refitted, but before fitting the sump, it is a good idea to check that the distributor will in fact be in the correct position when refitted. To do this, refit the distributor temporarily so that its drive spindle engages in the slot in the oil pump spindle. Check the rotor arm of the distributor lines up with the No 4 plug lead contact when the cap is in position.

## 46 Sump – refitting

1   The engine, if out of the car, should be inverted on the cylinder head surface. Make quite sure that all big-end bearing cap nuts are tight, all main bearing cap bolts are tight, and the oil pump has been refitted and tightened down. Fit a new sump gasket to the base of the cylinder block, having first made sure that the face has been thoroughly cleaned.

2   Clean off the mating face of the sump itself. The sump gasket comes in four pieces; two semi-circular cork seals which engage in the grooves of the bearing caps at each end of the crankshaft, and two side gaskets which fit the flanges of the sump pan. Fit the side gaskets first to the crankcase. It is not essential to use a jointing compound, although many people prefer to do so as a precaution. However, when fitting the cork seals into the grooves of the bearing caps, the ends of the seals should be treated with a quick setting jointing compound where they bear onto the ends of the side gaskets (see Figs. 1.20 and 1.21). Place the sump in position over the gaskets. Locate all the sump holding bolts into position before tightening them up (photos).

3   On engines fitted with aluminium sumps make sure that, if the baffle plate has been removed for cleaning, it is refitted before the sump is put back.

## 47 Flywheel – refitting

1   Before refitting the flywheel to the crankshaft flange, the mating faces must be examined carefully for any signs of dents or burrs and cleaned up as necessary. All traces of oil and grit must also be removed, and the locating dowel peg should be in position on the crankshaft flange. Offer up the flywheel to the flange squarely and locate it carefully into position without damaging the edges of the mating faces (photo).

2   Once the flywheel is mounted the set bolts should be fitted with new tab washers and progressively tightend up to the specified torque (photo).

3   If possible, it is a good idea to check the flywheel run-out at the outer edge of the clutch facing. If this exceeds a total of 0.003 in it means the flywheel is not fitted square with the crankshaft and serious vibration problems could result when the engine is running. A dial gauge will be required to carry out this check.

## 48 Valves and springs – reassembly to cylinder head

1   There are differences between the aluminium and cast iron heads in details of assembly, but these will be immediately apparent. The photographs used show an aluminium headed engine which was removed from the car and a cast iron headed version where the head was removed with the engine still in the car.

47.1 Refitting the flywheel ...

47.2 ... and tightening the bolts

2   With the head perfectly clean, lubricate the valve stem lightly for the first valve to be refitted and fit it in the guide. The valves should have been kept in order so that they may go in the correct places. Note that the arrangement of exhaust and inlet valves differs between aluminium and cast iron heads (photo).

3   On aluminium heads, place the spring seating washer over the valve, lip upwards, followed by the spring and collar. On cast iron heads, the lower spring seating washer is not fitted. The collars are fitted with sealing rings in their internal bores and these should be renewed. The seals are included in the head gasket set, and care should be taken to avoid damaging them during fitting (photos).

4   The valve spring compressing tool should be used to compress the spring sufficiently to enable the split collars to be refitted into the groove of the valve stem. A little grease may be used to assist holding them in position (photo).

5   Release the compressor slowly, watching that the collars do not move out of the groove. Remove the compressor. Tap the top of the valve stem sharply to bounce the spring, using a hammer-handle or soft mallet, thus verifying security of the assembly.

6   Repeat the procedure for each valve in turn.

## 49 Inlet and exhaust manifolds – refitting

1   If the engine is removed from the car, the manifolds may be refitted on the cylinder head whether or not the head is fitted itself. This is not possible on Holbay engines, however. With the engine in the car and the head removed, it is more convenient to fit them to the head before refitting the head to the engine. This is not possible on Holbay engines.

2   The two outer inlet ports are fitted with steel ring locating inserts. These should be clean and free from carbon or any sign of damage due to heat. Fit them before fitting the gasket (photo).

3   Fit the gasket to the cylinder head (photo).

### Single carburettor type

4   Assemble the two manifolds to each other with the deflector plate between them. No gasket is employed. Do not tighten the bolts excessively at this stage, but wait until the assembled manifolds are secured tightly to the cylinder head.

5   The remaining work is a reversal of the dismantling procedure given in Section 9, paragraphs 1 to 4.

6   Ensure the manifold bolts mentioned in paragraph 4 have been tightened.

7   It is recommended that, when the engine is out of the vehicle, the carburettor should not be refitted until the engine has been refitted.

8   The bolts securing the manifolds should be retightened when the engine is warm.

### Twin carburettor type

9   The dismantling procedure given in Section 9, paragraphs 5 to 13, should be followed in reverse.

10  The remarks in this Section, paragraphs 7 and 8, apply also to the twin-carburettor refitting procedure.

## 50 Cylinder head – refitting

1   Make sure the new cylinder head gasket is the correct one for the type of head. They are quite different for iron or aluminium.

2   Make sure the mating surfaces of the head and cylinder block are perfectly clean and flat. Place the gasket in position on the block. Do not use any sealing compound or grease when fitting it. Make sure it is put in position the right way up. It is marked 'top' on the upper side (photos).

3   If the tappet chest cover plate has been removed, make sure the tappets are back in position and the rocker oil supply pipe is refitted. Refit the cover with a new gasket and do the bolts up finger tight.

4   Hold the head over the block. Ensure that the oil feed pipe goes through the centre hole (in line with the pushrod holes). Lower the head into place on the two studs, taking care not to displace the tappet cover gasket (photos).

5   The tappet chest cover plate bolts should now be done up evenly but, at this stage, not excessively tightly. This will ensure that the mating faces of the cover and both the head and block are properly lined up before the head is immovably tightened down. If a new gasket is not being fitted to the tappet chest cover, it may help to guard against possible leaks if the top edge of the gasket is smeared with jointing compound before the head is refitted. This would normally apply only where the engine has not been removed from the car (photo).

6   Refit all the cylinder head bolts, washers and nuts (photo).

7   All the bolts and nuts should be tightened down lightly and to an equal extent. Then tighten them progressively by about 10 lbf ft at a time in the correct sequence as shown in Fig. 1.23 until the full correct torque has been applied (photo). Tighten the tappet cover bolts fully.

8   The length of the two projecting studs will prevent most sockets from reaching the single nut, so the second nut should be locked to it when both may be turned together. The top one may be slackened off by holding the bottom one with an open ended spanner after the full tightening has been completed.

9   If the engine is in the vehicle, continue as in Section 10, paragraphs 10 to 12 (in reverse order). Adjust the valve clearances.

## 51 Valve rocker gear – reassembly and refitting

1   As advised in Section 28, a note will have been made of the order of dismantling, and reassembly should be a reversal of this sequence. However, details are in any case clearly shown by Figs. 1.3 and 1.4.

2   When both halves are being assembled, check the two centres of the shaft are open-ended. These receive the lubricating oil from the T-piece, positioned between them and with the elbow facing the pushrods.

3   The rocker assembly should be fitted to the head after the head has been fitted to the block. Otherwise, some of the head bolts are not accessible for tightening with a conventional socket spanner. Also, unnecessary slackening of the rocker adjusters will be required to refit the pushrods.

4   Refit the pushrods into their appropriate holes and make sure the lower convex ends engage in the tappets (photo).

5   Place the complete rocker assembly into position on the cylinder

48.2 Refitting a valve in a guide

48.3a Refitting a stem oil seal

48.3b Refitting a valve collar (aluminium head)

48.3c Refitting a valve spring (iron head)

48.3d Refitting a valve collar (iron head)

48.4 Refitting valve collets

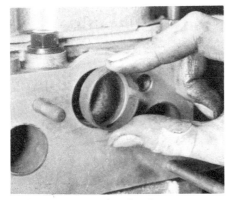

49.2 Refitting a port locating ring

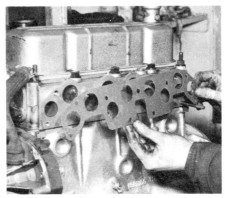

49.3 Fitting the manifold gasket

50.2a Fitting the cylinder head gasket (iron head)

50.2b Fitting the cylinder head gasket (aluminium head)

50.4a Refitting the cylinder head ...

50.4b ... over the two studs (iron head)

50.4c Refitting the aluminium cylinder head

50.5 Refitting the tappet cover bolts

50.6 Refitting the cylinder head bolts and nuts – arrow shows rocker oil supply pipe

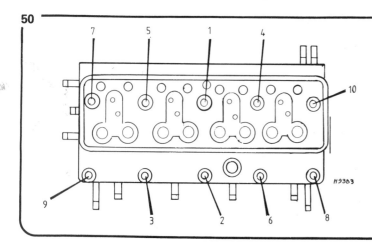

Fig. 1.23 Cylinder head bolts and nuts – tightening sequence (slacken in reverse order) (Sec 50)

H9383

50.7 Tightening cylinder head bolts and nuts

51.4 Refitting the pushrods

51.5a The rocker oil feed

51.5b Refitting the rocker assembly (iron head)

51.5c Refitting the rocker assembly (aluminium head)

51.6 Tightening down the rocker retaining nuts and bolts

51.7 Tightening the oil pipe union

52.9 Checking the valve clearances

52.10 Securing the tappet adjusting locknut

head, entering the oil pipe into the T-piece and the rocker arms into the pushrod cups. It will be noticed that the assembly will not sit flat because of the raised position of some of the pushrods (photos).

6 Refit all washers and nuts or bolts as appropriate and proceed to tighten them down a small and equal amount each in sequence to prevent any distortion caused by the resistance of the springs on the open valves. Check once more that the pushrods are correctly located. When the standards are all seated flat on the head, the nuts or bolts should be tightened to the correct torque (photo).

7 Tighten the oil pipe union (photo).

## 52 Valve rocker clearances – checking and adjustment

1 The valve rocker clearances are important. They affect the amount a valve opens and when it opens, and can thus affect the efficiency of the engine.

2 The clearances should be set by using a feeler blade between the rocker arm and encd of each valve stem. This is done when the valve is closed and the tappet is resting on the lowest point of the cam.

3 To enable each valve to be in the correct position for checking with the minimum amount of engine turning, the procedure and order of checking should follow the sequence given in the following tables. Note that the order is different, depending on which type of cylinder head (aluminium or cast iron) is fitted. In both the tables below the valves are numbered 1 to 8, starting from the front of the cylinder head. A valve is fully open when the rocker arm has pushed the valve down to its lowest point.

4 Revolve the engine by using a socket on the crankshaft pulley bolt and turning clockwise. If the engine is still in the vehicle, remove the spark plugs to assist turning the engine, and also the rocker cover.

5 Sequence table for cast iron head:

| Open valve | Adjust clearance (hot) |
|---|---|
| No 8 (ex) | No 1 (ex) |
| No 6 (in) | No 3 (in) |
| No 4 (ex) | No 5 (ex) |
| No 7 (in) | No 2 (in) |
| No 1 (ex) | No 8 (ex) |
| No 3 (in) | No 6 (in) |
| No 5 (ex) | No 4 (ex) |
| No 2 (in) | No 7 (in) |

6 Sequence table for aluminium head:

| Open valve | Adjust clearance (hot) |
|---|---|
| No 8 (ex) | No 1 (ex) |
| No 5 (in) | No 4 (in) |
| No 3 (ex) | No 6 (ex) |
| No 7 (in) | No 2 (in) |
| No 1 (ex) | No 8 (ex) |
| No 4 (in) | No 5 (in) |
| No 6 (ex) | No 3 (ex) |
| No 2 (in) | No 7 (in) |

7 The clearances will be found in the Specifications, and are correct for the engine when fully hot after a run. If the engine is being assembled cold, the gaps should be set 0.002 in greater than the figures given in the Specifications until the engine can be run.

8 Using a screwdriver and ring spanner, slacken the locknut on the adjusting stud and put the feeler blade, of thickness appropriate to the valve being adjusted, between the rocker arm and valve stem. Slacken the stud adjuster if the gap is too small to accept the blade.

9 Turn the adjusting screw until the feeler blade can be felt to drag lightly when it is drawn out of the gap (photo).

10 Hold the adjuster with a screwdriver and tighten the locknut. Check the gap once more to make sure it has not altered as a result of locking the stud (photo).

11 When a rebuilt engine has been run, and is thoroughly hot, the adjustment procedure must be carried out again, this time setting the clearances as given in the Specifications.

## 53 Engine reassembly – ancillaries

1 The remaining items, removed as described in Section 7, should now be refitted, with reference to Chapters giving detailed information as is necessary. It is advised that refitting the carburettors should be

left until the engine is in position in the vehicle, due to its vulnerable nature.

2 Refit the rocker cover, together with a new gasket.

## 54 Engine – refitting

1 Generally speaking, the engine removal procedure (fully detailed in Section 5) should be followed in reverse when refitting the engine.

2 If the engine and gearbox have been removed together, they should also be refitted as a single unit in view of the relative ease with which the units can be assembled together on the bench. There is, of course, no choice in this matter when dealing with automatic transmission. Additionally, with the Model 35, the following points should be noted:

(a) *Special washers are used beneath the head of the special bolts retaining the torque converter to the engine driveplate. Consult your dealer for replacement parts. Do not use ordinary bolts and washers, and ensure that the replacements are correctly torque tightened*

(b) *To ensure correct engagement of the oil pump drive, rotate the converter so that the drive fingers on the hub will be in the 9 o'clock and 3 o'clock positions. The slots in the oil pump driving gear are rotated to a similar position by using a screwdriver or similar tool*

(c) *Fill the transmission with new fluid on completion, then check the level*

With the Model 45, the following points should be noted:

(a) *Suitably jack-up the front end of the engine to facilitate alignment with the transmission*

(b) *Special washers are used beneath the heads of the special bolts retaining the torque converter to the engine driveplate. Consult your dealer for replacement parts. Do not use ordinary bolts and washers, and ensure that replacements are correctly torque tightened*

(c) *When refitting the filler tube, loosely attach the bracket to the converter housing, then align the tube in its seat in the sump and tighten the union nut. Do not strain the tube when tightening*

(d) *Ensure that the thick spacers are fitted between the rear engine mounting and transmission*

(e) *Adjust the selector linkage and downshift cable*

(f) *Fill the transmission with new fluid and check the level*

3 Double-check the condition of the hoist to be used, and of the lifting sling and its attachment to the engine. Serious injury, not to mention damage, may be caused if such a heavy weight should fall. When refitting the engine, take particular care of the hands and arms, which can easily become trapped between the engine and the vehicle body.

4 When lowering the unit, ensure that it is at the correct basic angle for re-entering the engine compartment, and make changes of angle gradually when required. Lower the unit gently, and watch around it all the time. Pipes and wires frequently seem to fall back into the path of the descending unit, and can be wrenched out by the weight, if not seen in time. Do not force anything; there is always a reason why it will not go where you want it to.

5 Once the engine is in place, the crankshaft pulley should be secured by engaging a gear and tightening the bolt. This is best done before fitting the radiator, thus providing easier access.

6 It is advised that new oil and air filters should always be fitted to a reassembled unit.

7 The following check list is felt to be useful:

*Fuel pipes to fuel pump and carburettor – connected and tight*
*Water hoses to radiator and heater – connected and clipped tight*
*Radiator and cylinder block water drain taps shut*
*Cooling system filled up*
*Sump drain plug screwed in tight*
*Oil filter element screwed on tight*
*Oil in sump*
*Oil in gearbox and level plug tight*
*LT wires connected to distributor and coil*
*Spark plugs clean and tight*
*Valve clearances set*

*HT leads from coil, distributor and spark plugs all connected correctly, and securely*
*Distributor rotor arm fitted*
*Choke and throttle cables connected and controls operating correctly over full range*
*Braided earthing cables from engine to body frame secure*
*Starter motor lead securely connected at both ends*
*Fan belt fitted and tensioned*
*Generator leads connected*
*Oil pressure pipe or sender wire conneccted*
*Temperature gauge wire connected*
*Battery charged and in good condition and leads securely connected to clean terminals*
*All loose tools removed from engine compartment*
*All jacks and blocks removed*
*Fuel in tank*

8    Once the engine has started, allow it to run at a fast tick-over and look all round for any leaks of coolant, oil or fuel. Check the exhaust for any leakage. Look for any loose items generally, and watch gauges and warning lights. At the first sign of any fault, stop the engine and investigate. Remember that it is usual for certain abnormal smells and smoke to be given off by a newly-assembled engine, due to burning-off of oil and other substances.

9    When the engine has run, and all seems in order, a short trip should be made in the vehicle to warm up the engine thoroughly. Immediately upon returning, and before the engine starts to cool, the valve clearances should be readjusted to the figures given in the Specifications.

10  During the initial period of use, a check should be kept upon fastenings in general, which can tend to loosen as things settle down.

11  When the engine has been rebuilt, or has had a new cylinder head gasket fitted, it is important to retighten the cylinder head fastenings after 500 miles have been covered. This must be done with the engine cold. Remove the rocker gear, unless Churchill Tool No 225A is available, in which case the rockers may remain in position. Check the tightness of each bolt (or nut, if applicable) in the order shown in Fig. 1.23 by first slackening each bolt by one flat, then retightening to the correct torque. Note that if Churchill Tool 225A is used, the torque wrench in this case should be set to 39 lbf ft (52.88 Nm), and the tool should be positioned at 180° to the torque wrench. Refit the rocker gear and set the valve clearances as described in Section 50, paragraph 7. Recheck when the engine is hot, as referred to in Section 52, paragraph 11.

## 55 Fault diagnosis – engine

| Symptom | Reason(s) |
| --- | --- |
| Engine fails to turn when starter switch is operated | Flat battery |
| | Dirty, loose or broken battery leads |
| | Defect in starter motor circuit |
| | Engine earthing strap broken or loose |
| Engine turns, but does not start | Fault in ignition system |
| | Fault in fuel system |
| | Excessive choke, leading to wet spark plugs |
| | Engine valve timing incorrectly assembled |
| Engine stops, and will not restart | Fault in ignition system |
| | Fault in fuel system |
| | Petrol tank empty |
| | Water in fuel system |
| Engine lacks power | Fault in ignition system |
| | Fault in fuel system |
| | Defective engine valves |
| | Defective engine valve clearances |
| | Brakes binding |
| | Incorrectly assembled engine valve timing |
| | Defective cylinder head gasket |
| | Defective manifold gasket |
| | Cylinder and piston wear |
| Engine misfires, or runs unevenly | Fault in ignition system |
| | Fault in fuel system |
| | Defective engine valves |
| | Defective engine valve clearances |
| | Defective cylinder head gasket |
| | Defective manifold gasket |
| | Cylinder and piston wear |
| | Crankcase ventilation regulator valve faulty |
| Excessive oil consumption | Defective engine valves and guides |
| | Defective engine valve stem seals |
| | Cylinder and piston wear |
| | Blocked engine breather |
| | Oil leaks |
| Engine noisy | Incorrect valve clearances |
| | Worn timing chain and sprockets |
| | Worn distributor drive |
| | Worn engine bearings |
| | Failed water pump bearing |
| | Cylinder and piston wear |
| | Worn rocker assembly |
| | Distributor faults |
| | Camshaft wear |

# Chapter 2 Cooling system

## Contents

| | |
|---|---|
| Antifreeze | 10 |
| Cooling system – draining | 3 |
| Cooling system – filling | 5 |
| Cooling system – flushing | 4 |
| Fanbelt – removal, refitting and adjustment | 11 |
| Fault diagnosis – cooling system | 13 |
| General description | 1 |
| Radiator – removal, inspection, cleaning and refitting | 6 |
| Routine maintenance | 2 |
| Thermostat – removal, testing and refitting | 7 |
| Viscous type cooling fan – removal and refitting | 9 |
| Water pump – removal, dismantling and refitting | 8 |
| Water temperature gauge – fault diagnosis and rectification | 12 |

---

## Specifications

**Type** ............................................................................... Pressurised; pump and fan assisted

### Capacity (with heater)
Sceptre, Hillman GT and Hunter GT ..................................... 13.75 pints (16.5 US pints) (7.8 litres)
All other models ............................................................... 12.65 pints (15.1 US pints) (7.2 litres)

### Radiator
Type ................................................................................ Two or three row, gilled tube
Cap opening pressure ........................................................ 9 lbf/in² (0.63 kgf/cm²)

### Thermostat
Opening temperature ......................................................... 82°C (180°F); Later models, 79°C/83°C (178°F/184°F)
Bypass port closed at ........................................................ 95°C (203°F)

### Water pump ..................................................................... Centrifugal, engine driven

### Torque wrench settings

| | lbf ft | Nm |
|---|---|---|
| Viscous fan-centre fixing bolt | 12 | 16 |
| Viscous drive unit to fan bolts | 5 | 6 |

---

## 1 General description

The engine cooling liquid is circulated on the thermosyphon principle, assisted by a belt-driven impeller type pump.

The system is pressurised so that boiling and evaporation will only occur at abnormally high temperatures. The radiator cap valve will lift at a pressure of 9 lbf/in². The pressure will then drop as vapour boils off and passes down the overflow pipe, until the valve re-seats. It is therefore important that the radiator cap is one designed for the system and in good condition. Testing equipment is available at most garages.

A thermostatically controlled valve restricts the amount of water passing through the radiator until the correct engine operating temperature is reached. This assists rapid warming up and keeps the engine at a constant running temperature regardless of ambient conditions.

The principle of operation is as follows. Water heated by the engine rises out of the cylinder head towards the thermostat which, if cold, is closed. It then diverts via the heater (or heater bypass pipe if the heater valve is shut) straight to the pump and thence back to the engine.

When the engine warms up a proportion of the warm water will pass via the thermostat valve to the top of the radiator down through which it will pass, thus cooling. The pump will then draw the cold water from the bottom of the radiator and pass it back to the engine (the pump has two inlets). If the engine temperature should rise excessively the thermostat valve will close off the bypass outlet thus directing all water through the radiator.

On models with a sealed system, water which may boil off down the radiator overflow pipe passes into a reservoir which maintains a level of liquid covering the end of the overflow pipe. Consequently, any liquid exhausted down the overflow is drawn back by the vacuum conditions created when the system cools down. This greatly reduces the need for regular topping-up.

On certain models, a viscous fan coupling unit is fitted between the water pump pulley and the fan blades. The unit is similar to a torque converter and acts in a manner similar to a slipping clutch. It has a limited torque output and restricts the fan speed to 3500 rpm in order to reduce noise and power absorption.

---

## 2 Routine maintenance

1 The coolant level should be checked at least weekly, and preferably more often. Any noticeable loss of water should be investigated. Rainwater is recommended for topping-up, to assist in keeping deposits to a minimum, and mixed (if appropriate) with antifreeze to the correct strength. Do not remove filler caps when the system is hot, or severe scalds may be sustained from the escape of pressurised coolant. To top-up the sealed system, examine the level of coolant in the radiator by removing the filler cap. Top-up to the neck level if necessary. Top-up the expansion bottle to a depth of one inch from the bottom if necessary. On non-sealed systems, the procedure is the same, but there is, of course, no expansion bottle to deal with.

2 Check the fanbelt for wear and correct tension and adjust or renew

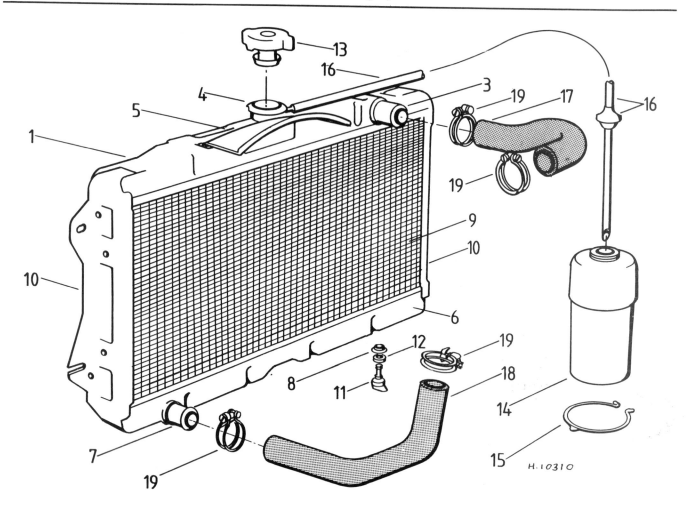

**Fig. 2.1 Radiator and hoses (Sec 1)**

| | | | | | | | |
|---|---|---|---|---|---|---|---|
| 1 | Top tank | 7 | Bottom outlet pipe | 12 | Washer | 16 | Expansion pipe and cap |
| 3 | Top inlet pipe | 8 | Drain tap boss | 13 | Filler cap | 17 | Top hose |
| 4 | Filler neck | 9 | Core | 14 | Expansion bottle | 18 | Bottom hose |
| 5 | Fan guard | 10 | Side strap | 15 | Clip | 19 | Hose clip |
| 6 | Bottom tank | 11 | Drain tap | | | | |

it if needed (see Section 11).

3    The water pump is sealed and need not be touched unless signs of leaking or shaft bearing failure are apparent.

4    In hard water areas removal of deposits using a proprietary chemical de-scaler may be needed from time to time – but not more than annually. A good time to do this is at the change of the seasons when antifreeze may be used.

### 3    Cooling system – draining

1    The vehicle should be on level ground. Remove the radiator cap, ensuring first that the system is sufficiently cool. Place a container beneath the radiator to catch re-usable coolant. Set the heater control to 'hot'. Unscrew the radiator drain tap, then unscrew the cylinder block drain tap. When the flow has ceased, the drain taps should be checked for possible blockages, by pushing a piece of wire through them (photo).

### 4    Cooling system – flushing

1    Every so often – particularly in hard water areas – it is good practice to flush out the system to remove loose sediment and scale. Do this when the coolant is being drained or before adding antifreeze.

With the expansion bottle system, however, the need for topping-up is very infrequent so that deposits from regular additions of new water are reduced. The need for flushing, therefore, is usually only caused by some other factor, such as a leak which allows air to enter the system and cause oxidisation, or the use of an antifreeze of a type which may cause corrosion.

2    To check the need for flushing, open the radiator drain tap. If the liquid coming out is obviously very dirty and full of solid particles, let it run out. If it clears as more runs out and the outflow is in no way restricted, there is no great problem. If, however, constant poking with a piece of wire is needed and the liquid continues very dirty then obviously a flush is required.

3    To flush, leave the radiator and block drain taps open and after removing the radiator cap, run a hose through the system for about fifteen minutes. If the taps show signs of blockage, keep poking them out. If the blocking is persistent, remove the tap completely so that a larger orifice may permit the obstruction to clear itself. In some bad cases a reverse flush may help and this is easily done by removing the radiator and running the hose into the bottom tank so it flows out of the filler neck.

4    If the radiator flow is restricted by something other than loose sediment, no amount of flushing will shift it and it is then that a proprietary chemical cleaner is needed. Use this according to the directions and make sure the residue is fully flushed out afterwards. If leaks develop after using a chemical cleaner, a proprietary radiator

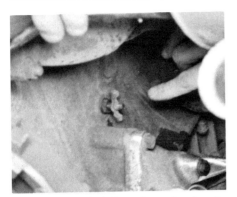

3.1 Cylinder block drain tap beneath exhaust manifold

6.2a Removing the radiator bottom hose

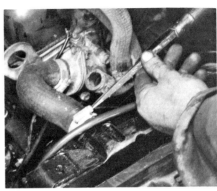

6.2b Removing the radiator top hose

6.4a Removing the radiator fixing screws

6.4b Lifting the radiator out

sealer may cure them. However, the signs probably mean the radiator has suffered considerable chemical corrosion and the metal is getting very thin in places.

## 5 Cooling system – filling

1  Always flush out before refilling.
2  Close both drain taps and fill up slowly. Mix antifreeze, if being used, with the water before putting it in, making up a total quantity about two pints less than the capacity of the system. Then top-up with water. Use clean rainwater if available. Pour it in slowly to avoid air-locks, up to the level of the bottom of the radiator filler neck. Fill the expansion bottle (if fitted) to a depth of one inch. Run the engine until the normal temperature is reached. Check for leaks. Check the function of the expansion bottle (where fitted), noting that the bottle should fill as the engine gets hot, and empty again as it cools.

## 6 Radiator – removal, inspection, cleaning and refitting

1  Drain the cooling system as described in Section 3.
2  Slacken the clip and remove the top radiator hose where it connects to the thermostat housing outlet or to the radiator. Slacken also the clip securing the bottom hose to the radiator and pull off the hose. Take care when pulling hoses away from the radiator, as damage can easily be caused to the stubs and joints (photos).
3  Disconnect and remove the expansion bottle (where fitted).
4  The radiator is held by four hexagon-headed speed screws. When these are removed the radiator may be lifted out. Keep the radiator in the normal upright position as far as is possible, to prevent sediment entering the internal tubes (photos).
5  Clean the exterior of the radiator, thoroughly.
6  Radiator tanks and connections are made of brass and can be repaired with solder where leaks are accessible. The technique of soldering is not discussed here but suffice it to say that the surfaces to be joined must be thoroughly cleaned, tinned, and the solder able to

'run' in the repair. It is fruitless merely to deposit blobs of solder about the place. It would be better to use a resin filler paste which in fact can be used for such repairs in limited applications. Care must be taken to localise any heat used, otherwise the radiator may start to disintegrate where you least want it to. A leak in the integral parts of the honey-comb, if not severe, can be cured with one of the specialist sealers added to the cooling liquid. If severe, professional attention will be needed. Another way for emergencies only is to block the whole of the honeycomb in the suspect area with resin filler paste. Old fashioned remedies such as mustard, egg whites and porridge oats added to the water, are not recommended as they have been known to have sinister effects on water pumps and thermostats.

## 7 Thermostat – removal, testing and refitting

1  If the engine gets too hot, stays too cool, or if the heater is inefficient, the thermostat is probably to blame.
2  Drain out sufficient coolant to lower the level about four inches (roughly a quart) so that no more will be lost when the top radiator hose is next detached from the thermostat housing.
3  Remove the two bolts securing the hose flange to the housing and remove the flange. The thermostat may then be taken out. If it is stuck round the edges clean carefully around the lip with a pointed tool to free it.
4  To test the thermostat, suspend it on a piece of cotton in a pan of water and see how it behaves at the necessary opening temperatures. The valve should start to open within 3°C of the normal operating temperature. Then after another two to three minutes it should open $\frac{3}{8}$ in (9.5 mm) to the 'bypass port closed' position. After being once more placed in cooler water it should close within fifteen to twenty seconds. On later type thermostats the bypass valve has been deleted.
5  If a thermostat does not operate correctly, it should be renewed. If one is not immediately available, leave the old one out to avoid damage by possible overheating of the engine.
6  Refit the thermostat to its housing carefully, with the jiggle pin at the top, and make sure it seats snugly. When refitting the housing

flange cover, use a new gasket and sealing compound on both sides. If the mating surfaces are badly pitted, it may be necessary to clean them up with a file, but make sure the surfaces remain flat.

7    Do not overtighten the securing bolts as the threads in the housing are easily stripped. This is why preparation of the mating surfaces is important to stop leaks.

## 8   Water pump – removal, dismantling and refitting

1    If the water pump leaks or the bearing is obviously worn, it needs to be removed for renewal or repair.

2    Drain the cooling system and then undo the hoses, which are connected to the pump.

3    Slacken the generator mounting bolts and belt tension adjuster bolt so the fan belt may be removed.

4    Remove the four bolts that hold the fan and pulley to the pulley centre and take the fan and pulley off (photo).

5    When removing a plastic type fan, undo the four screws and remove, together with the spring washers, the metal retaining plate and fan. When refitting the fan, ensure the retaining plate locates correctly on the locating peg of the fan before securing with the four screws and spring washers.

6    The pump is held to the block by four larger bolts (do not confuse them with the pump assembly bolts) which should be removed and the pump lifted off (photos).

7    Before attempting repairs to the pump, find out the relative cost of a new bearing assembly, seal and gasket and weigh this against the cost of a complete unit, new or secondhand, and the time factor involved.

8    Begin dismantling by removing the screws securing the impeller housing to the body and separating the two. To remove the bearing and spindle assembly, first remove the locating screw and then draw the pulley centre off the spindle with a suitable claw extractor (photo).

9    Warm the pump body in hot water (90°C) in order that the spindle, together with the bearing and impeller, may be pressed out.

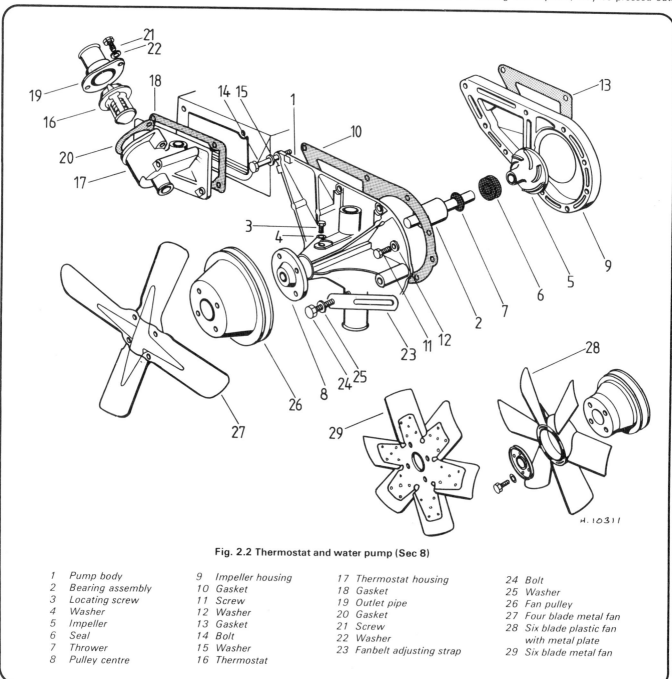

**Fig. 2.2 Thermostat and water pump (Sec 8)**

| | | | | | | | |
|---|---|---|---|---|---|---|---|
| 1 | Pump body | 9 | Impeller housing | 17 | Thermostat housing | 24 | Bolt |
| 2 | Bearing assembly | 10 | Gasket | 18 | Gasket | 25 | Washer |
| 3 | Locating screw | 11 | Screw | 19 | Outlet pipe | 26 | Fan pulley |
| 4 | Washer | 12 | Washer | 20 | Gasket | 27 | Four blade metal fan |
| 5 | Impeller | 13 | Gasket | 21 | Screw | 28 | Six blade plastic fan |
| 6 | Seal | 14 | Bolt | 22 | Washer | | with metal plate |
| 7 | Thrower | 15 | Washer | 23 | Fanbelt adjusting strap | 29 | Six blade metal fan |
| 8 | Pulley centre | 16 | Thermostat | | | | |

8.4 Removing the fan and pulley

8.6a Removing the pump securing bolts

8.6b Lifting away the pump

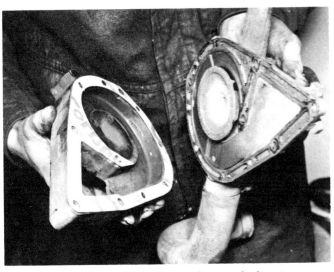

8.8 Separating the impeller housing from the pump body

When this has been done the impeller may be pressed off the spindle. Remove the seal assembly.

10  Unless one has the use of a press, reassembly is difficult, and for this reason pump overhaul should not be undertaken lightly.

11  To reassemble, heat the body as for removal. Align the locating holes, then press the bearing and shaft assembly into position. Whilst still warm, insert the tapered locating screw, which will position the unit correctly. No undue force should be required when fitting, if the heating temperature is correct.

12  Fit a new seal unit, having first refitted the water thrower disc. The seal should be smeared with a sealing compound to prevent water seepage. Make sure no traces of sealer get onto the carbon face, however. The seal and the mating face in the body must be completely free from surface defects.

13  Support the bearing spindle at the fan pulley end. Press on the impeller to the dimension 'B' given in Fig. 2.3. This can be checked in practical terms by inserting a 0.010 in (0.25 mm) feeler gauge at dimension 'C'.

14  Support the bearing spindle inside the impeller, and press on the fan pulley centre to dimension 'A'.

15  Assemble the pump body to the impeller housing, using a new gasket with grease. Insert temporarily two $\frac{5}{16}$ in bolts in the locating holes provided to align the two body parts accurately. Refit and tighten

the bolts evenly. Remove the $\frac{5}{16}$ in temporary bolts.

16  Before refitting the pump, clean the mating faces of the pump and block. Use a new gasket, coated with jointing compound. Refit and tighten the securing bolts.

17  Refit the fan and pulley. Refit the fan belt and adjust the tension. Connect the water hoses. Refill the system with coolant. Examine for leaks when cold and also at normal running temperature.

## 9  Viscous type cooling fan – removal and refitting

**Note**: *In some instances it may be necessary to remove the radiator from the car before the coupling and fan can be removed.*

1  Unscrew and remove the centre bolt which secures the drive unit to the water pump pulley flange.

2  Withdraw the fan complete with drive unit.

3  Unscrew and remove the four bolts which secure the fan to the drive unit and separate the two components.

4  Do not attempt to dismantle or repair the drive unit but renew it as an assembly if necessary.

5  Refitting is a reversal of removal, but tighten the centre bolt to the torque given in the Specifications Section.

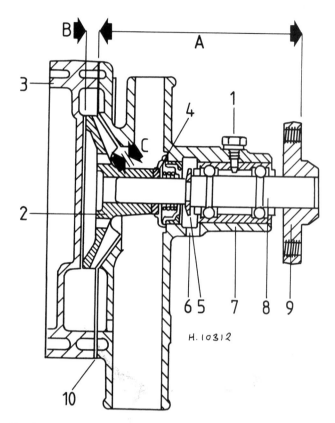

Fig. 2.3 Water pump – sectional drawing giving clearance details
(Sec 8)

| | | | |
|---|---|---|---|
| 1 | Bearing locating screw | 9 | Fan pulley centre |
| 2 | Impeller | 10 | Gasket |
| 3 | Impeller housing | | |
| 4 | Seal | | |
| 5 | Water thrower | | Dimensions: |
| 6 | Drain hole | | A  4.088 in (103.8 mm) |
| 7 | Pump body | | B  0.280 in (7.1 mm) |
| 8 | Bearing assembly | | C  0.010 in (0.25 mm) |

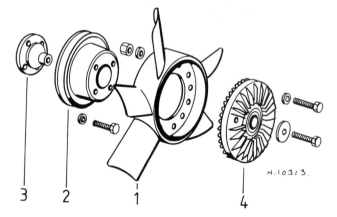

Fig. 2.4 Holset viscous fan unit (Sec 9)

| | | | |
|---|---|---|---|
| 1 | Plastic fan blades | 3 | Hub |
| 2 | Pulley | 4 | Drive unit |

## 10 Antifreeze

1    Antifreeze liquid added to the coolant is the accepted protection against cold which can freeze the coolant and crack the block. Even though a heater may be available whilst the car is garaged at night, daytime temperatures when the car is parked outside can be low enough to freeze. At very low temperatures a car without antifreeze can freeze up, whilst running, at the bottom of the radiator. Also, a small quantity of water will always remain in the block after draining which could freeze and cause damage.
2    Antifreeze has searching properties and if there are any leaks in the system it will accentuate them. You may notice coloured stains at the offending places. Make sure, therefore, that the cooling system is in good condition before adding antifreeze.
3    Use only antifreeze liquid to BS 3151/3152, an inhibited ethylene glycol mixture, inhibited to protect attacks on aluminium alloy components.
4    Mix the required quantity of antifreeze liquid with half the quantity of clean water required to fill the system. Pour this into the flushed-out radiator and top-up with clean water. Run the engine straight away to disperse the antifreeze thoroughly throughout.
5    The percentages of antifreeze to use (in relation to the total cooling liquid capacity) are given in the table below.

| Solution strength | Frost protection | Safe pump circulation |
|---|---|---|
| 25% | -15°F (-26°C) | 10°F (-12°C) |
| 30% | -28°F (-33°C) | 3°F (-16°C) |
| 35% | -38°F (-39°C) | -4°F (-20°C) |
| 40% | -42°F (-41°C) | -10°F (-23°C) |
| 50% | -53°F (-47°C) | -32°F (-36°C) |

## 11 Fanbelt – removal, refitting and adjustment

1    If the fanbelt is badly worn, or stretched so far that it is too slack at maximum adjustment, it should be renewed. It is wise to carry a spare at all times.
2    First, slacken the two nuts and bolts on which the generator pivots and then the bolts underneath which lock the long slotted adjusting brace. Do not slacken any of the bolts more than is necessary to just move the generator with a little force.
3    Move the generator so that the fanbelt may be removed.
4    Fit a new fanbelt over the pulleys and move the generator out until it is tight. Then tighten the bolts. This will be easier to do if the bolts are tight enough to allow the generator to move only when levered. Check the fanbelt tension by depressing it between the generator and water pump pulleys. It should not deflect more than $\frac{1}{2}$ in under 9lb pressure. Do not overtighten the belt or excessive strain will be put on the generator and pump bearings.
5    After a new belt has run for a few hundred miles, check the tension again – the initial stretch may require re-adjustment.
6    There are no definite rules as regards frequency of checking but it only takes a second every time the oil and water levels are checked.

## 12 Water temperature gauge – fault diagnosis and rectification

1    If no reading is recorded on the gauge when the engine is hot, the fault is in either the gauge, sender unit or wiring. Do not remove the wire from the sender unit and short it to earth to check whether a reading can be obtained. This will burn out the windings of the gauge.
2    If the fuel gauge is also not functioning, the cause may be that the instrument voltage stabiliser unit is faulty.
3    Otherwise, disconnect the terminal from the transmitter unit and insulate the end of the wire so that it will not short accidentally and damage the gauge (photo).
4    Measure the resistance in ohms between the transmitter terminal and earth when the engine is cold and again when hot. If there is no difference, then it is faulty and should be unscrewed and a new one fitted. If there is a variation in resistance measured, the gauge is probably faulty and will need renewal. Make sure first, however, that the wire from sender to gauge is in order. Details of instrument removal will be found in Chapter 10.

12.3 Disconnecting the transmitter lead

## 13 Fault diagnosis – cooling system

| Symptom | Reason(s) |
| --- | --- |
| Loss of coolant | Leaking hoses (at clips) |
| | Leaking hoses (damaged) |
| | Leak in radiator |
| | Leak in heater |
| | Leak at cooling system gaskets |
| | Defective cylinder head gasket |
| | Cracked or porous cylinder head or block |
| | Defective radiator cap |
| | Leaking water pump seal |
| | Leaking core plug in cylinder block |
| Overheating | Insufficient coolant |
| | Fan-belt slipping |
| | Radiator core blocked |
| | Vehicle front grille obstructed |
| | Water hose kinked, or collapsed internally, impeding flow |
| | Defective thermostat |
| | Ignition timing incorrect |
| | Carburettor incorrectly adjusted |
| | Defective radiator cap |
| | Insufficient engine oil |
| | Brakes binding |
| | New or rebuilt engine, still tight |
| | Corroded cooling system, impeding flow |
| | Water pump impeller shaft broken, hence impeller not revolving |
| Overcooling | Defective thermostat |
| | No thermostat fitted |

# Chapter 3 Fuel and exhaust systems

## Contents

Air cleaner: single and twin Stromberg 150 ED-3 – removal, cleaning and refitting ............................................................................ 7
Air cleaner: Stromberg 150 CDS – removal, cleaning and refitting ......................................................................................... 3
Air cleaner: Stromberg 150 CDSE – removal, cleaning and refitting ......................................................................................... 5
Air cleaner: SU HS4 – removal, cleaning and refitting .......... 8
Air cleaner: SU HS4C – removal, cleaning and refitting ....... 9
Air cleaner: twin Stromberg 150 CDS – removal, cleaning and refitting ................................................................... 4
Air cleaner: twin Weber 40 DCOE – removal, cleaning and refitting ........................................................................... 6
Choke control with twin Stromberg carburettors – renewal and adjustment ........................................................................ 16
Exhaust emission control ............................................................ 38
Exhaust system ........................................................................... 43
Fault diagnosis – fuel system .................................................... 44
Fuel gauge – tank sender unit .................................................. 41
Fuel pump – inspection, dismantling and reassembly ............. 40
Fuel pump – removal and refitting ........................................... 39
Fuel tank – removal and refitting ............................................. 42
General description ...................................................................... 1
Routine maintenance ................................................................... 2
Stromberg 150 CDS carburettor – description and principles of operation ................................................................................ 10
Stromberg 150 CDS carburettor – dismantling, inspection and reassembly .......................................................................... 13

Stromberg 150 CDS carburettor – removal and refitting .............. 11
Stromberg 150 CDS carburettor – setting and adjustments ........ 12
Stromberg 150 CDS twin carburettors – removal and refitting ... 15
Stromberg 150 CDS twin carburettors – slow running and synchronization ........................................................................... 14
Stromberg 150 CD-3 carburettor – general description ............... 21
Stromberg 150 CD-3 carburettor – operation, dismantling, cleaning and reassembly ............................................................. 22
Stromberg 150 CD-3 carburettor – setting and adjustment ........ 23
Stromberg 150 CD-3 twin carburettors – adjustment ................. 24
SU HS4 carburettor – adjustments and tuning ........................... 35
SU HS4 carburettor – dismantling and reassembly .................... 27
SU HS4 carburettor – examination and repair ........................... 28
SU HS4 carburettor – float chamber flooding ............................ 31
SU HS4 carburettor – float chamber fuel level adjustment ........ 32
SU HS4 carburettor – float needle sticking ................................ 30
SU HS4 carburettor – general description ................................... 25
SU HS4 carburettor – jet centering ............................................ 33
SU HS4 carburettor – needle renewal ......................................... 34
SU HS4 carburettor – piston sticking .......................................... 29
SU HS4 carburettor – removal and refitting ................................ 26
SU HS4C carburettor – adjustments ............................................ 37
SU HS4C carburettor – description .............................................. 36
Weber 40 DCOE carburettors – adjustments ............................... 18
Weber 40 DCOE carburettors – dismantling for cleaning ........... 20
Weber 40 DCOE carburettor – general description ...................... 17
Weber 40 DCOE carburettors – removal and refitting ................. 19

## Specifications

### Fuel pump
Type .................................................................................... AC mechanical
Delivery pressure ............................................................... 2.75 to 4.25 lbf/in$^2$ (0.19 to 0.29 kg/cm$^2$)

### Air cleaner
Holbay engine ..................................................................... Dry element type
All other engines ................................................................ AC Delco (single) or Fram (twin) – dry elements

### Carburettor
Type .................................................................................... Constant depression

### Stromberg 150 CDS

| | Single | Twin |
|---|---|---|
| Slow running speed | 700 to 800 rpm | 800 to 900 rpm |
| Needle: | | |
| Sea level to 5000 ft (1500m) | 6P (alum. head) 6Q (iron head) | GR |
| 5000 to 10 000 ft (1500 to 3000m) | 5R | 5AC |
| Over 10 000 ft (3000m) | 5T | 5AD |
| Spring | Red (all engines) | Blue |
| Fast idle adjustment (between screw head and cam) | 0.065 in (1.65 mm) for 12 coil spring on cam travel stop: 0.045 in (1.14 mm) for 6 coil spring on cam travel stop | 0.050 in (1.27 mm) |
| Choke control | Manual | Manual |

## Stromberg 150 CD-3 (up to 7 series)

| | Single | | Twin |
|---|---|---|---|
| | *Aluminium head* | *Iron head* | *Aluminium head* |
| Slow running speed | 870 to 930 rpm | 770 to 830 rpm | 900 to 960 rpm |
| Needle: | | | |
|    Sea level to 5000 ft (1500m) | B5CL | B5CM | B5CK |
|    5000 to 10 000 ft (1500 to 3000m) | B5CQ | B5CS | B5CV |
|    Over 10 000 ft (3000m) | B5CR | B5CT | B5CW |
| Spring | Red | Red | Blue |
| Fast idle adjustment (between screw head and cam) | 0.05 in (1.27 mm) | 0.045 in (1.14 mm) | 0.040 in (1.01 mm) |
| Choke control | Manual | Manual | Manual |

## Stromberg 150 CD-3 (commencing 7 series)
### 1725 cc engine

| | **Iron head** | | **Aluminium head** |
|---|---|---|---|
| | HC | LC | |
| Slow running speed | 770 to 830 rpm | 770 to 830 rpm | 870 to 930 rpm |
| Needle | B5ED | B5ED | B5EC |
| Spring | Red | Blue | Red |
| Fast idle adjustment | 0.045 in (1.14 mm) | 0.045 in (1.14 mm) | 0.045 in (1.14 mm) |
| Choke control | Manual | Manual | Manual |

### 1500cc engine (iron head)

| | |
|---|---|
| Slow running speed | 770 to 830 rpm |
| Needle | B5DZ |
| Spring | Blue |
| Fast idle adjustment | 0.045 in (1.14 mm) |
| Choke control | Manual |

## SU HS4

| | Iron head | Aluminium head |
|---|---|---|
| | 770 to 830 rpm | 870 to 930 rpm |
| Slow running speed | | |
| Needle | AAK | AAK |
| Spring | Green | Green |
| Choke control | Manual | Manual |

## SU HS4C

| | | |
|---|---|---|
| Slow running speed | 770 to 830 rpm | 870 to 930 rpm |
| Needle | ABW | ABZ |
| Spring | Yellow | Yellow |
| Choke control | Manual | Manual |

## Twin Weber 40 DCOE (Holbay engine)

| | Earlier models | | Later models |
|---|---|---|---|
| Slow running speed | 1000 rpm | | 1000 rpm |
| Choke size | 30 mm | 30 mm | 30 mm |
| Auxiliary venturi | 45 mm | 35 mm | 35 mm |
| Main jet | 100 | 115 | 115 |
| Pilot (idling) jet | 45F.4 | F.18/50 | F.18/50 |
| Air correction jet | 140 | 200 | 200 |
| Pump jet | 35 | 35 | 35 |
| Starting jet (fuel) | 60F.5 | F.1/120 | 140F.5 |
| Starting air jet | 100 | 100 | 100 |
| Starting mixture bush | 60 mm | 60 mm | 80 mm |
| Float level setting | 8.50 mm | 7.0 mm | 7.50 mm |

## Single Stromberg CDSE (Arrow Sedan engine)

| | |
|---|---|
| Slow running speed: | |
|    Manual transmission | 850 rpm |
|    Automatic transmission in D | 750 rpm |
| Needle | B 5A P |
| Spring | Red, 0.040 in (1.02 mm) dia. wire |
| Fast idle adjustment (between adjustment screw head and fast idle cam) | 0.045 to 0.055 in (1.14 to 1.39 mm) |

**Note:** *If a needle is renewed, be sure the new one has the same identification as the one removed*

## Fuel tank capacity

| | |
|---|---|
| All models | 10 gals/12 US gals (45.50 litres) |

## 1 General description

A ten gallon fuel tank is mounted under the rear of the car and from this fuel is drawn by an AC mechanical pump and delivered to the carburettor(s).

The pump is operated by an arm actuated by a cam on the camshaft and is located low down forward on the right-hand side of the engine block. The pump incorporates a filter screen. Fuel is delivered to a variety of carburettors according to model and the type of engine fitted. The output of the pump exceeds all normal requirements of the single or twin carburettors and fuel level within all carburettors is regulated by a float operated needle valve. When the valve is closed (shutting off the flow) the pump freewheels. The diaphragm is held up by the pressure in the line until such time as the carburettor needle valve opens, allowing the spring action of the pump to resume oscillating the diaphragm and to deliver more fuel.

The air taken in through the carburettor is filtered by a renewable paper element.

## 2   Routine maintenance

1   Every 5000 miles, or more frequently in very dusty circumstances, remove the air filter element and tap it smartly on a flat surface to dislodge any excess accumulations of dust on the outside. Wipe out the filter housing.

2   Lubricate all pivot points on the carburettor controls frequently, using engine oil from an oil can.

3   Other routine maintenance details are listed in the full maintenance schedule given at the beginning of the book. Details of the operations involved will be found in the relevant Sections.

## 3   Air cleaner: Stromberg 150 CDS – removal, cleaning and refitting

1   Unhook the throttle return spring where it hooks into an eye on the back of the air filter housing. Pull the rubber fume pipe off.

2   Unscrew the two bolts which hold the whole air cleaner assembly to the carburettor. Once these are clear, the whole unit may be lifted off and separated to give access to the filter element. Clean out the interior of the filter housing. If the same element is to be refitted, tap it on a flat surface to remove any loose accumulations of dust. Do *not* try to wash it, brush it – or blow it with compressed air.

3   When reassembling the unit, make sure the sealing rings are intact and in place. When fitting the element, it should seat snugly over the locating ridges in the housing.

4   When reassembling the unit, care should be taken that the gasket between the throttle spring plate and carburettor flange is the correct way up, otherwise the float chamber air vent will be blocked off.

5   The air intake pipe may be positioned for 'Summer' or 'Winter' conditions by revolving the casing, so that the appropriate arrows line up. In some cases, a duct will be fitted to the exhaust pipe and when the air cleaner intake pipe is required in the 'Winter' setting, it should be entered into the duct. To change the setting, the two fixing bolts should be removed, not merely loosened. If this is not done, damage can be caused to the threads in the mounting flange.

## 4   Air cleaner: twin Stromberg 150 CDS – removal, cleaning and refitting

1   The procedure is basically as described for fitting the single carburettor, except that four fixing bolts are employed.

2   The intake tube can be moved to any one of three positions. The 'Winter' position is at right angles to the air cleaner body, so that the end is near the exhaust manifold. The 'Summer' position is in line with the air cleaner body, and pointing directly forwards. The maintenance position – to improve access to certain adjacent items – is when turned to point towards the wing valance.

## 5   Air cleaner: Stromberg 150 CDSE – removal, cleaning and refitting

The procedure is basically as described for the Stromberg 150 CDS in Section 3.

## 6   Air cleaner: twin Weber 40 DCOE – removal, cleaning and refitting

1   Turn the front wheels on to right lock. Release the clip holding the air intake flexible pipe to the carburettor air box.

2   Pull off the flexible pipe.

3   Remove the two $\frac{7}{16}$ in AF screws and one $\frac{1}{2}$ in AF nut that secure the cleaner to the wing valance and lift away the cleaner. Do not lose the washers under the $\frac{1}{2}$ in AF nut.

4   Unscrew the wing nut on the air cleaner and remove the cover.

5   Take out the element, noting that rubber sealing rings are used

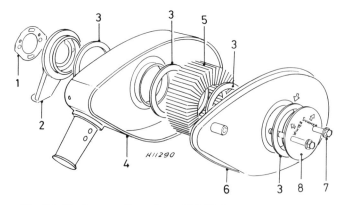

**Fig. 3.1 Air cleaner – Stromberg 150 CDS carburettor (Sec 3)**

| | | | |
|---|---|---|---|
| 1 | Gasket – cleaner to carburettor | 5 | Paper element |
| 2 | Throttle return spring plate | 6 | Cover |
| 3 | Sealing ring | 7 | Fixing bolt |
| 4 | Main body | 8 | Fixing plate |

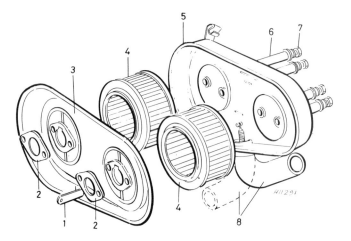

**Fig. 3.2 Air cleaners – twin Stromberg 150 CDS carburettors (Sec 4)**

| | | | |
|---|---|---|---|
| 1 | Throttle return spring attachment bracket | 5 | Air cleaner casing |
| 2 | Air cleaner to carburettor flange gaskets | 6 | Distance pieces – four |
| 3 | Air cleaner backplate | 7 | Air cleaner fixing bolts – four |
| 4 | Air cleaner elements | 8 | Air cleaner intake |

under each end of the filter element.

6   Clean out the casing and, if the element is to be refitted, tap it on a hard surface to remove surface dust. Use a low pressure air line directed sideways onto the filter surface (not directly at it) to remove any remaining dust.

7   If it is required to remove the air box from the carburettor, unscrew the retaining nuts. When refitting, use a gasket cement on the gasket fitted between the air box and backplate.

8   Reassembly and refitting is essentially a reversal of the removal procedure. Ensure that the element/cover sealing rings are undamaged and properly located.

9   When refitting the air cleaner to the wing valance, liberally grease the nut and screws to preclude rusting.

## 7   Air cleaner: single and twin Stromberg 150 CD-3 – removal, cleaning and refitting

The procedure is as described for the Stromberg 150 CDS in either Section 3 or Section 4, as relevant.

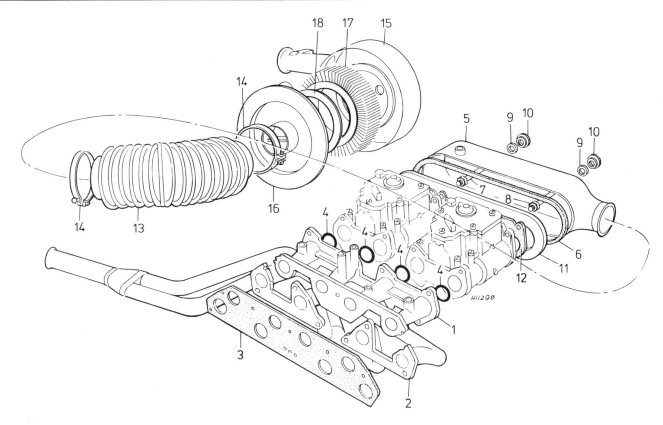

**Fig. 3.3 Air cleaner, manifolds and air box – twin Weber DCOE carburettors (Sec 6)**

| | | | | | |
|---|---|---|---|---|---|
| 1 | Inlet manifold | 6 | Gasket | 11 | Backplate |
| 2 | Exhaust manifold | 7 | Stud | 12 | Gasket |
| 3 | Manifold gasket | 8 | Locknut | 13 | Air hose |
| 4 | Sealing rings | 9 | Fibre washer | 14 | Clip |
| 5 | Air box | 10 | Nut | | |

| | |
|---|---|
| 15 | Air filter cover |
| 16 | Filter body |
| 17 | Filter element |
| 18 | Sealing ring |

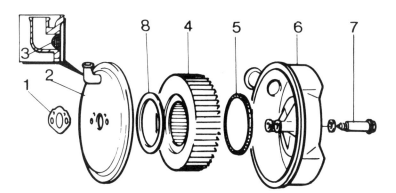

**Fig. 3.4 Air cleaner – SU HS4 carburettor (Sec 8)**

| | |
|---|---|
| 1 | Gasket |
| 2 | Cover |
| 3 | Gauze screen |
| 4 | Element |
| 5 | Sealing rings |
| 6 | Body |
| 7 | Securing bolts |
| 8 | Sealing ring |

## 8 Air cleaner: SU HS4 – removal, cleaning and refitting

1 The general procedure is as described in Section 3, except that the throttle spring is not clipped to the casing.
2 There is a gauze screen on the cover at the rocker housing hose connection which should be cleaned with paraffin or petrol, then blown dry with compressed air.

## 9 Air cleaner: SU HS4C – removal, cleaning and refitting

The procedures are similar to that for the air filter fitted to the HS4 carburettor, except that, after removing the two bolts securing the filter to the carburettor, four screws must be removed to separate the cover and body, to gain access to the filter element. The remainder of the removal sequence and the refitting follow the same lines as the HS4.

## 10 Stromberg 150 CDS carburettor – description and principle of operation

The Stromberg carburettor is a variable choke design with a single fuel delivery jet. This means that the cross-sectional area of the air intake passage through the carburettor varies according to demands made by the engine. The fuel, which is drawn into the air passage through a jet orifice, is metered by a tapered needle which moves in and out of the jet, thus varying the effective size of the orifice. This needle is attached to, and moves with the air valve piston which controls the variable choke opening.

At rest, the air valve piston is right down, choking off the air

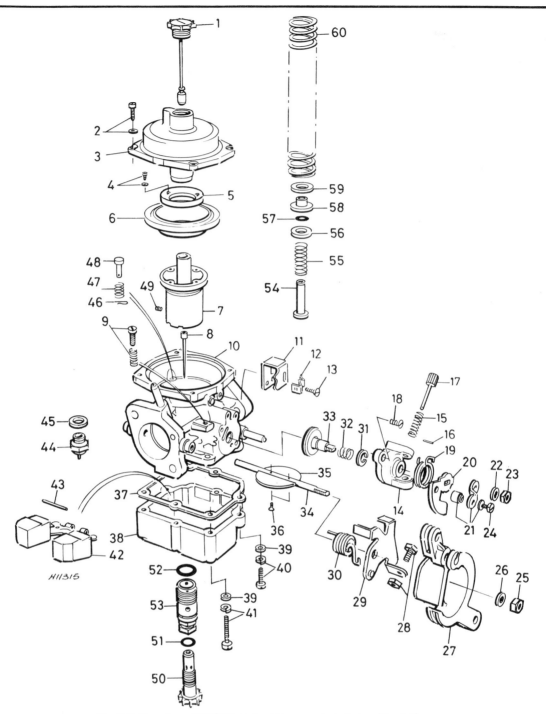

**Fig. 3.5 Stromberg 150 CDS carburettor – exploded view (Sec 10)**

| | | | |
|---|---|---|---|
| 1 | Air valve piston damper | 16 | Pin |
| 2 | Screw and spring washer | 17 | Travel stop |
| 3 | Suction cover chamber | 18 | Fixing screw |
| 4 | Screw and spring washer | 19 | Fast idle cam return spring |
| 5 | Diaphragm retaining ring | 20 | Fast idle cam |
| 6 | Diaphragm | 21 | Lever |
| 7 | Air valve piston | 22 | Washer |
| 8 | Metering needle | 23 | Nut |
| 9 | Slow running adjustment screw | 24 | Screw |
| 10 | Carburettor body | 25 | Nut |
| 11 | Choke cable bracket | 26 | Washer |
| 12 | Choke cable clip | 27 | Guide plate |
| 13 | Screw | 28 | Adjusting screw |
| 14 | Starter cover | 29 | Stop lever |
| 15 | Travel stop spring | 30 | Return spring |
| | | 31 | Spring retainer |

| | | | |
|---|---|---|---|
| 32 | Disc valve spring | 48 | Air valve piston lifting pin |
| 33 | Starter assembly disc valve | 49 | Locking screw |
| 34 | Throttle spindle | 50 | Jet adjustment |
| 35 | Throttle valve | 51 | O-ring jet adjustment |
| 36 | Throttle valve fixing screws | 52 | O-ring jet bushing retaining screw |
| 37 | Gasket | 53 | Jet bushing retaining screw |
| 38 | Float chamber | 54 | Jet |
| 39 | Washer | 55 | Jet spring |
| 40 | Screw (short) | 56 | Washer |
| 41 | Screw (long) | 57 | O-ring jet |
| 42 | Float assembly | 58 | Jet and centralising bush |
| 43 | Float pivot pin | 59 | Washer |
| 44 | Float valve assembly | 60 | Air valve piston return spring |
| 45 | Valve seat washer | | |
| 46 | Retainer | | |
| 47 | Spring | | |

supply. The tapered needle is fully home with the jet virtually cutting off the fuel outlet from the jet. For starting, the cold start lever is first pulled and this sets the cold start device so that fuel may be drawn into the main air passage via an independent passage which is opened up. It also opens the throttle flap a small amount. (On earlier types of Stromberg carburettors, the cold start device consisted of lifting the air valve a little mechanically, thus drawing the needle out of the jet to provide the richer mixture necessary).

As soon as the engine fires the suction from the engine, or manifold depression, is partially diverted to the upper side of the chamber in which the diaphragm (attached to the air valve piston) is positioned. This causes the valve to rise and provides sufficient air flow to enable the engine to run. As the throttle is opened further, manifold depression is reduced and now it is the speed of air through the venturi which causes the depression in the upper chamber, thus causing the piston to rise further. If the throttle is opened suddenly, the natural tendency of the air valve piston to rise – causing a weak mixture when it is least required (ie during acceleration) – is prevented by a hydraulic damper which delays the piston in its upward travel. The air intake is thus restricted and a proportionately larger quantity of fuel to air is drawn through.

Under constant speed running conditions, the air valve position is balanced by air speed through the venturi, throttle opening and the light pressure of the diaphragm return spring. The normal position for the starter assembly travel stop is shown in Fig. 3.7 (inset). At –23°C (–10°F) or below, the stop should be pushed in and turned to the position shown in the main figure, to assist cold starting.

11.2 Undoing the fuel pipe union

## 11 Stromberg 150 CDS carburettor – removal and refitting

1   The carburettor may be removed prior to engine removal or to dismantle and overhaul it.

2   Undo the fuel pipe union from the carburettor (photo).

3   Unhook the throttle return spring from the back of the air cleaner

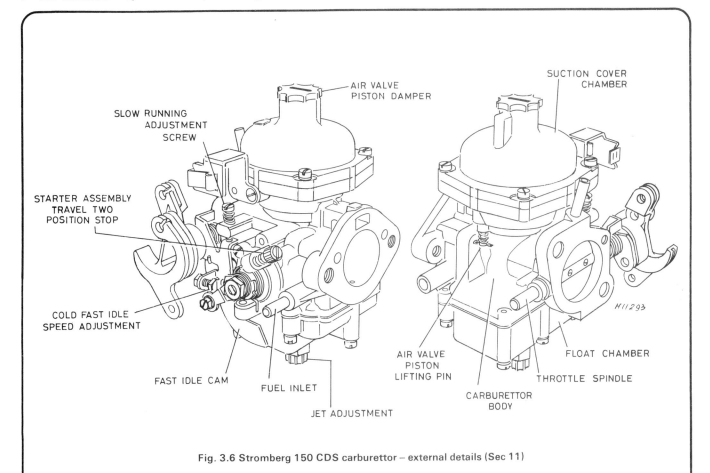

Fig. 3.6 Stromberg 150 CDS carburettor – external details (Sec 11)

11.3a Unhooking the throttle return spring

11.3b Removing the air cleaner

11.4 Detaching the vacuum pipe

11.5 Detaching the cold start cable

11.6 Detaching the throttle cable from the bracket ...

11.7 ... and throttle lever

11.8 Removing the carburettor by undoing the mounting stud nuts

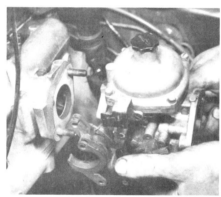
11.9 Lifting away the carburettor

11.11a Ensuring that the cold start outer cable clears ...

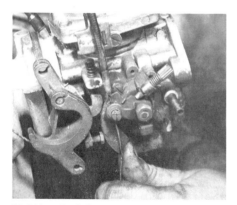
11.11b ... the fully open actuating arm

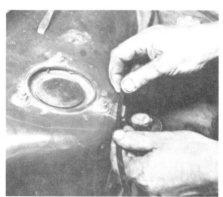
11.12a Ensure that the throttle and cold start cables ...

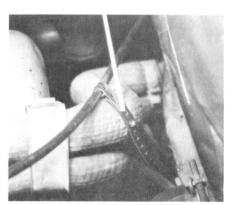
11.12b ... are correctly clipped

and then undo the two bolts securing the air cleaner to the carburettor and lift it away (photos).

4   Detach the vacuum pipe from the connection to the mounting flange (photo).

5   Slacken the screw securing the cold start inner cable to the operating lever, undo the clip over the outer cable and lift the cable away (photo).

6   Detach the throttle cable from the mounting bracket by undoing the locknut nearest the open end only (otherwise the positioning will be upset). Alternatively, the bracket and cable may be detached together by undoing the bolt holding the bracket to the inlet manifold (photo).

7   Unloop the cable from the throttle lever and take the nipple out of the recess (photo).

8   Undo the two mounting stud nuts holding the carburettor in position. One of these can only be removed completely whilst the carburettor is being drawn back off the studs. It may also be necessary to grind one jaw of the spanner, to enable it to engage fully with the partly-inaccessible nut (photo).

9   Lift away the carburettor (photo).

10  Refitting is the reverse of the removal procedure, with particular attention to the following points.

11  When refitting the cold start cable to the carburettor, do not clip the outer in position until the arm has been checked in the fully open position. If the outer is clipped in position, with the end too far down, the limit of travel of the operating arm will be restricted and result in

cold start difficulties (photos).

12  Make sure the throttle and cold start cables are properly clipped to keep their position. If this is not done, variations can result in the amount of movement at the operating levers on the carburettor (photos).

13  Top-up the air valve piston bore to 0.25 in (6.35 mm) from the top edge, using clean engine oil.

## 12  Stromberg 150 CDS carburettor – setting and adjustments

1   Before making any adjustments to the carburettor settings, make sure your reasons for the adjustment are sound and that you only do one at a time. Check the result of each adjustment after it is made. The Stromberg carburettor is a finely balanced and relatively delicate instrument and can easily be put off tune.

2   Control settings are important. Make sure the operation of the cold start cable moves the lever easily throughout its full range of movement and returns to its closed position when the control knob is pushed home. Adjustment can be made by repositioning the inner cable relative to the operating arm at the clamping screw. The outer cable can be repositioned as necessary where it clips to the bracket on the carburettor.

3   The throttle cable should also be checked for movement throughout its range. Make particularly sure that when the throttle flap is in the fully open position, the position of the accelerator pedal is as far

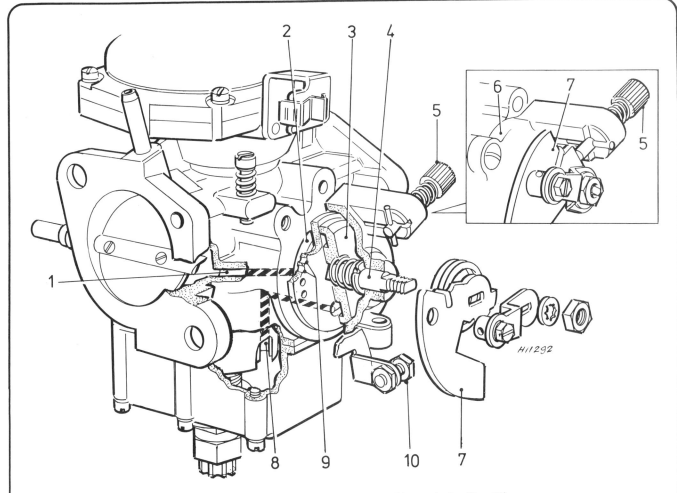

**Fig. 3.7 Stromberg 150 CDS carburettor – cold start device (Sec 12)**

| | |
|---|---|
| *1   Drilling for fuel from disc valve* | *6   Starter device outer housing* |
| *2   Port to fuel feed drilling from disc valve* | *7   Fast idle cam* |
| *3   Disc valve* | *8   Drilling for fuel from float chamber to disc valve* |
| *4   Disc valve spindle* | *9   Orifices for fuel in disc valve* |
| *5   Two position stop for cold start opening limit* | *10  Fast idle adjustment screw* |

down as it could possibly be, even with the cable disconnected. Otherwise, pressure on the pedal will impart strain on the cable and more important, on the throttle spindle and bearings. Adjustment should be made at the point where the end of the cable outer is located into the bracket near the carburettor. Slacken the two locknuts and move the outer cable so that when the accelerator pedal is fully depressed, the throttle is just fully open.

4    Slow running adjustment is controlled by the throttle stop screw, which in turn regulates the position of the throttle flap when the accelerator cable is at rest. The single jet controls fuel mixture throughout the full operational range. If satisfactory slow running cannot be achieved with the throttle stop screw adjustment, it will be necessary to proceed to the following check which affects the carburettor performance at all speeds.

5    If slow running indicates that further adjustment, other than on the throttle stop screw, is required, first remove the air valve piston damper from the top of the carburettor. Insert a thin rod or screwdriver into the top and use this to hold the piston down. At the same time turn the jet adjustment screw (Note: *not* the jet bush retainer) upwards so that the jet itself eventually touches the air valve piston. This will be felt when the adjusting screw meets resistance. Release the downward pressure on the valve piston, then check the piston moves freely. This can be done by lifting the pin and letting it fall. An audible 'click' should be heard as the piston hits the jet bridge. (If this does not occur, the jet will need centralising as described later). Back off the jet adjusting screw two complete turns.

6    Refill the piston damper bore to within 0.24 in (6 mm) of its upper edge with clean engine oil (do not use very low viscosity oils). Refit the damper piston. Run the engine until normal temperature is reached and adjust the throttle stop screw to obtain an idling speed of 700 to 800 rpm. It is permissible to move the jet adjuster screw not more than a half turn in either direction to achieve the desired smooth running. If no success is achieved, it will be necessary to check the needle position in the piston. This involves partial dismantling and is covered in the next Section.

7    The jet will need to be centralised if movement of the piston valve is binding the needle against the side of the jet orifice. The jet is located in a bush which permits it to move up and down when the jet adjusting screw is turned. The bush is locked into position by the jet bush retaining screw and when this is slackened the jet bushing, together with the jet, is free to move laterally. To centralise the jet, first slacken the jet bushing retainer by half a turn. Then turn the jet adjusting screw so the jet is level with the bridge face (as described in the previous adjustment). Then tap the jet bushing retainer to assist the jet to find its position round the needle. The jet bushing retainer screw should then be tightened and the piston lifted with the pin and allowed to drop. An audible click indicates that it is falling to the bottom of its stroke without hindrance. Then readjust the jet as described for the last adjustment in paragraph 6.

8    In certain cases of excessive fuel consumption or flooding, it may be that the floats or needle valve positions need resetting. For this, dismantling is necessary and the adjustment procedure is incorporated in the next Section.

9    The carburettor is so designed that when the cold start device is used, the throttle is automatically opened a specified amount. This ensures the engine speed is kept up; otherwise the rich mixture would stall the engine at low revolutions. The throttle opening is set by the fast idle adjustment screw. The head of this screw bears against the fast idle cam, mounted on the cold start device boss. The screw may be adjusted to give the correct gap between head and cam, with the cold start device closed, after slackening the locknut. The clearances are given in the Specifications.

10  If the engine oil is changed to meet very different climatic conditions, the oil in the air valve piston bore should be similarly changed, to avoid problems of poor starting and poor engine response.

## 13  Stromberg 150 CDS carburettor – dismantling, inspection and reassembly

1    Do not dismantle the carburettor unless absolutely necessary. This should only be for cleaning at intervals of 15 000 miles or when systematic diagnosis indicates that there is a fault with it. The internal mechanism is delicate and finely balanced and unnecessary tinkering will probably do more harm than good.

2    Although certain parts may be removed with the carburettor still

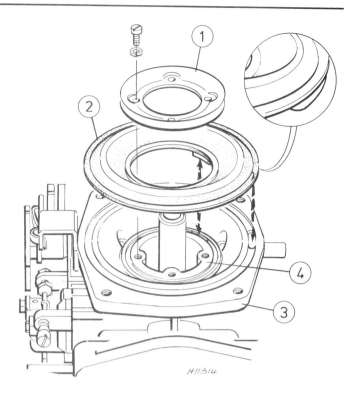

Fig. 3.8 Stromberg 150 CDS carburettor – diaphragm details (Sec 13)

| 1 | Clamping ring | 3 | Main body |
| 2 | Diaphragm | 4 | Air valve |

attached to the engine, nevertheless, it is considered safer to remove it and work over a bench.

3    Having removed the carburettor, take out the piston damper by unscrewing the top cap.

4    Undo the four screws holding the depression chamber cover in position. Mark the edge of the cover and carburettor body so it may be refitted in the same position. Then carefully lift it off, taking care the diaphragm return spring does not get stretched in the process. The return spring should be detached carefully from its upper and lower seatings and laid to one side. If this spring is kinked, stretched or treated in any way that may affect its pressure when fitted, the balance of the carburettor will be upset. Renew it (with one of the correct colour code) if in doubt.

5    Lift out the air valve piston and diaphragm together. If the diaphragm shows signs of perforation, cracking or other damage, it must be renewed. Remove the four screws and washers by which the retaining ring secures it to the piston. Note also that the diaphragm has tabs on its inner and outer edges which locate into slots in the piston and body of the carburettor. When refitting a diaphragm, it is most important that the centre section seats properly on the piston: it is easily dislodged when fitting the retaining ring. With the piston removed, it is possible to check the needle is correctly fitted. The shoulder of the needle should be flush with the face of the piston. If not, it may be re-set after slackening the needle locking screw in the side of the piston.

6    The float chamber may be removed next. First unscrew and remove the jet adjusting screw. Check the O-ring around it is in good condition. Undo the six screws which hold the float chamber to the carburettor body. The chamber may then be carefully pulled down over the jet bushing retainer. It is not essential to remove the jet and associated parts unless it is being renewed. The resistance to pulling off the float chamber will be the O-ring seal, fitted around the jet bushing retainer. This must be examined for condition.

7    With the float chamber removed, the carburettor may be cleaned with petrol or paraffin (nothing else). Use an air jet where possible to blow out the orifices in the body to the cold start device and the main jet area.

8   When the float chamber is removed, the floats may be checked for correct setting. With the carburettor in the inverted position and the needle valve in the closed position the highest point of the float should be 0.61 to 0.65 in (15.5 to 16.5 mm) above the joint face of the body. Both parts of the float should be equal and if necessary the arm that contacts the needle valve may be bent to adjust the float position. If the floats are apparently set correctly and excessive fuel consumption or flooding has been experienced, it is quite possible that the needle valve is worn, so a new one should be fitted. If the needle valve is one which can be separated from its seat, a ridge in the valve face indicates wear.

9   If there is any sign of play between the throttle spindle and the bushes in the body, it may be necessary to consider removing the spindle. This can be done after removing the nut holding the throttle operating lever, removing the two screws securing the throttle plate and drawing the spindle out.

10   Reassembly is a reversal of the dismantling procedure. The float chamber gasket need not necessarily be renewed but it is a good idea to fit three new O-rings on the jet, jet bushing and jet bushing retainer. When the diaphragm and piston assembly is refitted make sure the tabs fit the groves.

11   The jet centralisation and adjustment fast idle cam clearances may be set before refitting the carburettor on the engine.

## 14 Stromberg 150 CDS twin carburettors – slow running and synchronization

1   Synchronizing twin carburettors should only be carried out after checking spark plugs, points and valve clearances and the engine has reached operating temperature (not overheated under a closed bonnet).

2   Remove the air cleaner and both piston dampers.

3   Temporarily, tie the throttle return spring outer end to the fuel pipe T-piece between the carburettors.

4   Remove both depression chamber covers and lift out the air valve pistons and return springs.

5   Remove both needles from the air valve pistons, check their type with details given in the Specifications Section and refit as described for single carburettors in Section 13.

6   Refit the air valve pistons, return springs and depression chamber covers ensuring that the diaphragms are correctly located (Fig. 3.8).

7   Hold each air valve piston down (as described for single carburettors) in turn, screw up the jet adjuster (5) (Fig. 3.9) until it makes contact with the air valve piston.

8   Check that each air valve piston falls freely. If not, centralise the jets as described in Section 12.

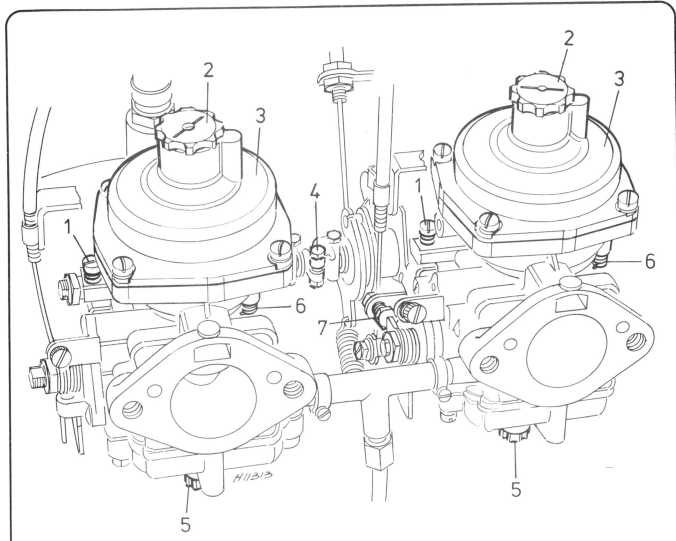

H11313

Fig. 3.9 Stromberg 150 CDS twin carburettors – throttle synchronization and jet adjustment (Sec 14)

| | | |
|---|---|---|
| 1   Slow running speed adjustment screw | 3   Depression chamber cover | 5   Jet adjustment | 7   Fast idle speed adjustment screw |
| 2   Air valve piston hydraulic damper | 4   Coupling clamping bolt | 6   Air valve piston lifting pin | |

9 Refill the damper bores with engine oil to within 0.25 in (6 mm) of the upper edge, and refit the dampers. Screw each jet adjuster down exactly two turns.
10 Unscrew the fast idle speed adjustment screw (7) until it is well clear of the cam on the rear carburettor.
11 Slacken the most accessible clamping bolt (4) on the carburettor throttle couplings.
12 Slacken the slow running screws (1) until they are well clear of the throttle levers, then rotate each screw until a 0.002 in (0.050 mm) feeler gauge is just gripped between them and the throttle levers, with the throttle butterflies held in the closed position. Now rotate each screw clockwise by two turns.
13 Tighten the clamp bolt (4).
14 Start and run the engine until it regains normal operating temperature. If needed, adjust the jet adjusters not more than half a turn each way from the previously set position and readjust each slow running screw by an equal amount to improve the overall idling conditions.
15 Obtain a length of small bore hose, place it at the same point on each carburettor in turn, and listen to the 'hiss' of incoming air with the engine running. If the 'hiss' is greater at one than the other, slacken the clamp bolt (4) and adjust the screw (1), on each carburettor if necessary, until synchronized.
16 With the clamp bolt still loose, adjust each carburettor slow running mixture screw (5) until the highest engine speed is obtained without moving the throttle. Always commence with a weak setting (ie mixture screw high) and work towards a rich setting (ie mixture screw down), when adjusting the slow running mixture.
17 Retighten the clamp bolt whilst making sure the slow running screws rest on their abutment points on the throttle levers.
18 Adjust the fast idle speed screw (7) to obtain the specified adjustment between its domed head and the fast idle cam (ensure that the choke control knob is pushed fully home).
19 On completion, refit the air cleaner and throttle return spring.

## 15 Stromberg 150 CDS twin carburettors – removal and refitting

1 Removal of twin carburettors is similar to removal of a single carburettor as detailed in Section 11. There are, however, four bolts retaining the air cleaner and only the rear carburettor has a vacuum pipe connection.
2 When withdrawing the carburettors, take care not to bend the coupling, which must be removed if any work is to be undertaken on either carburettor.
3 When refitting carburettors, ensure that they are synchronized correctly. Refitting is otherwise a reversal of the removal procedure.

## 16 Choke control with twin Stromberg carburettors – renewal and adjustment

1 Disconnect both outer and inner cables at the carburettor ends.
2 Draw the cables through the bulkhead grommets into the inside of the car.

3 Thread a $\frac{3}{4}$ in (19 mm) AF box spanner over the two cables and remove the nut behind the instrument panel to permit the assembly to be withdrawn.
4 Refit the rear cables in the reverse order to removal.
5 To adjust the cables, set the control knob $\frac{1}{8}$ in (3 mm) from the fully home position, then tighten the pinch bolt on the carburettor starter assembly operating lever.

## 17 Weber 40 DCOE carburettor – general description

The Weber DCOE carburettor has two throttle barrels of equal diameter, each barrel being fitted with similar size venturis, jets and fuel passageways, which are fed from a single float chamber between the two barrels. A single accelerator pump feeds the two accelerator pump jets when the accelerator pedal is depressed, and a single cold starting device feeds fuel into each barrel when brought into action by operation of the choke control.

By using two of these carburettors fitted to a manifold with four separate ports connecting the four throttle barrels of the two carburettors to the four inlet ports of the cylinder head, the advantages of one carburettor for each cylinder are obtained. The throttle shafts of the two carburettors are linked and synchronized so that all four throttles operate together.

This arrangement gives increased power and torque because the carburettors supply each cylinder individually, and are not restricted by the limitations of a common inlet manifold system.

## 18 Weber 40 DCOE carburettors – adjustments

1 Before carrying out any adjustments to the Weber carburettors read Section 12, paragraphs 1 to 3 which apply equally to the Weber instruments.
2 Referring to Fig. 3.10, slow running adjustment is controlled by the screw (3) between the two carburettors. Clockwise rotation increases the idling speed and anticlockwise rotation decreases it. If, after obtaining the correct idling speed of 1000 rpm, the running appears to be uneven, the carburettors will have to be synchronized.
3 Warm up the engine thoroughly, then remove the carburettor air box. Check the tightness of all manifold and carburettor retaining nuts and bolts to ensure there are no leaks which could cause the uneven running (see Section 6).
4 Screw the mixture control screws (1) lightly onto their seats, then back them off half a turn each. Start up the engine and adjust the throttle stop screw until the engine runs at 1000 to 1200 rpm.
5 Listen, with a suitable length of pipe, at the same point on each air intake. A similar 'hiss' should be heard from each one. If the 'hiss' is different adjust the synchronizing screw (2) until a similar hiss is obtained.
6 Listening to the engine very carefully, or with an assistant in the car watching the tachometer, adjust each mixture control screw by no more than 1/12th of a turn at a time untill the highest engine speed is obtained as each screw is adjusted. Clockwise movement of the screws weakens the mixture and anticlockwise richens it. If there is no

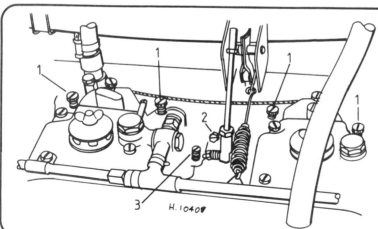

Fig. 3.10 Weber 40 DCOE carburettors – slow running and synchronizing adjustments (Sec 18)

1 Slow running mixture volume control screws
2 Carburettor synchronizing adjustment screw
3 Slow running speed adjustment screw

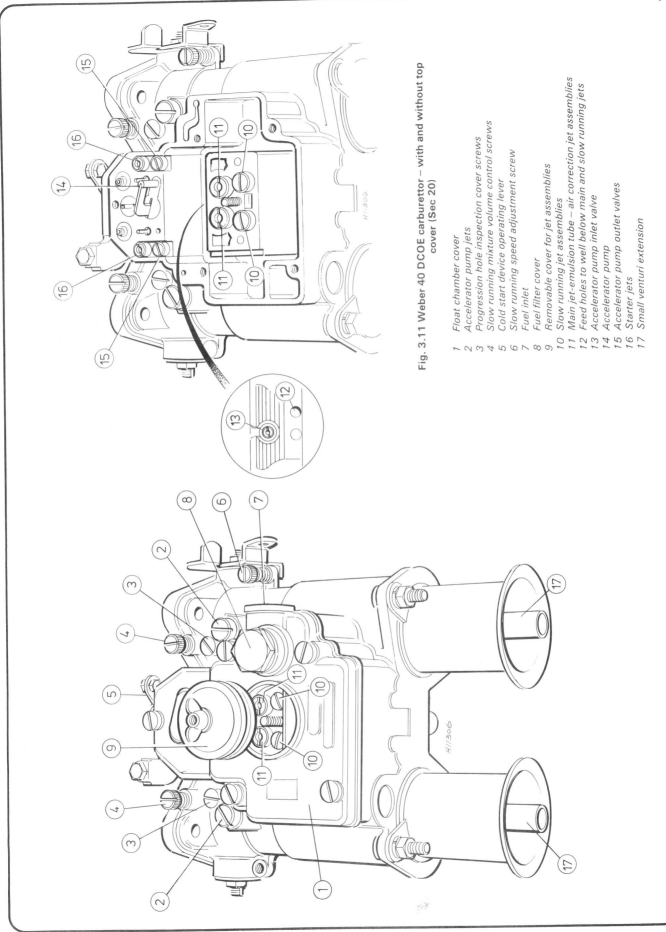

Fig. 3.11 Weber 40 DCOE carburettor – with and without top cover (Sec 20)

1 Float chamber cover
2 Accelerator pump jets
3 Progression hole inspection cover screws
4 Slow running mixture volume control screws
5 Cold start device operating lever
6 Slow running speed adjustment screw
7 Fuel inlet
8 Fuel filter cover
9 Removable cover for jet assemblies
10 Slow running jet assemblies
11 Main jet-emulsion tube – air correction jet assemblies
12 Feed holes to well below main and slow running jets
13 Accelerator pump inlet valve
14 Accelerator pump
15 Accelerator pump outlet valves
16 Starter jets
17 Small venturi extension

H11294

response to these adjustments it indicates that there is an air leak either at the inlet manifold gasket or at the joint between the carburettor and the inlet manifold.

7    Finally, adjust the slow running to 1000 rpm with the adjustment screw (3). Short out each spark plug in turn and if the adjustments have been done correctly, there should be the same falling off of revs as each plug is shorted out.

8    Refit the air box, and recheck idling speed.

## 19 Weber 40 DCOE carburettors – removal and refitting

1    The operations for removing the Weber 40 DCOE carburettors are much the same as those for removing the Stromberg 150 CDS units described previously, so only brief instructions will be given in this Section.

2    Disconnect the air cleaner hose at the carburettor air box end by releasing the clip (Fig. 3.3).

3    Remove the air box from the carburettor by undoing the two long through-bolts and nuts.

### Fig. 3.12 Weber 40 DCOE carburettors – exploded view (Sec 20)

| | |
|---|---|
| 1   Fuel inlet union | 47   Gasket |
| 2   Washer | 48   Cover plate |
| 3   Washer | 49   Accelerator pump control |
| 4   Filter gauze | lever |
| 5   Bushing | 50   Pin |
| 6   Washer | 51   Carburettor body |
| 7   Filter cover plug | 52   Gasket |
| 8   Float chamber air vent | 53   Cover plate |
| 9   Jet inspection cover | 54   Screw |
| 10   Screw | 55   Screw |
| 11   Spring washer | 56   Spring washer |
| 12   Brass washer | 57   Washer |
| 13   Float chamber cover | 58   Nut |
| 14   Gasket | 59   Spring washer |
| 15   Washer | 60   Choke cable attachment |
| 16   Needle valve body | 61   Starter device operating |
| 17   Needle valve | lever |
| 18   Pin | 62   Screw |
| 19   Twin floats | 63   Return spring |
| 20   Emulsion tube holder | 64   Cold start device body |
| 21   Air correction jet | 65   Starter shaft |
| 22   Emulsion tube | 66   Gauze |
| 23   Main jet | 67   Screw |
| 24   Slow running jet holder | 68   Cold start device assembly |
| 25   Slow running jet | 69   Throttle lever |
| 26   Cover plate | 70   Starter valve |
| 27   Spring and anchorage | 71   Return spring |
| 28   Stud | 72   Spring guide and retainer |
| 29   Accelerator pump inlet | 73   Spring ring |
| valve | 74   Retainer plate |
| 30   Air inlet | 75   Accelerator pump control rod |
| 31   Nut | 76   Return spring |
| 32   Spring washer | 77   Piston |
| 33   Plate | 78   Slow running adjustment |
| 34   Auxiliary venturi | screw |
| 35   Large venturi | 79   Volume control screw |
| 36   Stud | 80   Spring |
| 37   Bearing | 81   Spring |
| 38   Dust cover | 82   Progression hole cover screw |
| 39   Spring | 83   Gasket washer |
| 40   Cover | 84   Accelerator pump jet |
| 41   Distance washer | 85   Sealing ring |
| 42   Lock washer | 86   Screw plug |
| 43   Nut | 87   Starting jet |
| 44   Throttle spindle | 88   Ball valve |
| 45   Throttle plates | 89   Weight |
| 46   Screw | 90   Screw |

4    Disconnect the fuel pipe at the T-piece between the carburettors and disconnect the throttle operating rod at its upper end at its balljoint with the cable lever. Pull off the servo pipe at the rear T-piece.

5    Disconnect both choke cables at the carburettor ends, then remove all eight nuts, spring and flat washers holding the carburettors to the inlet manifold, and withdraw the carburettors, still connected together. Note the rubber sealing rings between the carburettors and the manifold.

6    To refit the carburettors, reverse the above procedure but note the following points:

7    The rubber sealing rings mentioned above are used to make an airtight joint between the carburettors and the manifold in conjunction with double coil spring washers under the carburettor flange fixing nuts. This set up gives a certain amount of flexibility to the carburettor mounting, minimising the vibration which can cause excessive aeration of the fuel.

8    The rubber sealing rings can be re-used if they are in good condition, but the coil spring washers should always be replaced by new ones once the carburettors have been removed.

9    The carburettor flange fixing nuts must be tightened evenly so that there is a gap of 0.020 to 0.025 in (0.5 to 0.6 mm) between the spring washer coils when the gaps between the carburettor and inlet manifold flanges are parallel.

10    This can be achieved on the lower nuts by tightening them down until the spring washers are just fully compressed and then undoing each nut a quarter of a turn. This must be done after all the easily accessible nuts have been correctly tightened and the coil gaps set correctly.

## 20 Weber 40 DCOE carburettors – dismantling for cleaning

1    Do not dismantle the carburettor unless you are absolutely certain there is a fault within it, as unnecessary tinkering can well upset the fine balance within the instrument.

2    Referring to Fig. 3.11, remove the circular cover (9) by undoing the wing nut on its top, and remove the slow running jets (10) and the air correction jets (11).

3    Now remove the two accelerator pump jets (2) and undo the progression hole inspection cover screws (3).

4    Remove the float chamber cover (1) by undoing the five retaining screws and take out the starter jets (16).

5    Undo and remove the fuel filter cover plug (8) from the float chamber cover and take off the gauze filter. Wash it in petrol and dry it with low pressure compressed air, if available.

6    Allow the floats to hang down as low as possible and with compressed air, blow through the fuel feed hole (7) which is normally covered by the filter.

7    Remove all fuel and any dirt or water that may have accumulated from the float chamber and the well below the main jets which is accessible through the small hole (12).

8    Carefully, blow through all the jets previously removed with compressed air. *Do not* under any circumstances use wire or any hard object to clean the jets, as this will enlarge or score them and thereby upset the workings of the carburettor.

9    Having cleaned all the jets, refit them in their locations. Before refitting the float chamber cover it is worth checking that the float level is correct.

10    Fig. 3.13 shows the method of checking the float level and gives dimensional details of a small gauge that needs to be made up.

11    Check the float can move freely on its fulcrum pin (3). Also, examine the float lever (5) for signs of pitting where it contacts the needle valve. If wear is present, it must be renewed as it can cause faulty operation of the needle valve.

12    Check the needle valve body (1) is screwed tightly into its housing and that the pin ball end (4) of the spring-loaded damping device in the needle valve is not jammed.

13    Hold the float chamber cover (8) in a vertical position so the weight of the float allows the float lever to just contact the needle valve. It must not move the ball end of the needle damper pin. In this position, both floats should just contact the 8.5 mm steps on the gauge when placed between the cover gasket face and the floats at their highest points. The soldered seams on the floats must not make contact with the gauge.

14    If the float level is found to be incorrect, bend the lever tab (5) to correct it. Take care when bending the tab to keep its face at right

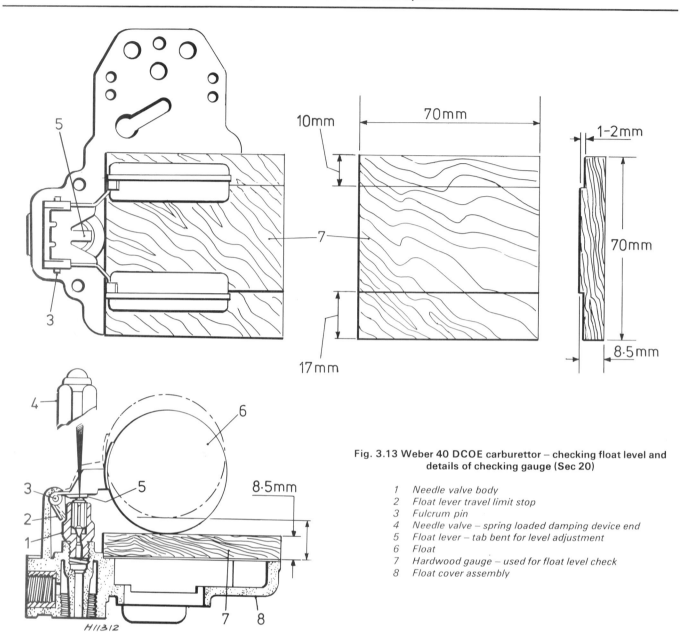

**Fig. 3.13 Weber 40 DCOE carburettor – checking float level and details of checking gauge (Sec 20)**

1  *Needle valve body*
2  *Float lever travel limit stop*
3  *Fulcrum pin*
4  *Needle valve – spring loaded damping device end*
5  *Float lever – tab bent for level adjustment*
6  *Float*
7  *Hardwood gauge – used for float level check*
8  *Float cover assembly*

angles to the needle centre line.

15  Having got the float level correct, check that the total float movement from its level position to its lowest point is 0.256 in (6.5 mm). This is in fact 0.591 in (15 mm) from the gasket face on the cover. This movement, if wrong, can be corrected by bending the lug (2).

16  Once all is correct, refit the float chamber cover.

## 21  Stromberg 150 CD-3 carburettor – general description

This unit differs from the model CDS by having a fixed metering jet but an adjustable metering needle. This is adjusted internally by means of a special tool (Fig. 3.15) which can be purchased through main dealers.

## 22  Stromberg 150 CD-3 carburettor – operation, dismantling, cleaning and reassembly

This is similar to the 150 CDS, and reference should therefore be made to Sections 10, 11 and 13.

## 23  Stromberg 150 CD-3 carburettor – setting and adjustment

1  To adjust the slow running speed, raise the engine to normal operating temperature on the road, and raise the bonnet immediately on stopping to prevent excessive engine heat build-up. Adjust the slow running speed in accordance with that specified by turning the screw (4) (Fig. 3.15).

2  Where adjustment of the mixture is required, a special tool must be obtained from a Stromberg/Zenith agent or a vehicle main dealer. The tool comprises an inner member similar to an Allen key which engages with the metering needle adjustment screw, and an outer tubular member which incorporates a peg to engage with the air valve piston damper bore slot. During adjustment, the inner member is turned while the outer member is held quite still to prevent the rubber diaphragm twisting or tearing.

3  Before raising or lowering the metering needle, check that the basic setting of the needle is correct. To do this, unscrew and pull out the air valve piston damper (1) (Fig. 3.14). Remove the carburettor top cover (3). Invert the assembly and then withdraw the air valve piston/rubber diaphragm assembly, allowing the oil to drain, and, using a straight edge, check that the shoulder of the metering needle or its Delrin washer (if fitted) is flush with the air valve piston lower face. If

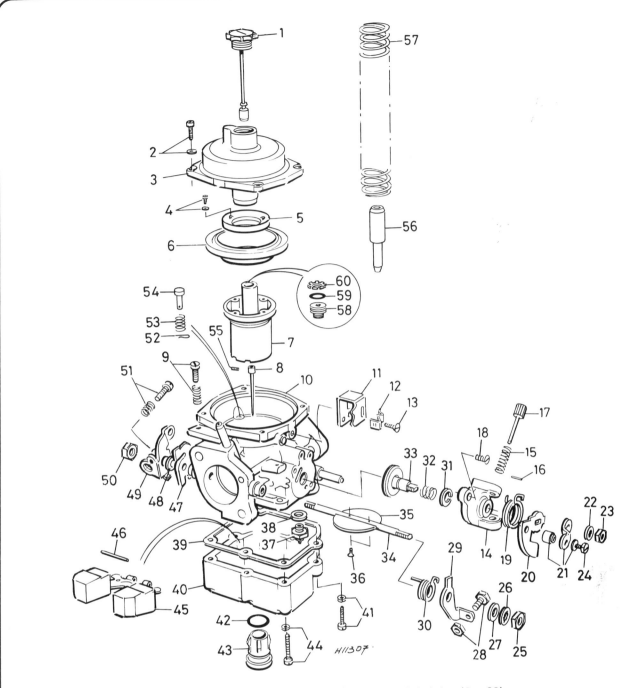

**Fig. 3.14 Stromberg 150 CD3 carburettor – exploded view (Sec 23)**

| | | | |
|---|---|---|---|
| 1 | Damper | 17 | Stop | 33 | Disc valve | 47 | Lever |
| 2 | Cover screw | 18 | Screw | 34 | Throttle valve spindle | 48 | Bush |
| 3 | Cover | 19 | Spring | 35 | Throttle valve plate | 49 | Lever |
| 4 | Diaphragm ring screw | 20 | Cam | 36 | Retaining screws | 50 | Nut |
| 5 | Diaphragm retaining ring | 21 | Lever | 37 | Fuel inlet valve | 51 | Throttle spindle free |
| 6 | Diaphragm | 22 | Washer | 38 | Washer | | movement screw |
| 7 | Air valve piston | 23 | Nut | 39 | Gasket | 52 | Spring clip |
| 8 | Metering needle | 24 | Screw | 40 | Float chamber | 53 | Coil spring |
| 9 | Slow running screw | 25 | Nut | 41 | Retaining screw and | 54 | Lifting pin |
| 10 | Body | 26 | Lockwasher | | lockwasher | 55 | Metering needle screw |
| 11 | Bracket | 27 | Washer | 42 | O-ring | 56 | Metering jet |
| 12 | Clip | 28 | Fast idle screw and locknut | 43 | Plug | 57 | Spring |
| 13 | Screw | 29 | Lever | 44 | Retaining screw and | 58 | Metering needle adjustment |
| 14 | Cover | 30 | Spring | | lockwasher | | screw |
| 15 | Spring | 31 | Circlip | 45 | Float | 59 | O-ring |
| 16 | Retaining pin | 32 | Coil spring | 46 | Float pivot | 60 | Retainer |

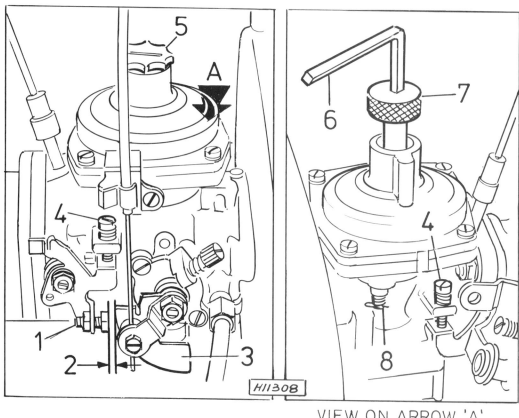

Fig. 3.15 Stromberg 150 CD3 carburettor – adjustment details (Sec 23)

1  Fast idle
2  Fast idle screw to cam gap
3  Fast idle cam
4  Slow running adjustment screw (alternative positions)

5  Air valve piston damper
6  Metering needle adjustment tool – inner component
7  Metering needle adjustment tool – outer component
8  Air valve piston lifting pin

not, engage the inner member of the adjusting tool and rotate the metering needle until the correct basic setting is obtained.

4    Refit the air valve piston/diaphragm, ensuring the alignment lug on the periphery of the diaphragm locates correctly in the recess in the carburettor body. Refit the carburettor top cover and check the air valve piston rises and falls freely by operating the lifting pin. If the piston sticks, loosen the cover screws and tap the cover gently then retighten the screws. If it still sticks, lift the cover and rotate it through 90° at a time and test in each new cover position until the piston rises and falls freely.

5    Insert both components of the adjuster tool into the carburettor damper orifice, ensuring the outer member engages securely with the air valve piston bore slot. If the carburettor is being adjusted without having first checked the basic setting of the metering needle, then the damper bore will contain oil. This will make it very difficult to insert the adjuster tool and even pressure will have to be exerted on the outer member until the damped oil is ejected through the channels provided in the tool.

6    To enrich the mixture, rotate the inner member of the tool clockwise and to weaken it, in an anti-clockwise direction. Do not rotate the inner member of the tool more than one turn in either direction from the basic setting position or the metering needle will become disengaged from its holder. Should this happen, remove the air valve piston/diaphragm assembly and re-engage the metering needle with its holder by supporting the lower face of the needle while exerting pressure on the holder with the adjuster tool and turning it at the same time.

7    The mixture can be adjusted by rotating the tool with the engine running, but any downward pressure on the tool will close the air valve piston and stall the engine. It will therefore be more satisfactory if the

tool is rotated not more than $\frac{1}{8}$th of a turn at a time and removed from the carburettor before starting the engine and checking the effect of the needle adjustment as previously described in paragraph 3. Where adjustment is being carried out with the engine running and it stalls, rev the engine on restarting to clear the inlet manifold before checking the idling quality.

8    Reset the fast idle gap in accordance with that given in the Specifications and refill the damper bore with engine oil to within 0.25 in (6 mm) of the upper edge. Refit the piston damper.

### 24  Stromberg 150 CD-3 twin carburettors – adjustment

1    Carry out the procedures laid down in Section 14, paragraphs 1 to 4.

2    Check the basic needle setting as described in Section 23, paragraph 3.

3    Refit the air valve piston, and check as laid down in Section 23, paragraph 4.

4    Unscrew the fast idle speed adjustment screw (1) (Fig. 3.15) until it is well clear of the cam on the front carburettor.

5    Slacken the more accessible clamp bolt on the couplings located between the carburettors.

6    Check the accelerator cable is not holding the throttle open. Slacken off both carburettor slow running speed adjustment screws until their ends are well clear of the throttle levers. From this position rotate each screw in a clockwise direction until a 0.002 in (0.050 mm) feeler gauge (or a strip of thin paper) is lightly held between the levers and screw ends. Rotate each screw exactly two turns in a clockwise direction to open each throttle by a similar amount. Tighten the

interconnecting coupling clamp bolt.

7    With the engine at normal operating temperature, start the engine and check the mixture as described in the previous Section, adjusting each carburettor, if necessary, with the special tool.

8    Check for synchronization by referring to the procedure given in Section 14, paragraph 15.

9    Reset the fast idle gap in accordance with that given in the Specifications and refill the damper bores with engine oil to within 0.25 in (6 mm) of the upper edge.

10   On completion, refit the piston damper, air cleaner and throttle return spring.

## 25 SU HS4 carburettor – general description

1    The variable choke SU carburettor, is a relatively simple instrument. It is similar to the Stromberg carburettor in that it has only one variable jet fitted to deal with all possible conditions.

2    Air passing rapidly through the carburettor draws petrol from the jet so forming the petrol/air mixture. The amount of petrol drawn from the jet depends on the position of the tapered carburettor needle, which moves up and down the jet orifice according to the engine load and throttle opening, thus effectively altering the size of jet so that exactly the right amount of fuel is metered for the prevailing road conditions.

3    The position of the tapered needle in the jet is determined by engine vacuum. The shank of the needle is held, at its top end, in a piston which slides up and down the dashpot in response to the degree of manifold vacuum.

4    With the throttle fully open, the full effect of the inlet manifold vacuum is felt by the piston, which has an air bleed into the choke tube on the outside of the throttle. This causes the piston to rise fully, bringing the needle with it. With the accelerator partially closed, only slight inlet manifold vacuum is felt by the piston (although, of course, on the engine side of the throttle the vacuum is greater), and the piston only rises a little, blocking most of the jet orifice with the metering needle.

5    To prevent the piston fluttering and giving a richer mixture when the accelerator pedal is suddenly depressed, an oil damper and light spring are fitted inside the dashpot.

6    The only portion of the piston assembly to come into contact with the piston chamber or dashpot is the actual piston rod. All the other parts of the piston assembly, including the lower choke portion, have sufficient clearance to prevent any direct metal to metal contact which is essential if the carburettor is to function correctly.

7    The correct level of the petrol in the carburettor is determined by the level of the float chamber. When the level is correct the float rises, and, by means of a lever resting on top of it, closes the needle valve in the cover of the float chamber. This closes off the supply of fuel from the pump. When the level in the float chamber drops (as fuel is used in the carburettor), the float drops. As it does, the float needle is unseated, so allowing more fuel to enter the float chamber and restore the correct level.

## 26 SU HS4 carburettor – removal and refitting

1    Disconnect the fuel feed pipe at the inlet to the float chamber.

2    Remove the air cleaner.

3    Disconnect the throttle and choke operating cables at the carburettor.

4    Pull off the vacuum connection.

5    Remove the nuts and spring washers securing the carburettor to the manifold, then pull the carburettor, joint washer, abutment bracket and insulator away.

6    Refitting is a reversal of the removal procedure, following which it will be necessary to top up the piston damper oil level (see next Section) and adjust the choke and throttle cables.

## 27 SU HS4 carburettor – dismantling and reassembly

1    Unscrew the piston damper and lift it away from the chamber and piston assembly. Recover the fibre washer.

2    Using a screwdriver or small file, scratch identification marks on

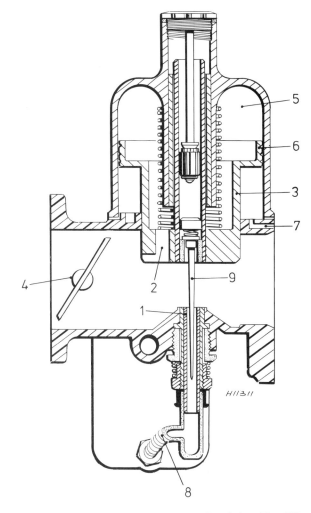

**Fig. 3.16 SU HS4 carburettor – sectional view (Sec 25)**

| | | | |
|---|---|---|---|
| 1 | Jet | 6 | Piston |
| 2 | Drilling | 7 | Vent |
| 3 | Piston | 8 | Fuel feed tube |
| 4 | Butterfly | 9 | Needle |
| 5 | Suction chamber | | |

the suction chamber and carburettor body so they may be fitted together again in their original position. Remove the three suction chamber retaining screws and lift the suction chamber from the carburettor body leaving the piston assembly in place.

3    Lift the piston spring from the piston, noting which way round it is fitted, and remove the piston. Invert it and allow the oil in the damper bore to drain out. Place the piston in a safe place so the needle will not be touched or the piston roll onto the floor. It is recommended that the piston be placed on the neck of a narrow jar with the needle inside so acting as a stand.

4    Mark the position of the float chamber lid relative to the body, and unscrew the three screws holding the float chamber lid to the float chamber body. Remove the lid and withdraw the pin, thereby releasing the float and float lever. Using a spanner or socket, remove the needle valve assembly.

5    Release the pick-up return spring from its retaining lug.

6    Support the plastic moulded base of the jet and remove the screw retaining the jet pick-up link and link bracket.

7    Carefully, unscrew the flexible jet tube sleeve nut from the float chamber and lift the jet assembly away from the underside of the carburettor body. Note the gland, washer and ferrule at the end of the jet tube.

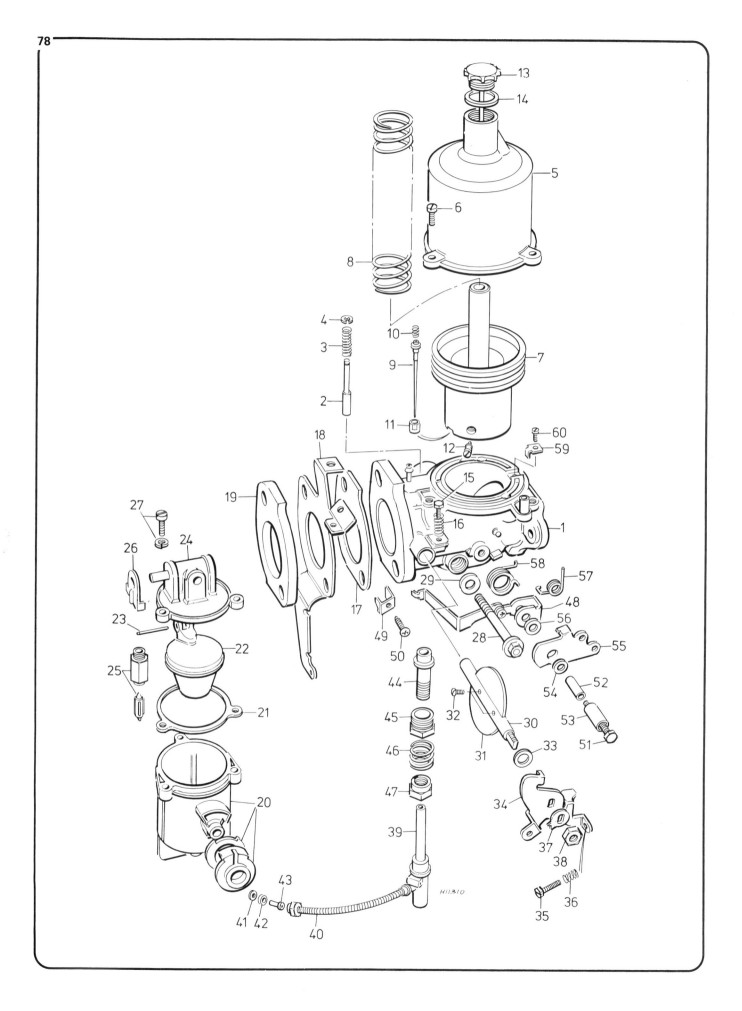

H11310

8 Undo and remove the jet adjustment nut and spring. Also unscrew the jet locknut and lift away, together with the brass washer and jet bearing.

9 Unscrew and remove the lever pivot bolt and spacer. Detach the lever assembly and return the springs noting the pivot bolt tubes, skid washer and the locations of the cam and pick-up lever springs.

10 Close the throttle and mark lightly the relative position of the throttle disc and carburettor flange.

11 Unscrew the disc retaining screws, open the throttle and ease the disc from its slot in the throttle spindle.

12 Bend back the tabs of the lockwasher securing the spindle nut. Undo and remove the nut and detach the lever arm, washer and throttle spindle.

13 Should it be necessary to remove the piston lifting pin, push it upwards and remove the securing clip. Lift away the pin and spring.

14 Reassembly is a straight reversal of the dismantling sequence, following which the piston damper should be topped up with engine oil to within 0.5 in (13 mm) of the top of the hollow piston rod.

## 28 SU HS4 carburettor – examination and repair

1 The SU carburettor is most reliable, but even so, it may develop one of several faults which may not be readily apparent unless a careful inspection is carried out *piston sticking, float needle sticking, or float chamber flooding*. These are dealt with in Sections 29 to 31. In addition, the parts described in the following paragraphs are susceptible to wear after high mileages. They vitally affect the economy of the engine, and should be checked every 24 000 miles (38 600 km) and renewed where necessary.

2 The carburettor needle: If this has been incorrectly fitted at some time so it was not centrally located in the jet orifice, then the metering needle will have a tiny ridge worn on it. If a ridge can be seen, the needle must be renewed. SU carburettor needles are made to very fine tolerances and, should a ridge be apparent, no attempt should be made to rub the needle down with fine emery paper.

3 The carburettor jet: If the needle is worn it is likely the rim of the jet will be damaged where the needle has been striking it. It should be

Fig. 3.17 SU HS4 carburettor – exploded view (Sec 27)

| | | | |
|---|---|---|---|
| 1 | Body | 31 | Throttle butterfly |
| 2 | Piston lifting pin | 32 | Screw |
| 3 | Spring | 33 | Washer |
| 4 | Circlip | 34 | Throttle return lever |
| 5 | Piston chamber | 35 | Fast-idle screw |
| 6 | Screw | 36 | Spring |
| 7 | Piston | 37 | Lockwasher |
| 8 | Spring | 38 | Nut |
| 9 | Needle | 39 | Jet assembly |
| 10 | Spring | 40 | Sleeve nut |
| 11 | Support guide | 41 | Washer |
| 12 | Locking screw – needle support guide | 42 | Gland |
| | | 43 | Ferrule |
| 13 | Piston damper | 44 | Jet bearing |
| 14 | Sealing washer | 45 | Jet bearing locking nut |
| 15 | Throttle adjusting screw | 46 | Spring |
| 16 | Spring for screw | 47 | Jet adjusting nut |
| 17 | Gasket | 48 | Pick-up lever |
| 18 | Abutment bracket | 49 | Link – pick-up lever |
| 19 | Insulator block | 50 | Screw |
| 20 | Float chamber, mounting rubber and spacer | 51 | Pivot bolt |
| | | 52 | Pivot bolt tube – inner |
| 21 | Gasket | 53 | Pivot bolt tube – outer |
| 22 | Float | 54 | Distance washer |
| 23 | Hinge pin | 55 | Cam lever |
| 24 | Lid | 56 | Washer |
| 25 | Needle and seat | 57 | Spring – cam lever |
| 26 | Baffle plate | 58 | Spring – pick-up lever |
| 27 | Screw and spring washer | 59 | Guide – suction chamber piston |
| 28 | Bolt | | |
| 29 | Rubber washer | 60 | Screw |
| 30 | Throttle spindle | | |

renewed, otherwise fuel consumption will suffer. The jet can also be badly worn or ridged on the outside from where it has been sliding up and down between the jet bearing every time the choke has been pulled out. Removal and renewal is the only answer.

4 Check the edges of the throttle and choke tube for wear. Renew if worn. The washers fitted to the base of the jet and under the float chamber lid may leak after a time and can cause a great deal of fuel wastage. It is wise to renew them automatically when the carburettor is stripped down.

5 After high mileages, the float chamber needle and seat are bound to be ridged. They are not expensive items to replace and must be renewed as a set. They should never be renewed separately.

## 29 SU HS4 carburettor – piston sticking

1 The hardened piston rod which slides in the centre guide tube in the middle of the dashpot is the only part of the piston assembly (which comprises the jet needle, suction disc, and piston choke) which should make contact with the dashpot. The piston rim and the choke periphery are machined to very fine tolerances so they will not touch the dashpot or the choke tube walls.

2 After high mileages, wear in the centre guide tube may allow the piston to touch the dashpot wall. This condition is known as sticking.

3 If piston sticking is suspected and it is wished to test for this condition, rotate the piston about the centre guide tube at the same time sliding it up and down inside the dashpot wall. Where the piston is found to interfere, that portion of the wall must be polished with a metal polish until clearance exists. In extreme cases, fine emery cloth can be used. The greatest care should be taken to remove only the minimum amount of metal to provide the clearance, as too large a gap will cause air leakage and upset the function of the carburettor. Clean down the walls of the dashpot and the piston rim and ensure that there is no oil on them. A trace of oil may be judiciously applied to the piston rod.

4 If the piston is sticking, under no circumstances try to clear it by trying to alter the tension of the light return spring.

## 30 SU HS4 carburettor – float needle sticking

1 If the float needle sticks, the carburettor will soon run dry and the engine will stop, despite there being fuel in the tank. The easiest way to check a suspected sticking float needle is to remove the inlet pipe at the carburettor and turn the engine over on the starter motor. Remove the LT lead on the ignition coil so the engine does not start. If fuel spurts from the end of the pipe (direct it towards the ground, into a wad of cloth or into a jar) then the fault is almost certain to be a sticking float needle.

2 Remove the float chamber, dismantle the valve and clean the housing and float chamber out thoroughly.

## 31 SU HS4 carburettor – float chamber flooding

If fuel emerges from the small breather hole in the cover of the float chamber, this is known as flooding. It is caused by the float chamber needle not seating properly in its housing; normally, this is because a piece of foreign matter is jammed between the needle and needle housing. Alternatively, the float may have developed a leak or be maladjusted to hold the float chamber needle valve open even though the chamber is full of petrol. Remove the float chamber cover, clean the needle assembly, check the setting of the float as described later in this Chapter and shake the float to verify if any petrol has leaked into it. If this has happened, the float should be renewed.

## 32 SU HS4 carburettor – float chamber fuel level adjustment

1 It is essential that the fuel level in the float chamber is always correct otherwise excessive fuel consumption may occur.

2 Remove the float chamber/lid assembly and invert it.

3 With the needle valve held closed by the weight of the float only, there should be a gap of 0.062 to 0.187 in (1.6 to 4.76 mm) between the float and the rim of the float chamber lid. If the gap is outside these limits, the float must be renewed (Fig. 3.18).

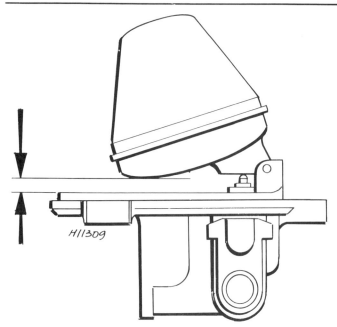

Fig. 3.18 SU HS4 carburettor – measuring the float height
(Sec 32)

### 33 SU HS4 carburettor – jet centering

1    This operation is always necessary if the carburettor has been dismantled. To check if this is necessary on a carburettor in service, first lift the piston by means of the piston lifting pin and then let it fall under its own weight. It should fall onto the bridge, making a soft metallic click.

2    Disconnect the jet link from the bottom of the jet, and the nylon flexible tube from the underside of the float chamber. Gently, slide the jet and nylon tube from the underside of the carburettor body. Next unscrew the jet adjusting nut and lift away the nut and the locking spring. Refit the adjusting nut without the locking spring and screw it up as far as possible without forcing it. Refit the jet and tube, but there is no need to reconnect the tube.

3    Slacken the jet locking nut so it may be rotated with the fingers only. Unscrew the piston damper and lift away the damper. Gently, press the piston down onto the bridge and tighten the locknut. Lift the piston using the lifting pin and check it is able to fall freely under its own weight. Now lower the adjusting nut and check once again. If this time there is a difference in the two metallic clicks, repeat the centering procedure until the sound is the same for both tests.

4    Remove the jet gently and unscrew the adjusting nut. Refit the locking spring and jet adjusting nut. Top-up the damper with oil, if necessary, and refit the damper. Connect the nylon flexible tube to the underside of the float chamber and finally reconnect the jet link.

### 34 SU HS4 carburettor – needle renewal

1    Should it be necessary to fit a new needle, first remove the piston and suction chamber assembly, marking the chamber for correct reassembly in its original position.

2    Slacken the needle clamping screw and withdraw the needle, guide and spring from the underside of the piston.

3    To refit the needle assembly, fit the spring and guide to the needle and insert the assembly into the piston, making sure the guide is fitted flush with the face of the piston, and the flat on the guide positioned adjacent to the needle guide locking screw. Screw in the guide locking screw.

### 35 SU HS4 carburettor – adjustments and tuning

1    Top-up the piston damper with engine oil until it is 0.5 in (13 mm) above the top of the hollow piston rod.

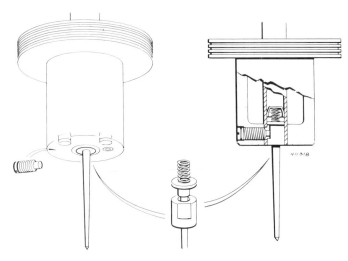

Fig. 3.19 SU HS4 carburettor – needle location (Sec 34)

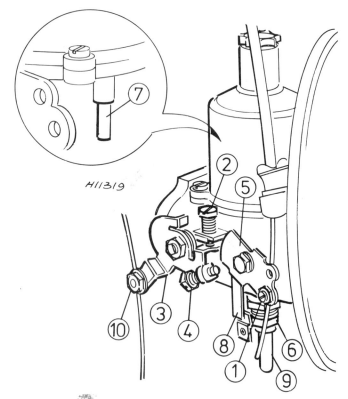

Fig. 3.20 SU HS4 carburettor – adjustment points (Sec 35)

| | | | |
|---|---|---|---|
| 1 | Choke control wire attachment | 6 | Jet adjusting nut |
| 2 | Throttle adjusting screw | 7 | Piston lifting pin |
| 3 | Throttle lever arm | 8 | Jet lever |
| 4 | Fast idle screw | 9 | Jet |
| 5 | Mixture control cam lever | 10 | Throttle control wire attachment |

2    Run the engine up to normal operating temperature then switch off and disconnect the choke control wire (see Fig. 3.20).

3    Unscrew the throttle adjusting screw until just clear of the throttle lever arm when the throttle is closed. Check the fast idle screw is not touching the mixture control cam lever.

4    Turn the throttle adjusting screw one and a half turns clockwise.

5    Check the piston falls freely and the jet is centred correctly (see Sections 29 and 33).

6   Turn the jet adjusting nut two turns downwards then restart the engine and adjust the throttle adjusting screw to obtain the correct idling speed.

7   Turn the jet adjusting nut down to richen or up to weaken the mixture until the fastest idling speed, consistent with even running, is obtained. Readjust the idling speed if necessary.

8   Raise the piston lifting pin about 1/32 in (0.8 mm) after all free movement has been taken up. If the engine speed increases considerably the mixture is too rich; if it decreases immediately, the mixture is too weak. If the mixture is correct, a momentary slight increase in idling speed wil occur, then the normal idling speed will be resumed. Readjust the mixture if necessary.

9   Reassemble the choke control cable through the pivot pin and clamp the wire so that there is approximately $\frac{1}{16}$ in (1. 6 mm) free movement at the control knob before the jet lever moves.

10  Run the engine up to normal operating temperature, pull the choke knob out to just take up the free play, then adjust the fast idling to approximately 1000 rpm.

## 36  SU HS4C carburettor – description

The HS4C carburettor is very similar to the HS4 and most of the procedures apply to both carburettors. The main differences, however, lie in the throttle, choke and jet adjustment linkages. Also, the air filters are of a different design and layout. The differences between the two carburettors are shown in the relevant illustrations.

## 37  SU HS4C carburettor – adjustments

1   When idling, fuel is supplied through the jet to give the correct fuel discharge for idling with the engine at its normal operating temperature. The effective discharge area is determined by the position of the jet, which is set, through a linkage, by a jet adjusting screw.

### *Idling adjustment*
2   Check the throttle for correct operation and signs of sticking.

3   Referring to Fig. 3.21, disconnect the choke cable (1) and remove the air filter (see Section 9).

4   Ensuring that the fast idle screw (4) remains clear of the control cam (5), unscrew the throttle screw (2) until it is just clear of the throttle lever with the throttle closed, then turn the screw clockwise one and a half turns.

5   Lift the piston with the lifting pin (7), and check it falls freely with a 'click' onto the jet bridge when the pin is released. If the piston shows any tendency to stick, remove the suction chamber and piston

as follows:

*(a)  Clean the exterior of the carburettor*

*(b)  Unscrew and remove the piston damper (with washer, if fitted)*

*(c)  Remove the suction chamber screws and lift the chamber from the body*

*(d)  Remove the piston spring, lift out the piston assembly and empty away any oil remaining in the piston rod*

*(e)  Thoroughly clean the bore of the suction chamber and the piston using a cloth moistened with petrol or methylated spirit.* **Do not use any abrasive compounds for cleaning**

*(f)  Check the needle for damage or if the jet is obstructed by dirt. Check that the needle shank is flush with the underside of the piston*

6   Refit the piston and suction chamber and, using the lifting pin, check the piston falls freely onto the bridge.

7   Lift the piston until the jet is visible. Turn the adjusting screw (6) anti-clockwise until the jet is flush with the bridge, or as high as possible without exceeding the bridge height.

8   Turn the jet adjusting screw (6) two turns clockwise.

9   Unscrew the piston damper and remove from the piston. Top-up with engine oil until the level is 0.5 in (13 mm) above the top of the hollow piston rod. Refit the damper and the air cleaner.

10  Start the engine and run it at a fast idle speed until it reaches its normal operating temperature, then allow to run for a further five minutes. Increase the engine speed to 2500 rpm for thirty seconds, and then allow the engine to idle.

11  Adjust the throttle screw (2) to give the correct idling speed.

12  Turn the jet screw (6) clockwise to enrich, or anti-clockwise to weaken, until the fastest idle speed is obtained. Turn the screw anti-clockwise until the engine speed just begins to drop. Now turn in a clockwise direction the minimum amount necessary to regain the fastest speed.

13  Check the idling speed and adjust if necessary.

14  Check for correct mixture strength by gently raising the lifting pin (7) by about 1/32 in (0.8 mm) after first taking up any free movement. If the mixture is correct, the engine speed will increase for a moment and then resume its former speed. If the mixture is too rich, the engine speed will increase and if it is too weak, will decrease. Re-adjust if necessary.

15  Reconnect the choke cable and adjust if necessary as described in the following paragraphs.

### *Choke cable adjustment*
16  Reconnect the choke cable into the pivot pin, ensuring that with the fast idle cam against its stop, a $\frac{1}{16}$ in (1.5 mm) movement exists

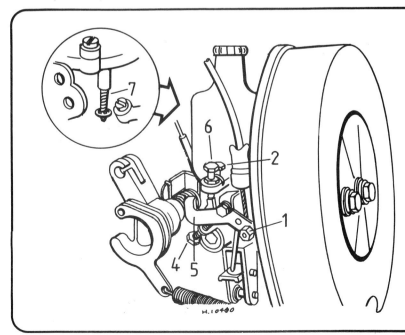

**Fig. 3.21 SU HS4C carburettor – idling, throttle cable and choke control adjustments (Sec 37)**

1   Mixture control (choke) cable
2   Throttle adjusting screw
4   Fast idle adjusting screw
5   Mixture control cam
6   Jet adjusting screw
7   Piston lifting pin

H.10400

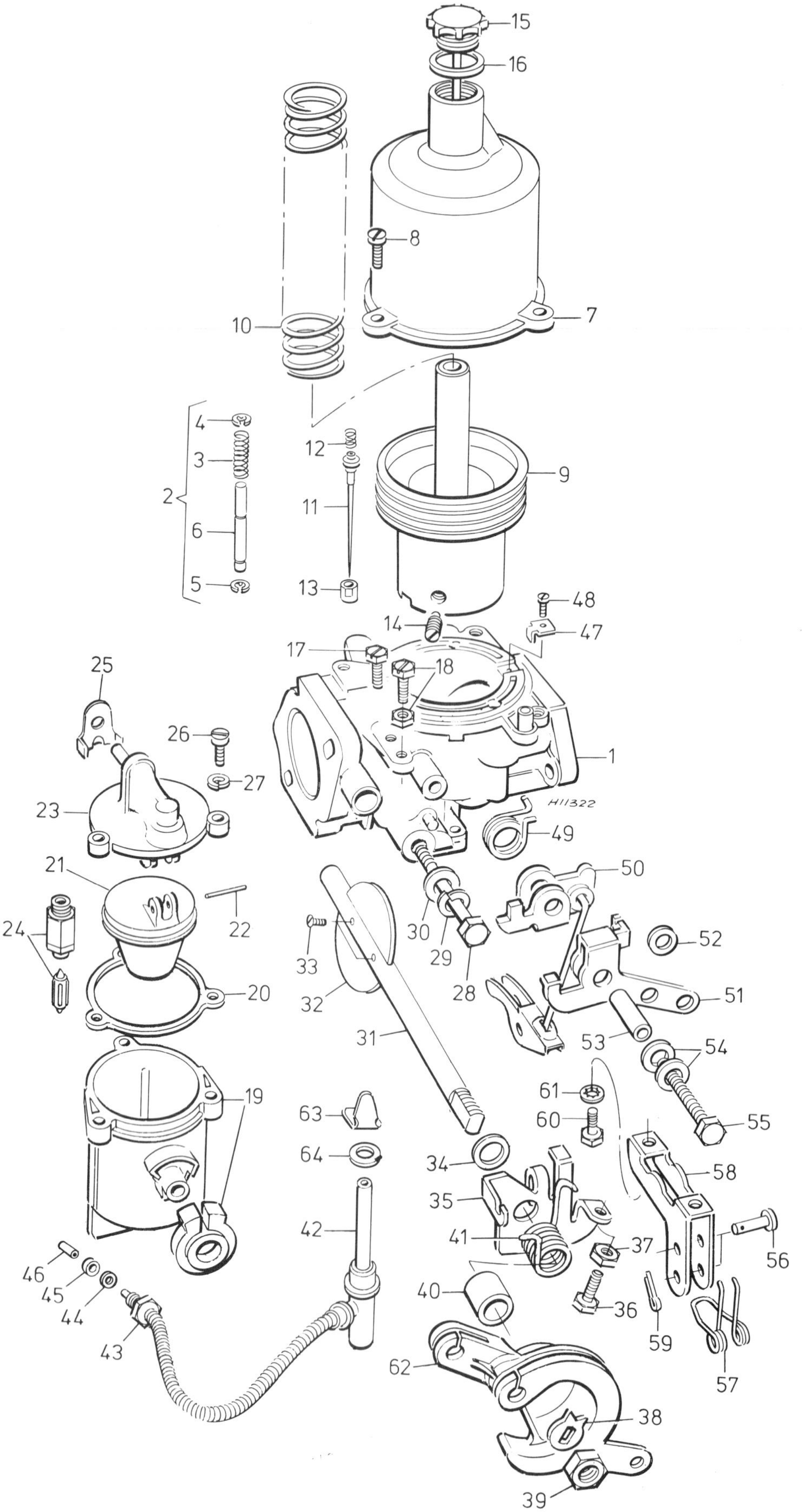

15

16

8

7

10

4

3

2

6

5

12

11

13

14

48

47

17

18

9

25

26

27

23

24

21

22

20

33

32

31

30

29

28

50

52

51

53

54

61

60

55

34

58

35

41

37

56

40

36

46

45

44

43

42

63

64

19

59

57

62

38

39

1

49

H11322

**Fig. 3.22 SU HS4 carburettor – exploded view (Sec 37)**

1    Body
2    Piston lifting pin assembly
3    Lifting pin spring
4    Circlip
5    Circlip
6    Lifting pin
7    Suction chamber
8    Suction chamber screw
9    Piston
10   Spring
11   Jet needle with collar
12   Needle spring
13   Needle guide
14   Needle guide locking screw
15   Piston damper
16   Damper sealing washer
17   Throttle adjusting screw
18   Jet adjusting screw and locknut
19   Float chamber and spacer
20   Chamber gasket
21   Float
22   Float hinge pin
23   Float chamber lid
24   Float needle and seat
25   Baffle plate
26   Float chamber lid screw
27   Spring washer
28   Float chamber securing bolt
29   Spring washer
30   Plain washer
31   Throttle spindle
32   Throttle disc
33   Throttle disc securing screw
34   Throttle spindle washer
35   Throttle return lever
36   Fast-idle screw
37   Fast-idle screw locknut
38   Throttle spindle nut lockwasher
39   Throttle spindle nut
40   Spacer
41   Throttle return spring
42   Jet assembly
43   Jet assembly sleeve nut
44   Washer
45   Gland
46   Ferrule
47   Piston guide key
48   Key securing screw
49   Pick-up lever spring
50   Jet fork assembly pick-up lever
51   Cam lever
52   Skid washer
53   Pivot bolt tube
54   Washer
55   Pivot bolt
56   Clevis pin
57   Jet return spring
58   Jet assembly securing bracket
59   Split pins
60   Securing bracket bolt
61   Starlock washer
62   Throttle actuating lever
63   Jet fork centering washer
64   Washer

before the cam moves. Pull out the choke knob until the jet is about to move. Adjust the fast idle screw until a speed of 1750 rpm is reached (engine at its normal operating temperature). Lock the screw with the locknut.

*Throttle cable adjustment*

17   Adjust the cable by means of the threaded end of its outer cable at the bracket, so that correct idling is achieved when the pedal is released and full throttle opening just obtained when the pedal is pushed down onto the floor covering.

## 38 Exhaust emission control

1    Legislation is being progressively introduced into all EEC countries to control exhaust emissions of new cars, and variations may arise because of this. In particular, the Sunbeam Arrow range supplied to North America has been brought to the standard necessary to meet the stringent regulations existing there.
2    The purpose of the system is to decrease the emission of both hydrocarbons (unburnt fuel) and of carbon monoxide in the exhaust gases, thus decreasing atmospheric pollution.
3    Basically, the system needs a modified variable choke carburettor – such as the Stromberg 150 CDS – and a modified distributor. Most of the polluting gases reach atmosphere via the exhaust on overrun conditions when the throttle is shut. Normally the exhaust gases excessively dilute the slow running mixture reaching the engine in these conditions and so prevent proper combustion. The modified system uses the manifold depression, which is at maximum on overrun, to operate this. A control valve which in turn operates a throttle bypass valve permits a proper mixture to reach the cylinders. This, in turn, increases the engine power and so cuts out the overrun engine braking effect. To counteract this an automatic vacuum retard device is fitted to the distributor which retards the ignition twelve crankshaft degrees. The throttle bypass valve is incorporated as part of the Stromberg CDSE carburettor (Figs. 3.23 and 3.24).
4    Other refinements on the carburettor include a temperature controlled valve which weakens the mixture under light load and idling conditions when the engine is hot. Furthermore, the main jet is fixed and the needle is spring-loaded to run off-centre in the jet to improve atomisation. The manifold depression must reach 21 in Hg before the system comes into operation and cuts out when it drops to 18 in Hg (allowing air through the bleed to return the valves to closed positions).
5    It must be appreciated, of course, that all other aspects of engine condition and settings must be as near perfect as possible to achieve the sought-after reduction in emission fumes. Valve clearances, plug gaps, points gap, centrifugal and vacuum automatic advance curves and static timing are all equally important.
6    The overall requirement is, therefore, an engine in a very good state of tune at all times. The extra expense of maintaining this is offset by improved performance and fuel consumption and the knowledge that one is not feeding unwanted elements into the air we breathe.
7    Cars supplied for the US marked should, in general, never be tampered with. Where any adjustment or repair is required, it should be carried out by a properly equipped main dealer or carburettor specialist, since in all cases it is necessary to carry out a rigorous step-by-step fault diagnosis procedure.
8    After the first 600 miles (from new) it is necessary for the following service checks to be carried out:

   (a)   Check valve/rocker clearance
   (b)   Check contact points gap
   (c)   Check idling speed and quality
   (d)   Check dynamic ignition timing when idling
   (e)   Check time for engine speed to fall from 2500 rpm to idle – four to six seconds permitted

9    At intervals of 4000 miles it is necessary for the following service checks to be carried out: Items c, d and e in paragraph 8.
10   At intervals of 8000 miles it is necessary for the following service checks to be carried out:

   (a)   Check the spark plug gap
   (b)   Check all the items in paragraph 8

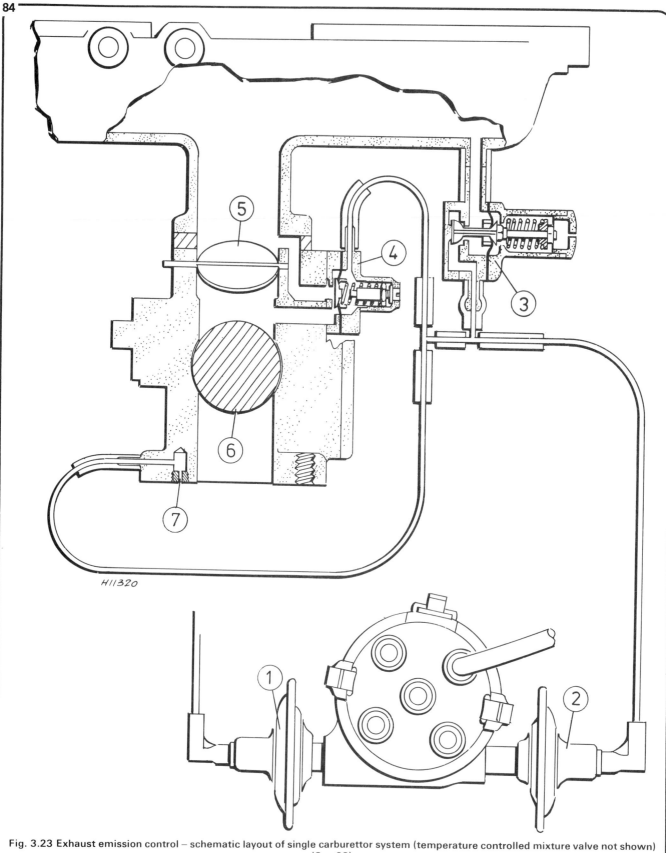

H11320

Fig. 3.23 Exhaust emission control – schematic layout of single carburettor system (temperature controlled mixture valve not shown)
(Sec 38)

| | | | |
|---|---|---|---|
| 1 | Distributor vacuum advance diaphragm | 3 | Manifold depression control valve |
| 2 | Distributor vacuum retard diaphragm | 4 | Throttle bypass valve |
| | | 5 | Throttle flap |

6   Carburettor air-valve piston
7   Calibrated air bleed (closing valves when manifold depression goes below 18 in Hg)

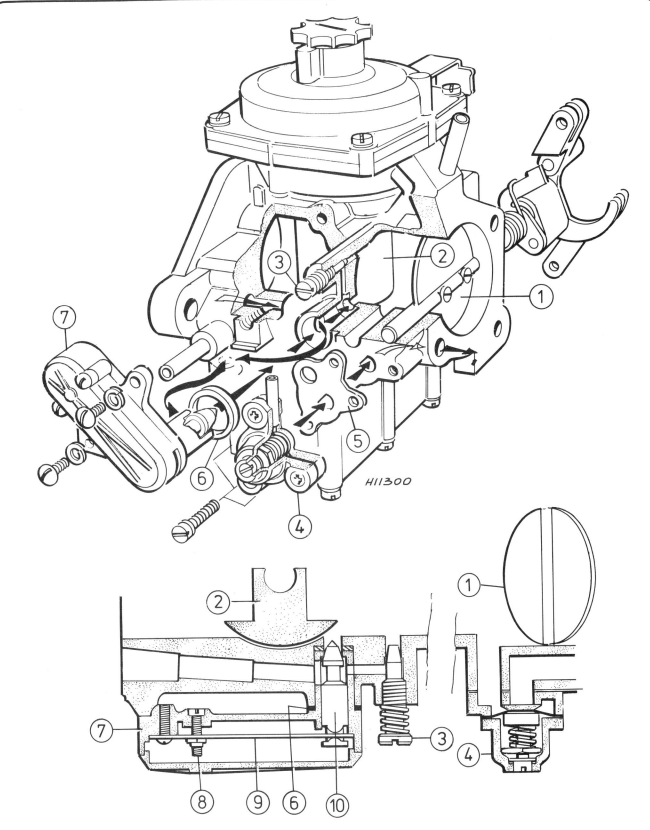

H11300

Fig. 3.24 Stromberg CDSE carburettor – cutaway view with details of throttle bypass valve and temperature controlled mixture valve (Sec 38)

| | | | |
|---|---|---|---|
| 1 Throttle flap | 4 Throttle bypass valve | 7 Temperature controlled valve body | 9 Bi-metal spring |
| 2 Air valve piston | 5 Gasket valve to body | 8 Adjustment screw | 10 Valve plunger |
| 3 Slow running air bleed screw | 6 Joint ring | | |

39.3a Refitting fuel pump gaskets

39.3b Refitting fuel pump securing nuts

39.3c Reconnecting fuel feed pipe

## 39 Fuel pump – removal and refitting

1   The fuel pump will need removing if it is to be dismantled for overhaul. Disconnect the fuel lines on the inlet and outlet sides by undoing the union on the inlet side and pulling off the connector pipe on the outlet side.
2   Undo the two nuts holding the pump flange to the crankcase and take the pump off. Keep the spacer and gaskets together and do not discard them. If necessary, blank off the fuel line from the tank to prevent loss of fuel.
3   Refitting is a reversal of the removal procedure. Make sure the total thickness of gaskets and spacer is the same as came off. Check the fuel line connections are not leaking after starting the engine (photos).

## 40 Fuel pump – inspection, dismantling and reassembly

1   First clean the pump exterior thoroughly and mark the edges of the two halves of the body.
2   Undo the cover retaining clip and lift off the cover. The gasket and gauze filter may then be removed.
3   Remove the six screws and washers holding the two halves of the pump together and the top half may then be lifted off.
4   The diaphragm and pullrod should then be pushed down a little against the pressure of the return spring and turned clockwise a quarter of a turn. This will disengage the pullrod from the operating link and the diaphragm may be lifted out.
5   If there are signs of wear in the rocker arm pivot pin, and rocker arm and link bushes then they should be renewed. They can be taken from the pump body by first clamping the rocker arm in a vice and then tapping the body away with a soft-faced hammer.
6   The valve assemblies should only be removed from the upper body if renewal is necessary. They are staked into the body and are destroyed when levered out.
7   Examine the diaphragm for signs of cracking or perforation and renew if necessary.
8   The oil seal and retainer in the base of the pump (round the pullrod) should be renewed as a matter of course if the diaphragm is also being renewed. They can be levered out with a screwdriver. The new ones should be pressed in carefully, keeping them square.
9   When fitting new valve assemblies to the body, first fit the seating washers and then place the valves, making sure they are the correct way up according to inlet and outlet. Press the valves into place using a piece of tube with suitable internal and external diameters, proceeding carefully to avoid damage to the valves. The body will have to be restaked at six (different) places round the edge so the assemblies are held firmly in their positions. If this is not done properly and leakage occurs between the valve assembly and the seating ring, the pump will not operate efficiently.
10  The rocker arm assembly is refitted to the body by first assembling the link, rocker arm, pivot pin and washers and placing them in position in the pump body. Then locate the spring over the pip on the rocker arm and in the pump body recess. Tap the pin retainers into the slots in the body so they are hard up to the pin. The slots should then

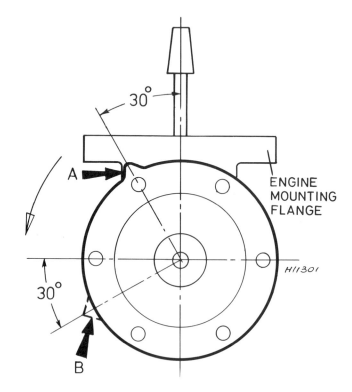

**Fig. 3.25 Diagram of fuel pump diaphragm to show position of tabs when inserting the stem (A) and after locking on to the operating link (B) (Sec 40)**

be staked with a suitable punch so the retainers are held tightly in position.
11  Place the diaphragm return spring in position in the lower half of the pump. To refit the diaphragm, first fit the stem carefully through the oil seals then position the diaphragm so the tab is in the position shown in Fig. 3.25. Then press the centre of the diaphragm down which will pass the stem end through the operating link slot. Then, by turning 90° anti-clockwise, the stem will hook into position correctly.
12  Fit the upper half of the pump body and line up the mating marks. In order to assemble the two halves and the diaphragm properly, push the rocker arm upwards so the diaphragm is drawn level. Then place the six screws in position lightly. It is best if the base of the pump is held in a vice whilst the rocker arm is pushed right up to bring the diaphragm to the bottom of its stroke. A short piece of tube over the rocker arm will provide easy leverage. In this position, the six screws should be tightened evenly and alternately.
13  Fit a new filter bowl gasket carefully in the groove of the upper body, making sure it does not twist or buckle in the process. Refit the cover and the retaining clip and screw it tight.
14  When the pump is reassembled, the suction and delivery pressure can be felt at the inlet and outlet ports when the rocker arm is

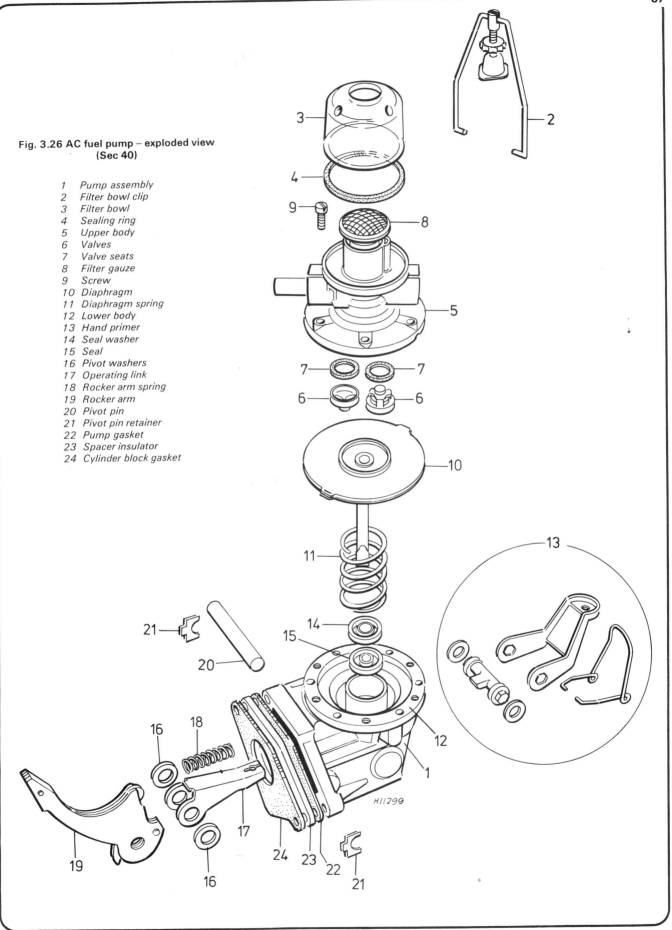

Fig. 3.26 AC fuel pump – exploded view
(Sec 40)

1   Pump assembly
2   Filter bowl clip
3   Filter bowl
4   Sealing ring
5   Upper body
6   Valves
7   Valve seats
8   Filter gauze
9   Screw
10  Diaphragm
11  Diaphragm spring
12  Lower body
13  Hand primer
14  Seal washer
15  Seal
16  Pivot washers
17  Operating link
18  Rocker arm spring
19  Rocker arm
20  Pivot pin
21  Pivot pin retainer
22  Pump gasket
23  Spacer insulator
24  Cylinder block gasket

H11299

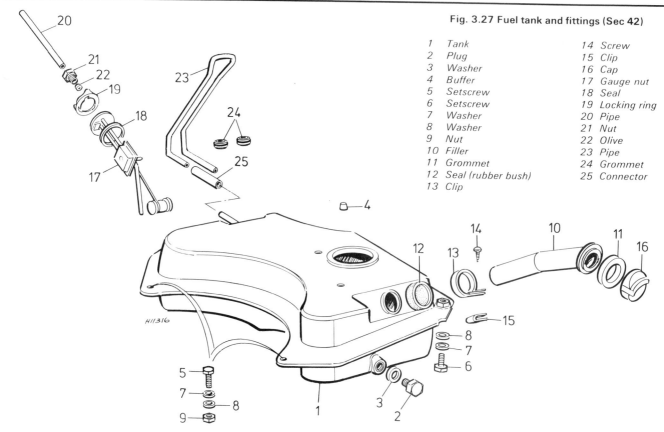

Fig. 3.27 Fuel tank and fittings (Sec 42)

| | | | |
|---|---|---|---|
| 1 | Tank | 14 | Screw |
| 2 | Plug | 15 | Clip |
| 3 | Washer | 16 | Cap |
| 4 | Buffer | 17 | Gauge nut |
| 5 | Setscrew | 18 | Seal |
| 6 | Setscrew | 19 | Locking ring |
| 7 | Washer | 20 | Pipe |
| 8 | Washer | 21 | Nut |
| 9 | Nut | 22 | Olive |
| 10 | Filler | 23 | Pipe |
| 11 | Grommet | 24 | Grommet |
| 12 | Seal (rubber bush) | 25 | Connector |
| 13 | Clip | | |

operated. Be careful not to block the inlet port completely when testing suction. If the rocker arm were to be operated strongly and the inlet side was blocked, the diaphragm could be damaged.

## 41 Fuel gauge – tank sender unit

1   The fuel gauge sender unit is mounted on the side of the tank where the fuel outlet pipe connection is also made. If the gauge becomes faulty, first check that the sender unit, which is a variable resistance, is giving different resistance readings with both a full and empty tank. If not, it should be renewed. Otherwise, the gauge is faulty.
2   To remove the sender unit, first disconnect the fuel pipe union. Then engage the locking plate lugs with a suitable tool and turn it anti-clockwise. The unit can be lifted out. Take care when refitting that the washer is correctly fitted and both joining surfaces are clean and undistorted.

## 42 Fuel tank – removal and refitting

The following instructions refer specifically to removal and refitting procedures for saloon models. Slight variations will be encountered when dealing with estate models, but the principle is basically the same.
1   To remove the fuel tank, begin by disconnecting the battery earth lead.
2   Referring to Fig. 3.27, remove the drain plug (2) and washer (3) from the fuel tank and drain the contents off.
3   Pull off the vent hose connector (25), then disconnect all electrical leads from the gauge unit (17).
4   Disconnect the fuel line (20) from the gauge unit.
5   Next, pull the filler neck tube (10) from the rubber bush (12) outwards from the tank face.
6   Remove the fuel tank finally by unscrewing the two bolts with washers (6 to 8) and the two nuts with washers (8 and 9).
7   Refitting is a reversal of the removal procedure, but take care that the tank unit electrical connections do not become trapped in the process. It is advisable at this point to check the condition of the drain

plug washer (3), and renew it if necessary.

## 43 Exhaust system

1   When any one section of the exhaust system needs renewal, it often follows that the whole lot is best renewed (photo).
2   On new cars, the front pipe and silencer is fitted as a single piece. In view of the fact that the front pipe deteriorates less quickly than the rest, replacements are supplied in two parts. Thus it is possible to cut the original pipe and fit the silencer section only. Fig. 3.28 shows the position at which the cut should be made.
3   It is most important when fitting exhausts that the twists and contours are followed carefully and each connecting joint overlaps by

43.1 Removing exhaust manifold to exhaust pipe nuts

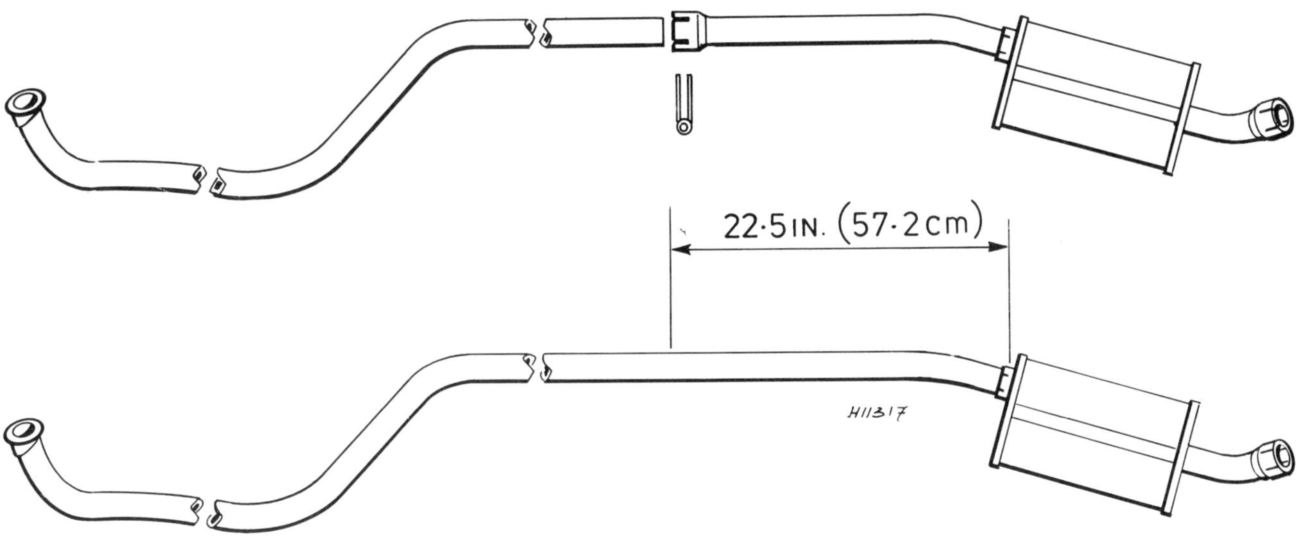

22·5 IN. (57·2 cm)

H11317

Fig. 3.28 Method of cutting the old exhaust pipe when fitting a new silencer (Sec 43)

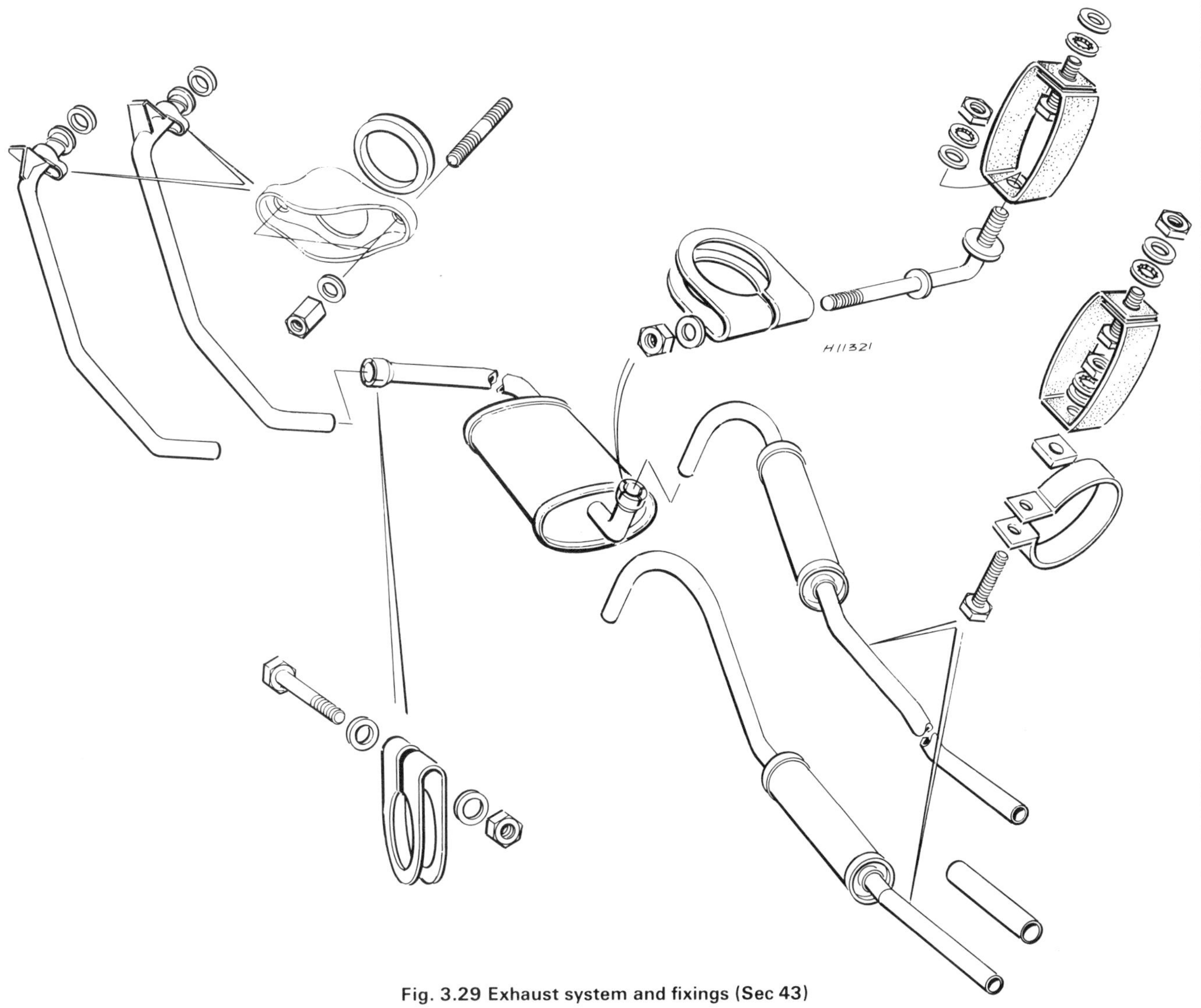

H11321

Fig. 3.29 Exhaust system and fixings (Sec 43)

the correct distance. Any stresses or strain imparted to force the system to fit the hangar clips will result in early fractures and failures.
4  When fitting a new part or a complete system it is well worth removing *all* the system from the car and cleaning up all the joints so they fit together easily. The time spent struggling with obstinate joints whilst flat on your back under the car is eliminated and the likelihood of distorting or even breaking a section is greatly reduced. Do not waste a lot of time trying to undo rusted and corroded clamps and bolts. Cut them off. New ones will be required anyway if they are that bad.

## 44  Fault diagnosis – fuel system

*Unsatisfactory engine performance and excessive fuel consumption are not necessarily the fault of the fuel system. In fact, they more commonly occur as a result of faults in the ignition system, which should be checked first. The fault-finding table assumes the ignition system is in order, and also that the engine is in an acceptable mechanical condition.*

| Symptom/s | Reason/s |
| --- | --- |
| Smell of petrol – engine stopped | Leaking fuel lines or unions<br>Leaking fuel tank |
| Smell of petrol – engine idling | Leaking fuel lines or unions between pump and carburettor<br>Float level incorrect<br>Punctured float<br>Faulty needle valve |
| Excessive fuel consumption, which is not covered by leaks | Carburettor setting incorrect<br>Air valve piston operating incorrectly<br>Diaphragm faulty<br>Flange/air cleaner gasket upside down<br>Float chamber vent blocked<br>Brakes binding<br>Tyres underinflated |
| Difficult starting, uneven running, lack of power, stalling | Carburettor incorrectly set<br>Fuel restriction in delivery system<br>Pump delivering insufficient fuel<br>Incorrect metering needle fitted<br>Leak in vacuum system<br>Incorrect float level<br>Jets or emulsion tubes blocked or restricted<br>Water in fuel<br>Insufficient fuel in tank<br>Incorrect float level<br>Diaphragm faulty<br>Air valve piston operating incorrectly<br>Leak at inlet manifold<br>Blocked air cleaner<br>Vapour lock in fuel lines (hot conditions only) |

# Chapter 4 Ignition system

## Contents

Ducellier distributor contact breaker points – cleaning and adjusting ............................................................. 18
Ducellier distributor contact breaker points – removal and refitting ................................................................. 17
Ducellier distributor – description and operation ........................... 15
Ducellier distributor – dismantling, examination and reassembly . 20
Ducellier distributor – maintenance ........................................ 16
Ducellier distributor – removal and refitting .................................. 19
Fault diagnosis – ignition system ........................................... 22
General description ....................................................... 1
Lucas 23D4 distributor – maintenance, dismantling and ignition timing ............................................................. 9
Lucas 25D4 distributor condenser – testing, renewal and refitting ................................................................. 5
Lucas 25D4 distributor contact breaker points – adjustment ....... 3
Lucas 25D4 distributor contact breaker points – removal and refitting ................................................................. 4
Lucas 25D4 distributor – dismantling, inspection and reassembly ................................................................. 7
Lucas 25D4 distributor – ignition timing ................................... 8
Lucas 25D4 distributor – removal and refitting .......................... 6
Lucas 43D4 and 45D4 distributors – dismantling, inspection and reassembly ............................................................. 14
Lucas 43D4 and 45D4 distributors – general note ..................... 10
Lucas 43D4 and 45D4 distributors – ignition timing ................... 11
Lucas 43D4 and 45D4 distributors – maintenance and adjustment ................................................................. 12
Lucas 43D4 and 45D4 distributors – removal and refitting .......... 13
Routine maintenance ..................................................... 2
Spark plugs and HT leads ................................................. 21

## Specifications

*Ignition system (general)*

**Type** ................................................................................. Coil and distributor

**Firing order** ....................................................................... 1–3–4–2

**Coil type** .......................................................................... Lucas 11C12 (HA12 on some export models)
AC Delco Remy 100329
AC Delco Remy 7992170 (5 Series)

*All models except Holbay and Arrow Sedan*

**Spark plugs**
Type ................................................................................ Champion N9Y or AC 42XLS
Gap ................................................................................. 0.030 in (0.76 mm)

**Distributor**
Type ................................................................................ Lucas 25D4, Lucas 45D4 or Ducellier
Rotation ........................................................................... Anti-clockwise (viewed from above)
Contact breaker gap:
    Lucas distributors ............................................................ 0.015 in (0.38 mm)
    Ducellier distributor ......................................................... 0.016 in (0.4 mm) initial setting only
Dwell angle:
    Lucas 25D4 .................................................................. 60° ± 3°
    Lucas 45D4 .................................................................. 51° ± 5°
    Ducellier ..................................................................... 56° ± 1°
Ignition advance control ......................................................... Fully automatic-vacuum and centrifugal

**Ignition timing (nominal) static** ............................................. 7° to 9° BTDC (1500LC 2° to 6° BTDC)

**Ignition timing (dynamic, at 3000 rpm with vacuum advance pipe disconnected)**

Pre 7-Series models .............................................................

7-Series models ..................................................................

| Engine | Head | Carbs | Timing |
|--------|------|-------|--------|
| 1500 HC | Iron | Single | 39° to 41° BTDC |
| 1725 HC | Iron | Single | 29° to 31° BTDC |
| 1725 LC | Iron | Single | 30° to 32° BTDC |
| 1725 | Aluminium | Single | 31° to 33° BTDC |
| 1725 | Aluminium | Twin | 33° to 35° BTDC |
| 1500 | Iron | Single | 30° to 32° BTDC |
| 1725 | Iron | Single | 32° to 34° BTDC |
| 1725 | Aluminium | Single | 32° to 34° BTDC |

*Holbay engine*
## Spark plugs
Type ........................................................................... Champion N9Y
Gap ............................................................................ 0.030 in (0.76 mm)

## Distributor
Type:
    Series 5 ............................................................ Lucas 45D4
    Except Series 5 ................................................ Lucas 23D4 or Lucas 43D4
Rotation ..................................................................... Anti-clockwise (viewed from above)
Contact breaker gap .................................................. 0.015 in (0.38 mm)
Dwell angle:
    Lucas 23D4 ...................................................... 60° ± 3°
    Lucas 43D4 ...................................................... 51° ± 5°
    Lucas 45D4 ...................................................... 51° ± 5°
Ignition advance control:
    5 Series ........................................................... Fully automatic centrifugal with vacuum retard
    Except 5 Series ................................................ Fully automatic centrifugal

## Ignition timing (static)
5 Series ..................................................................... 13° to 15° BTDC
Except 5 Series .......................................................... 6° to 8° BTDC

## Ignition timing (dynamic, at 3000 rpm)
5 Series ..................................................................... 25° BTDC
Except 5 Series .......................................................... 26° BTDC

*Arrow Sedan engine*
## Spark plugs
Type ........................................................................... N9Y
Gap ............................................................................ 0.025 in (0.63 mm)

## Distributor
Type ........................................................................... Lucas 25D4
Rotation ..................................................................... Anti-clockwise (viewed from above)
Contact breaker gap .................................................. 0.015 in (0.38 mm)
Dwell angle ............................................................... 60° ± 3°

## Ignition timing ................................................ 7° BTDC static and running at correct idling speed

## Torque wrench setting

| | lbf ft | Nm |
|---|---|---|
| Spark plugs | 12 | 16 |

## 1  General description

1  In order that the internal combustion engine with spark ignition can operate properly, it is essential that the spark is delivered at the spark plug electrodes at the precise moment it is required. This moment varies – in relation to the position of the pistons and crankshaft – depending on the speed and loading of the engine. This control of the spark timing is automatic (on early cars, the control was manual). When it is realised that at 50 mph approximately 100 sparks per second are being produced, the importance of the need for precise setting can be appreciated. Many minor faults, and cases of poor performance and heavy fuel consumption, can be traced to the ignition system.

2  The ignition coil is a high voltage transformer, and is the means of transforming the twelve volts available from the battery into the high voltage required at the spark plugs. When the contact points close, the twelve volt battery supply is applied across the primary winding of the coil (ie across terminals CB and SW, signifying 'contact breaker' and 'ignition switch'). When the contact points open, the magnetic field of the coil collapses and a very high voltage is induced in the secondary winding of the coil. This occurrence is a basic electrical phenomenon, the principle of which need not be discussed here. The HT lead and the case of the coil are the terminals of the secondary winding, and current at high voltage is thus fed through the circuit, consisting of the HT lead from the coil, the rotor arm, to each of the four segments in the distributor cap in turn, and thence via the individual HT leads to the spark plugs. The condenser in the distributor has a dual function: Firstly, it acts as an accelerator to make the field collapse rapidly, thereby causing the HT voltage to increase and give a better spark. Secondly, the condenser serves to damp the arc (or sparking) across

the contact points, thereby helping to prolong their life.

3  Obviously, the timing of the break in the circuit decides the moment at which the spark is made. The contact points (or breaker points!) are in effect a switch. Not only do they open and close four times for every two revolutions of the crankshaft – delivering a spark to the four plugs in turn – they also open earlier or later in relation to the position of the crankshaft/pistons. Ignition advance and retard are the terms used to express this condition and it is measured in degrees – being degrees of angle of any crank on the shaft. Zero degrees is top dead centre, being the highest point on the arc made by a crank. Timing setting is therefore expressed as so many degrees BTDC (before top dead centre).

4  To vary the ignition timing, the contact points mounting plate can rotate a limited amount relative to the centre spindle. This is controlled by the vacuum advance device which works from the suction (depression) in the engine inlet manifold. In addition, the contact opening cam is able to revolve a certain amount round the centre spindle. This is controlled by spring-loaded weights which move out under centrifugal force. When they move out, the spindle to cam position is altered.

5  Timing varies with different engines but normally ranges from the static (at rest) advance of approximately 8° BTDC to 36° BTDC. The vacuum advance device is concerned only with smooth running and economy at the lower engine speeds and part throttle openings. When accelerating and under open throttle conditions, the centrifugal control is the only one in operation. The static timing is important of course as the two automatic timing advance devices start from this point and consequently if it is incorrect, the whole range is affected. The vernier adjustment on the vacuum advance unit alters the static ignition setting entirely – not just for the vacuum advance part.

6  To provide for identification of distributors, the service number

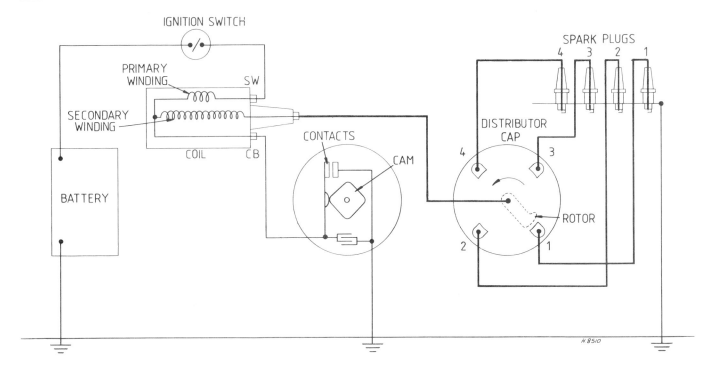

Fig. 4.1 Ignition system – the HT circuit is shown in bold lines (Sec 1)

stamped on the body is used. The vacuum advance units have the identifying details stamped on the capsule.

## 2 Routine maintenance

1 *Spark plugs (5000 miles):* Remove the plugs and thoroughly clean away all traces of carbon. Examine the porcelain insulation round the central electrode inside the plug and if damaged, discard the plug. Reset the gap between the electrodes. Do not use a set of plugs for more than 10 000 miles. It is false economy.

2 *Distributor (5000 miles):* Remove the cap and rotor arm and put one or two drops of engine oil into the centre of the cam recess. Smear the surfaces of the cam itself with petroleum jelly. Do not over lubricate as any excess could get onto the contact point surfaces and cause ignition difficulties. Examine the contact point surfaces. If there is a build-up of deposits on one face and a pit in the other it will be impossible to set the gap correctly and they should be refaced or renewed. Set the gap when the contact surfaces are in order.

3 *General:* Examine all leads and terminals for signs of broken or cracked insulation. Also check all terminal connections for slackness or signs of fracturing of some strands of wire. Partly broken wire should be renewed. The HT leads are particularly important as any insulation faults will cause the high voltage to 'jump' to the nearest earth and this will prevent a spark at the plug. Check that no HT leads are loose or in a position where the insulation could wear due to rubbing against part of the engine.

## 3 Lucas 25D4 distributor contact breaker points – adjustment

1 Remove the distributor cap by unclipping the two leaf springs, one each side of the distributor.

2 Pull off the rotor arm from the cam spindle.

3 First examine the points by carefully levering them apart with a small screwdriver or something similar. If the faces of the circular contacts are pitted or rough then they cannot be properly set and should be removed for renewal or cleaning up.

4 If the faces are clean then turn the engine so that the moving arm of the breaker rests with the follower on one of the four high points on

the cam. The engine can be turned by engaging a gear and moving the car.

5 Select a feeler blade (see Specifications) and place it between the points. If the gap is too great, slacken the fixed point locking screw and move the plate to alter the gap. If the gap is too small, the feeler blade may still fit between the points as the spring-loaded arm can simply move back. When setting them, therefore, the feeler gauge blade should only be a very light touch on each contact face.

6 Lock the fixed plate screw and recheck the gap. Refit the rotor arm making sure that the lug in the rotor recess is fully engaged in the slot on the cam spindle.

7 Check the inside of the distributor cap before refitting it and verify that the four segments are clean and the centre carbon brush is intact and moves freely.

## 4 Lucas 25D4 distributor contact breaker points – removal and refitting

1 The contact points should be removed if the surfaces are damaged or worn sufficiently to require renewal or refacing. Generally it is best to renew the contacts completely as refacing never produces a surface as good as the original (unless done professionally which would cost more than the new ones!) and they will deteriorate again much more rapidly.

2 Remove the distributor cap and rotor arm as described in the previous Section and remove the fixed plate locking screw.

3 Undo the small nut on the terminal post which also secures the end of the spring, and lift off the washer and nylon insulating sleeve. The two circular tags from the coil and condenser leads may then be taken off and the spring contact lifted off at the pivot post. The fixed contact can also now be lifted out.

4 Refitting is a reversal of the removal procedure. Modern contact sets are sometimes supplied as a complete assembly which can be fitted and connected as a single unit. If the new points are in separate pieces, the assembly on the terminal post is important. If you did not notice the order in which the pieces came off, the correct order of refitting is: Fixed contact onto the baseplate, insulating washer over the terminal post, insulating washer over the pivot post, spring contact, lead connectors onto terminal post, nylon sleeve on terminal post, plain washer and nut. This assembly insulates the spring side of the contacts from earth except when the points are closed.

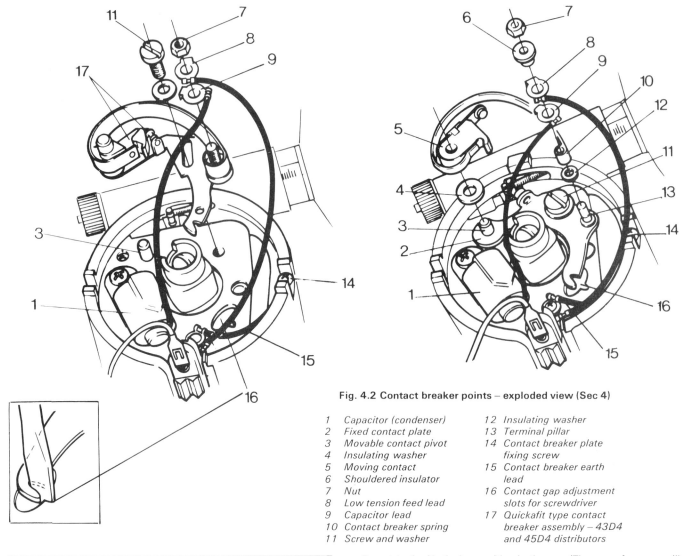

Fig. 4.2 Contact breaker points – exploded view (Sec 4)

1   Capacitor (condenser)
2   Fixed contact plate
3   Movable contact pivot
4   Insulating washer
5   Moving contact
6   Shouldered insulator
7   Nut
8   Low tension feed lead
9   Capacitor lead
10  Contact breaker spring
11  Screw and washer

12  Insulating washer
13  Terminal pillar
14  Contact breaker plate
    fixing screw
15  Contact breaker earth
    lead
16  Contact gap adjustment
    slots for screwdriver
17  Quickafit type contact
    breaker assembly – 43D4
    and 45D4 distributors

## 5   Lucas 25D4 distributor condenser – testing, removal and refitting

1   A faulty condenser causes interruptions in the ignition circuit or total failure. Elaborate testing methods are pointless as the item is cheap to renew.
2   If the contact points become pitted after a relatively small mileage (under 1000) and if starting is difficult, it is a good idea to renew the condenser with the points. Another way to check is to remove the distributor cap and turn the engine so the points are closed. Then switch on the ignition and open the points using an insulated screwdriver. There should be a small blue spark visible, but if the condenser is faulty, there will be a very strong blue spark.
3   To remove the condenser, disconnect the lead from the contacts terminal post and remove the crosshead screw securing the condenser mounting bracket to the plate. Fit a new one in the reverse order.

## 6   Lucas 25D4 distributor – removal and refitting

1   The distributor should be removed if there are indications that the drive spindle is a sloppy fit in the bushes ( causing contact gap setting difficulties) or if it is to be dismantled and cleaned thoroughly and checked. It should also be removed before the oil pump is taken out.
2   Before removing the distributor, it is helpful to prevent future confusion if the engine is positioned with No 1 piston at TDC on the firing stroke. This can be done by noting the position of the No 1 plug lead in the cap and then turning the engine to TDC so the rotor is

adjacent to the No 1 plug position in the cap. (The cap, of course, will be removed to do this.) For details see Section 8, dealing with ignition timing.
3   Detach the plug leads from the spark plug and the coil HT lead from the distributor cap or coil. Remove the cap by unclipping the leaf spring clip at each side (photo).
4   Pull off the LT wire connector at the distributor and remove the suction pipe from the vacuum advance unit (photos).
5   Undo the two bolts securing the flange of the distributor body to the block. Do not undo the upper clamp bolts or clamp unless the distributor is being renewed. It will at least keep the timing in the right area (photo).
6   Lift the distributor out. Before proceeding any further, note the position of the eccentric slot in the end of the driveshaft inside the distributor mounting recess in the block. This will give a firm timing reference if the oil pump is to be removed.
7   Refitting is a reversal of the removal procedure. Check that the rubber sealing ring between the flange and block is in good condition. Line up the eccentric tongue on the distributor shaft with the slot in the driveshaft and when the sleeve of the body is being pushed down, be prepared to rotate the shaft either way a little to engage the drive (photo).

## 7   Lucas 25D4 distributor – dismantling, inspection and re-assembly

1   If the distributor is causing trouble with the ignition system, it is often a good idea to fit a completely new unit. Without the proper test

6.3 Removing the distributor cap

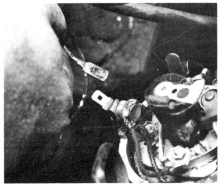

6.4a Disconnecting the LT wire from the distributor

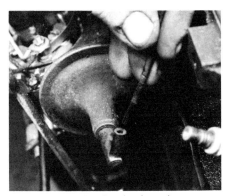

6.4b Disconnecting the pipe from the vacuum advance unit

6.5 Removing the distributor flange bolts

6.7 Checking the condition of the distributor sealing ring

equipment it is difficult to diagnose whether or not the centrifugal and vacuum automatic advance mechanisms are performing as they should. However, play in the shaft bushes can be detected by removing the rotor arm and gripping the end and trying to move it sideways. If there is any movement, it means the cam cannot accurately control the contact points gap. This must receive attention.

2    With the distributor removed, take off the rotor, condenser and contact points as described in Section 4.

3    Unhook the vacuum advance link from the edge of the contact breaker moving plate and then take out the two screws at the edge of the base plate which secure it to the body of the distributor.

4    Pull the nylon LT lead terminal from the groove in the side of the distributor and the two plates may then be lifted out.

5    If the shaft is being removed to renew the bushes do *not* dismantle the centrifugal advance mechanism as it is not necessary. Remove the small circlip from the end of the threaded shank of the vacuum advance vernier adjustment. This will enable the knurled screw to be taken right off. Note the position of the vernier scale on the advance unit. The vacuum unit can then be also withdrawn.

6    Remove the pin securing the offset driving dog with a flat-nosed punch and the shaft, complete with cam and centrifugal advance mechanism, may be taken out. Note the relative position of the dog offset to the cam rotor slot.

7    To renew the bush, first press or drive out the old one from inside the distributor body.

8    The bush is stepped at its lower end for 0.75 in (19 mm). Before fitting a new bush it should be soaked in engine oil for at least twenty four hours – or hot oil for two hours – before fitting. It is made of sintered copper/iron and retains its lubricant due to porosity. The new bush should be pushed in from the lower end, the small diameter part first. When the shoulder part reaches the body, the bush should be pressed in with a shouldered mandrel in a press or vice. Any attempt to drive it in – even using blocks of wood – will almost certainly cause it to break up. The bottom of the bush should be flush with the distributor body and it should protrude very slightly at the top inside.

9    When fitted, the bush should be drilled through in line with the shaft oil drain hole in the body. Make sure there are no burrs or loose metal particles anywhere in the bush.

10   Refit the shaft, lubricated with engine oil. If it is tight, it will need 'running in' by hand until there are no traces of binding. The bush must not be reamed as this will impair its self-lubricating properties. Do not forget the distance collar on the shaft under the action plate.

11   If the centrifugal advance device is to be dismantled, first remove the two springs very carefully so as not to kink, distort or stretch them. Then note the position of the cam rotor arm slot relative to the offset drive dog on the bottom of the shaft and undo the screw in the top of the cam securing it to the shaft. The cam may then be lifted off, followed by the counter weights.

12   Reassembly of the distributor is a reversal of the dismantling process. Take care the cam rotor arm slot is in the same relative position with the driving dog as before and do not stretch the centrifugal springs. Smear the contact breaker baseplate with a thin film of oil or grease between it and the moving plate. Make sure the drive dog retaining pin is peened over sufficiently to prevent it working loose.

## 8   Lucas 25D4 distributor – ignition timing

1    It is necessary to time the ignition when it has been upset due to overhauling or dismantling which may have altered the relationship between the position of the pistons and the moment at which the distributor delivers the spark. Alternatively, it may simply be felt the engine performance is not all it might be, and that a timing check is therefore desirable. It is assumed that fuel of the recommended octane rating is being used.

2    The static or datum timing is that setting which causes the spark to arrive at a given position of the crankshaft (or, put another way, to arrive at a given position of the No 1 piston before TDC). The setting of the crankshaft is normally given in relevant specifications, and is quoted in degrees. From the specifications we know that the static timing is say, 8° Before Top Dead Centre. The range of 6° to 10° given is intentional. No two engines are identical. Neither are the combined operations of their components. Se we start in the middle of

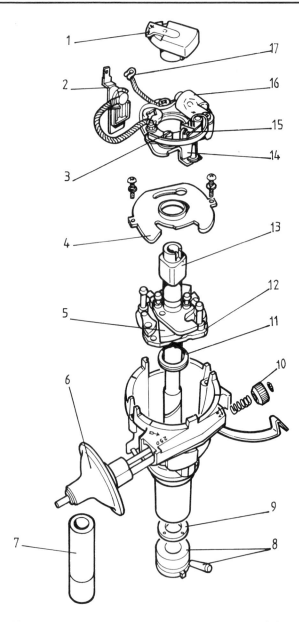

position. Should the rotor arm still be way out, check whether the distributor body can be rotated enough to compensate by slackening the clamp and trying it. It may be possible, with alterations to plug lead lengths. Such a state of affairs usually indicates that the oil pump drive spindle is out of position. With luck it will not have to be repositioned. (See Chapter 1, Section 45).

4    Now the engine should be set at the correct static advance position. Each notch, or line, represents 5°, so for 8° advance turn the engine back, then forwards to one and a half notches/lines from the TDC mark.

5    As discussed in the opening Section, the spark is produced when the contact points in the LT circuit open. It is now necessary to slacken the distributor clamping screw so the body of the distributor may be turned (whilst the rotor spindle stays still). Also, the vernier control on the vacuum advance should be set in the centre of the range to give scope for equal fine adjustment either way later. This central position is with two divisions of the scale showing. The distributor should now be turned slightly, one way or the other, so the contact points are fully open on the cam. The contact gap MUST be set correctly. As it is difficult to see exactly when the points are just opening a means of doing this electrically is necessary. Use a continuity tester or a twelve volt bulb and a jumper lead. If the latter is used, put one lead to the terminal where the coil LT lead joins the distributor and the other to a good earth on the engine block. With the ignition swiched on the bulb will now light with the points open. Turn the body of the distributor anti-clockwise until the light just goes out. Then, holding the rotor arm lightly, with clockwise pressure, turn the body clockwise again until the light just comes on again. Then tighten the clamping screw. If desired, the correctness of the setting can be checked with a stroboscopic timing light but such a device is not essential for accurate setting of the static timing.

6    The performance of the engine should now be checked by road testing. Make any adjustments by turning the vernier adjustment wheel a measured number of 'clicks' – start by increasing the advance – and road test after each adjustment. One complete revolution of the vernier adjuster is equivalent to a 3° crankshaft movement and one division on the scale represents 4°.

## 9  Lucas 23D4 distributor – maintenance, dismantling and ignition timing

Apart from the fact that no vacuum unit is fitted, this distributor is similar to the 25D4 unit described in earlier Sections.

## 10  Lucas 43D4 and 45D4 distributors – general note

These distributors are slightly smaller than the earlier 23D4 and 25D4 distributors which they supersede. No vacuum unit is fitted on the 43D4 and there is no vernier adjuster on the 45D4.

## 11  Lucas 43D4 and 45D4 distributors – ignition timing

The procedure for ignition timing is identical to that given in Section 8. Note, however, that the coil LT lead terminates inside the distributor on a terminal assembly.

## 12  Lucas 43D4 and 45D4 distributors – maintenance and adjustment

1    Every 5000 miles (8000 km), release the two spring clips which retain the distributor cap in position, and remove the distributor cap and rotor arm. Apply two or three drops of engine oil to the felt pad which is located in the distributor cam recess.

2    Refer to Fig. 4.5 and remove the movable contact breaker arm by lifting the spring (4) out of the white nylon insulator (5) and the contact point from its hollow pivot (2). Apply a thin smear of high melting point grease to the outside of the hollow pivot.

3    Apply a smear of the same grease to the high points of the distributor cam.

4    Apply one drop of engine oil through the centre plate holes (15) (Fig. 4.6). This operation applies only to the type 45D4 distributor and it should be noted that neither type of distributor requires lubrication

**Fig. 4.3 Lucas 25D4 distributor – exploded view, omitting distributor cap (Sec 7)**

| | |
|---|---|
| 1   Rotor arm | 9    Thrust washer |
| 2   LT terminal | 10   Vernier adjustment nut |
| 3   Fixed contact plate securing screw | 11   Distance collar |
| | 12   Action plate |
| 4   Contact breaker baseplate | 13   Cam |
| 5   Centrifugal advance control weights | 14   Contact breaker moving plate |
| 6   Vacuum advance control unit | 15   Contacts |
| 7   Bearing bush | 16   Condenser |
| 8   Dog and pin | 17   CB earth connector |

the possible range.

3    The crankshaft pulley wheel, keyed to the front of the crankshaft, is marked with a series of notches (or lines on those models with damper pulley wheels). A pointer is fitted to the front of the timing gear cover. If the engine is revolved clockwise, TDC on No 1 piston will be achieved when the *last* notch (or line) comes up to the pointer. Do this and then look at the distributor cap and see at which position the HT lead from No 1 spark plug connects. Then remove the cap and see whether the top of the rotor arm is facing the No 1 plug contact. If it is, good! If not, the engine must be turned another complete revolution to the TDC mark again. The rotor arm should then be in the correct

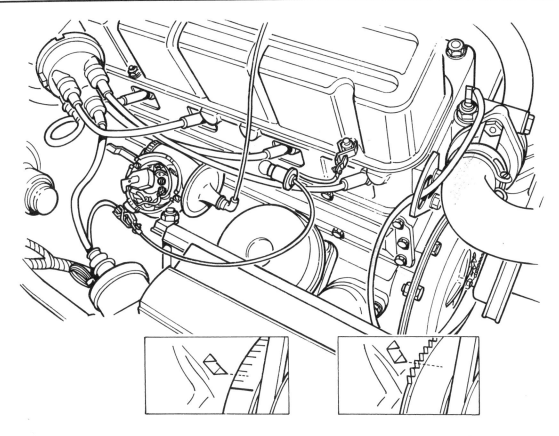

Fig. 4.4 Static ignition timing – insets show pointer set at 8° advance (Sec 8)

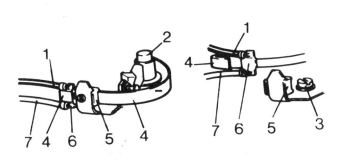

Fig. 4.5 Lucas distributors types 45D4 and 43D4 – LT terminals
(Sec 12)

1   LT lead
2   Pivot post
3   Fixed contact locking screw
4   Moving contact spring arm
5   Insulator
6   LT connecting plate
7   Capacitor lead

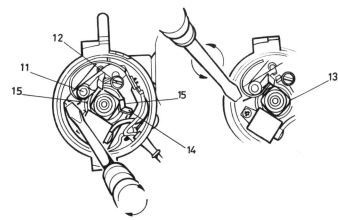

Fig. 4.6 Lucas distributor type 45D4 – contact breaker adjustment
(Sec 12)

11  Pivot
12  Fixed contact locking
     screw
13  Cam
14  Felt lubricating wick
15  Lubrication holes

of the centrifugal advance mechanism.

5   Prise the contact points apart and check their faces for pitting. Minor 'pips' or 'craters' may be removed from the contact point faces by dressing them squarely on an oilstone or by drawing a strip of fine emery cloth between them. If the points are badly pitted or burned then they must be renewed.

6   To remove the points, push the LT and condenser (capacitor) lead connecting plate (6) from the looped end of the movable contact spring arm (4) (Fig. 4.5).

7   Unscrew and remove the locking screw and washers which secure the fixed contact breaker arm and lift the complete contact breaker set from the distributor baseplate.

8   Separate the two points simply by pulling the movable arm from the hollow pivot.

9   Refitting the points is a reversal of the removal procedure, but do not tighten the fixed contact screw fully – just enough to allow the

contact to slide stiffly.

10  With a socket spanner applied to the crankshaft pulley bolt turn the engine until the heel of the movable contact breaker arm is located exactly at the centre of a high point of the distributor cam. Using a screwdriver in the adjustment slots, move the fixed arm until, using feeler gauges, the points gap is as specified. Tighten the locking screw.

11  Check the ignition timing by one of the two methods recommended (test bulb or stroboscope). If necessary, any adjustment of the distributor will have to be carried out by loosening the clamp plate pinch bolt and turning the distributor body, as no vernier screw adjuster is fitted.

12  Refit the rotor arm and distributor cap.

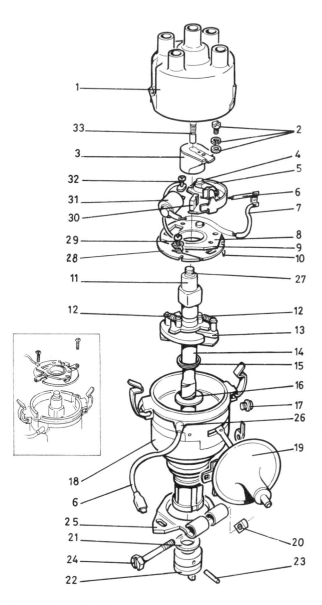

**Fig. 4.7 Lucas distributor type 45D4 – exploded view (Sec 14)**
**(Type 43D4 is similar except that a blanking plate is fitted in place**
**of the vacuum advance capsule). Inset: Alternative baseplate**
**fixing**

| | |
|---|---|
| 1   Cap | 18   Body |
| 2   Contact securing screw | 19   Vacuum capsule |
| 3   Rotor | 20   Pinch bolt nut |
| 4   Pivot post | 21   Thrust washer |
| 5   Movable contact arm | 22   Driving dog |
| 6   LT lead and terminal plate | 23   Pin |
| 7   Condenser (capacitor) lead | 24   Pinch bolt |
| 8   Movable baseplate | 25   Clamp plate |
| 9   Fixed baseplate | 26   Insulating sleeve |
| 10  Baseplate locating prongs | 27   Felt lubricating pad |
| 11  Cam | 28   Baseplate expanding |
| 12  Centrifugal advance springs |      section |
| 13  Centrifugal advance | 29   Wedge screw |
|     mechanism | 30   Cam lubricating wick |
| 14  Shaft | 31   Capacitor (condenser) |
| 15  Nylon washer | 32   Retaining screw |
| 16  Steel washer | 33   Carbon bush |
| 17  Vacuum capsule or | |
|     blanking plate screws | |

## 13  Lucas 43D4 and 45D4 distributors – removal and refitting

The procedure is similar to that given in Section 6, except that the LT lead must be detached at the coil end.

## 14  Lucas 43D4 and 45D4 distributors – dismantling, inspection and reassembly

1    Remove the distributor cap, rotor arm and felt lubrication pad.
2    On type 45D4 units, remove the vacuum unit screws (17) (Fig. 4.7). (Note the two baseplate prongs which locate beneath one screw). Disengage the vacuum unit link from the moving plate pin and remove the vacuum unit.
3    Push back the LT lead (6) and rubber sleeve (26) into the centre of the distributor.
4    Remove the baseplate wedge screw (29) and then, using a small screwdriver, prise the expanded segment (28) of the fixed baseplate (9) inwards so that the complete baseplate/contact breaker assembly can be lifted from the distributor body.
5    Refer to Fig. 4.7 and drive out the drive dog securing pin (23). Note the relative positions of the dog driving tongue and the rotor locating slot, then pull off the dog and thrust washer.
6    The shaft, complete with centrifugal advance mechanism, can now be withdrawn through the distributor body. Retain the O-ring (1) (see Fig. 4.8).
7    If the centrifugal advance mechanism is worn, it should be renewed as a complete shaft/advance mechanism assembly. Any servicing should be limited to renewal of the springs if they have stretched or broken.
8    Check the shaft for side movement in the bearings. If evident, then the complete distributor should be renewed on an exchange basis.
9    Reassembly is a reversal of the dismantling procedure, but the following points should be observed. Smear all friction surfaces of internal components with a molybdenum disulphide grease before assembly. Insert the baseplate assembly into its approximate position in the distributor body so the two prongs are located either side of the hole through which the vacuum unit securing screw passes. On type 45D4 distributors, connect and screw the vacuum unit into position, then snap the baseplate into position in the body, ensuring that it is pressed down against the ledge inside the body so that the chamfered edges will engage the undercut in the body side. Should there be any tendency for the baseplate not to be a tight fit in its groove, renew it. Fit and tighten the securing screw. Later distributors have a second screw fitted for additional security, and the baseplate has two lugs by which the plate is secured to the body by the two screws. See Fig. 4.7.
10   Fit the thrust washer (raised side of pips towards dog) and the drive dog, noting particularly the alignment of the large and small segments in relation to the electrode of the rotor arm. See Fig. 4.8.
11   Fit the pin which secures the dog to the shaft and stake the holes at both ends. Should a new shaft be fitted, these are supplied undrilled and should be drilled to accept the pin using a $\frac{3}{16}$ in (4.76 mm) twist

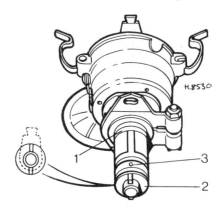

**Fig. 4.8 Lucas distributor types 45D4 and 43D4 – location of the**
**driving dog relative to the rotor arm (Sec 14)**

| | |
|---|---|
| 1   O-ring seal | 3   Pin |
| 2   Driving dog | |

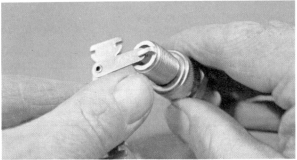

**Measuring plug gap.** A feeler gauge of the correct size (see ignition system specifications) should have a slight 'drag' when slid between the electrodes. Adjust gap if necessary

**Adjusting plug gap.** The plug gap is adjusted by bending the earth electrode inwards, or outwards, as necessary until the correct clearance is obtained. Note the use of the correct tool

**Normal.** Grey-brown deposits, lightly coated core nose. Gap increasing by around 0.001 in (0.025 mm) per 1000 miles (1600 km). Plugs ideally suited to engine, and engine in good condition

**Carbon fouling.** Dry, black, sooty deposits. Will cause weak spark and eventually misfire. Fault: over-rich fuel mixture. Check: carburettor mixture settings, float level and jet sizes; choke operation and cleanliness of air filter. Plugs can be re-used after cleaning

**Oil fouling.** Wet, oily deposits. Will cause weak spark and eventually misfire. Fault: worn bores/piston rings or valve guides; sometimes occurs (temporarily) during running-in period. Plugs can be re-used after thorough cleaning

**Overheating.** Electrodes have glazed appearance, core nose very white – few deposits. Fault: plug overheating. Check: plug value, ignition timing, fuel octane rating (too low) and fuel mixture (too weak). Discard plugs and cure fault immediately

**Electrode damage.** Electrodes burned away; core nose has burned, glazed appearance. Fault: pre-ignition. Check: as for 'Overheating' but may be more severe. Discard plugs and remedy fault before piston or valve damage occurs

**Split core nose (may appear initially as a crack).** Damage is self-evident, but cracks will only show after cleaning. Fault: pre-ignition or wrong gap-setting technique. Check: ignition timing, cooling system, fuel octane rating (too low) and fuel mixture (too weak). Discard plugs, rectify fault immediately

drill. Use the dog as a guide to position the hole and press down on the cam end of the shaft whilst drilling, to compress the dog and washer against the shank. Where a new thrust washer is installed, assemble the drive dog and washer and pin and then tap the end face of the drive dog to slightly compress and flatten the 'pips' on the thrust washer to provide the specified shaft endfloat of between 0.010 and 0.020 in (0.2540 and 0.5080 mm).

## 15  Ducellier distributor – description and operation

Certain models within the Hunter range have this distributor fitted in place of the more normally found Lucas unit. The Ducellier distributor, however, has a few unusual features not to be found on the other distributor, namely:

(a)  *A floating driving dog*
(b)  *Balanced rotor arm*
(c)  *Spring loaded slipper to bias the distributor shaft and provide a light brake to reduce oscillation at low engine speeds*
(d)  *Adjustments that provide fine control of the dwell angle, dwell variation with increase of speed, primary and secondary centrifugal advance curves and the commencement of vacuum advance*

The vacuum advance pullrod operates a pivoted arm that slides the moving contact point across the domed fixed contact (see Fig. 4.9). Consequently sparking is not confined to one part of the points and the usual pitting is virtually eliminated. The points are also self-cleaning throughout their service life. This action is due to the movement of the moving contact point across the face of the fixed contact point.

Every throttle opening position, when the engine is running, will change the degree of vacuum in the manifold and advance capsule. This, in turn, will move the capsule pullrod and turn the arm on its pivot, moving the heel towards the cam on the spindle and sliding the moving contact point across the face of the fixed contact point. The arm of the lever alters the angle of the contact breaker arm, bringing the heel closer to the cam, advancing the ignition timing and reducing the dwell angle. The height and contour of the fixed contact point will increase the gap and dwell angle in inverse proportion once the lever arm is correctly set.

The operating end of the lever arm has a cam which can be adjusted to compensate for manufacturing tolerances of the arm and points assembly. The dwell angle should not change by more than -2° once set.

A serrated cam (see Fig. 4.9) can be adjusted to set the tension of the vacuum capsule return spring, thus providing a means of correctly setting the commencement of the vacuum advance. This is set in production and does not normally need to be disturbed.

## 16  Ducellier distributor – maintenance

1   Keep the inside and outside of the distributor cap clean by wiping with a soft cloth. Clean the HT leads, the plug caps and exteriors of the plugs and finally the coil. Dampness on these components can make starting a problem. This can be remedied by the use of a waterproof sealant, liberally sprayed over the ignition components.
2   *Every 5000 miles (8000 km) or 5 months:* Lubricate the distributor. Release the spring clips, remove the cap and rotor arm and apply two drops of engine oil to the contact breaker pivot and to the felt pad in the spindle. Lightly grease the distributor cam. Refit the rotor arm and cap.

## 17  Ducellier distributor contact breaker points – removal and refitting

1   Remove the cap and rotor.
2   Disconnect the LT lead at the connector.
3   Pull the condenser lead from the LT insulator and pull the insulator from the distributor body.
4   Remove the clip and insulating washer from the moving contact pivot post.
5   Press the terminal end of the contact breaker spring towards the spindle and remove it from the insulator on the fixed post. Lift out the

moving contact and LT lead assembly.
6   Remove the fixed contact securing screw and lift away the contact.
7   Refitting is the reverse of the removal sequence, but remember to lubricate the various parts as described in Section 16, paragraph 2.

## 18  Ducellier distributor contact breaker points – cleaning and adjusting

1   The contact breaker points must not be cleaned with an abrasive when worn, but renewed, as the contour of the domed contact is critical to ensure the correct dwell angle. If the surfaces show signs of burning, the points must again be renewed and no attempt made to reface them. Clean the points with a soft cloth only.
2   To adjust the points using feeler gauges is never a very accurate method and it is recommended that a dwell angle meter be used. The dwell angle indicates the period that the points are closed.
3   Connect the dwell meter according to the manufacturer's instructions. Switch on the ignition and crank the engine with the starter motor. Note the reading, which should be as specified.
4   If the reading is not within the limits specified, slacken the fixed contact point plate screw and move as necessary to obtain the correct reading. Tighten the screw and recheck the adjustment.
5   Refit the rotor and cap, start the engine, disconnect the vacuum pipe from the distributor and set the idle speed to 1500 to 2000 rpm. The dwell angle reading should be within the limits specified previously, if not, it is likely that a mechanical fault exists within the distributor and must be traced and remedied. Reconnect the vacuum pipe and remove the dwell meter.

## 19  Ducellier distributor – removal and refitting

1   Turn the crankshaft so the TDC timing mark on the crankshaft pulley is adjacent to the pointer on the timing case.
2   Remove the cap and note if the rotor arm is pointing to No 1 or 4 electrode.
3   Disconnect the LT lead at the connector and the vacuum pipe from the distributor.
4   Remove the bolt securing the clamp plate to the mounting bracket and lift away the distributor.
5   Note the position of the slots in the driving shaft.
6   Refitting is a reverse of the removal procedure but the following point must be noted. It is important that the driving dog is in correct engagement with the slots. A combination of wear on the driving surfaces could easily result in the distributor becoming 180° out, resulting in wrong timing.
7   Start the engine and reset the ignition if necessary.

## 20  Ducellier distributor – dismantling, examination and re-assembly

1   Remove the distributor as described in Section 19.
2   Remove the rotor and contact breakers as described in Section 9.
3   Remove the securing screw and lift off the condenser.
4   Prise out the lubricating felt pad from the spindle.
5   Remove the clip from the D-shaped post; if available, use tool number 15518Q to release the spring tension. Rotate the tool in a clockwise direction, after noting the position of the cam.
6   Remove the vacuum unit securing screw and the cap clip. Tilt the vacuum unit so as to disengage the serrated cam and vacuum pullrod from the D-shaped post. Lift away the vacuum unit and the serrated cam, noting its position.
7   Remove the remaining baseplate screw and the second cap clip. Pull the slipper away from the spindle and lift the baseplate out of the body. Remove the arm from the plate.
8   Remove the circlips from the centrifugal weight posts. Disconnect the springs from the cam plate, taking care not to overstretch them. Note the relationship of the dog drive offset and rotor slot. Remove the cam securing screw and washers and lift the cam from the spindle. Unhook the springs from the fixed post. Remove the circlips from the pivots and lift off the balance weights.
9   Further dismantling is not recommended unless the driving dog is to be renewed. Renewing the spindle alone would not be an

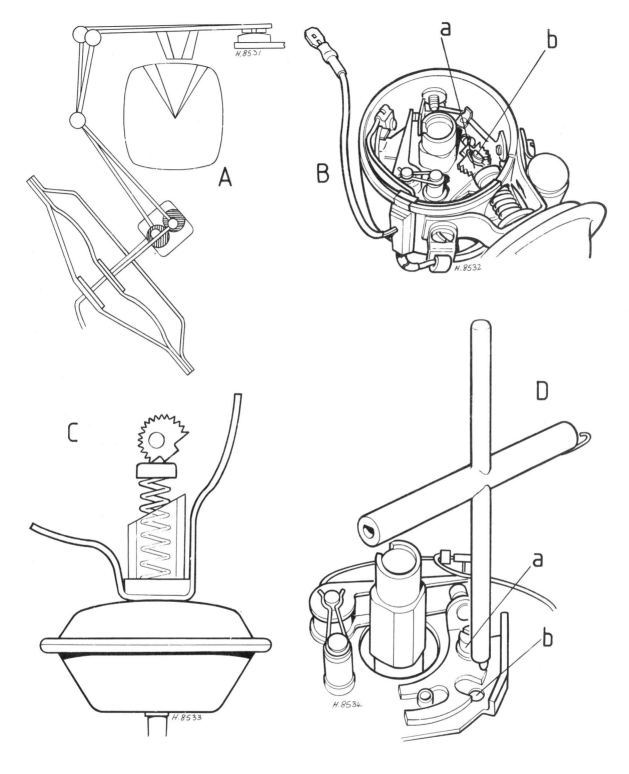

**Fig. 4.9 Details of the Ducellier distributor (Sec 15)**

A   Movement of contact breaker arm with operation of the vacuum
    pullrod
B   Details of distributor baseplate
    (a) serrated cam    (b) D-post
C   Position of serrated cam on pullrod
D   Use of special tool to adjust dwell angle
    (a) locking screw,    (b) hole for eccentric on special tool

economical repair, as the body is likely to be worn also.

10 If dismantling further, lift the end of the coil that surrounds the driving dog pin and wind the spring off. Clamp the dog in a vice and drive out the pin. Remove the dog, shims and washer.

11 Remove any burrs on the shaft before removing the shaft assembly from the body. Remove the thrust washer and O-ring.

12 Check for cracks or tracking in the distributor cap or on the rotor arm. Slight burning of the segments within the cap or on the edge of the rotor arm electrode is acceptable. The carbon brush should have free movement within its housing and the length protruding from the cap should not be less than 0.156 in (4 mm). If below this figure, renew the brush.

13 Check the spindle for scoring on the bearing surfaces. Place the spindle in the body and check for side play. None should be present. Now check for endfloat which must not exceed 0.008 in (0.2 mm). Measure the endfloat by placing two equal thickness feeler gauges opposite each other between the dog drive and the shims under the body. Excessive endfloat can be eliminated by removing the dog drive and placing thicker shims between the body and the dog.

14 Reassembly can commence once all components have been checked and renewed where necessary.

15 Lubricate the upper part of the spindle and the weight pivots with grease. Fit the weights and circlips. Place the cam assembly over the slots and engage the slots with the balance weight posts. If the spindle is already fitted in the body, with the driving dog fitted, align the rotor slot with the dog as shown in Fig. 4.8.

16 Fit the advance springs, taking care that they are not over-stretched. Note that the closed end of the primary (weaker) spring and the oval end of the secondary (stronger) spring are attached to the fixed posts.

17 Fit the circlips to the balance weight posts and refit the cam securing screw with spring and plain washers.

18 Lubricate the lower end of the distributor shaft and the bushes in the body with engine oil, ensuring that oil goes between the bushes. Place the thick thrust washer on the shaft, insert the shaft into the body, and place the lower washers (thin thrust washer with a steel shim either side) on the lower part, followed by the driving dog.

19 Align the dog and rotor as shown in Fig. 4.8. Drive in the pin, making sure that it is free in the dog to provide the 'floating dog' characteristic. Check that the shaft is free to rotate.

20 Refit the coil spring in the groove by winding it over the dog.

21 Fit the slipper, with the step uppermost, and spring into the groove in the baseplate. Align the baseplate lugs with the securing screw holes, depress the slipper and fit the baseplate into the body.

22 Lubricate the lever arm pivot with engine oil and place the lever arm in position, engaging the cam with the aperture in the baseplate. Lubricate the D-shaped post with engine oil.

23 Fit the serrated cam over the pullrod of the vacuum capsule with the cam in the minimum tension position, serrated teeth to the left as viewed from above and the hole offset toward the vacuum unit (see Fig. 4.9).

24 Align the long edge of the dust cover and the long arm of the vacuum unit. Insert the pullrod and cam through the hole in the body and engage them with the D-shaped post on the lever arm.

25 Fit the vacuum unit securing screws, together with the condenser and second cap clip and tighten the screws.

26 Refit the fixed contact to the baseplate and lightly tighten the securing screw. Lubricate the moving contact pivot with engine oil. Fit the moving contact onto the post and engage the spring with the insulator. Fit the insulating washer and spring clip.

27 Refit the LT insulator into the distributor and insert the condenser lead. Fit the clip to the D-shaped post.

28 Soak the felt pad in engine oil, squeeze out the excess and fit to the top of the shaft.

29 Before the final adjustment can take place (refitted to the engine) using the dwell meter, some preliminary adjustments must be made. Rotate the D-shaped post until the moving contact point is central upon the fixed contact. Turn the serrated cam anti-clockwise six clicks from the fitted position, and adjust the points gap to that specified.

30 Refit the distributor to the engine and adjust, if necessary, to obtain the correct dwell angle as described in Section 18. As the distributor has been completely stripped, it will be necessary to check the mechanical efficiency of the distributor.

31 With the engine running, the dwell meter connected and the vacuum pipe disconnected, increase the engine speed to 2000 rpm and note the dwell angle. It should be within the limits described in

Section 18. Any reading outside these figures indicates a mechanical fault within the distributor.

32 To check for dwell variation with vacuum advance, reconnect the vacuum pipe and accelerate the engine quickly from idling speed to 2000 rpm, release the throttle and note the dwell angle reading. It must not exceed a + 0° – 2° variation, if it does, rotate the D-post in very small amounts to obtain the correct setting.

33 Finally, recheck the dwell angle as described in Section 18.

## 21 Spark plugs and HT leads

1 With the development of modern technology and materials, spark plugs are generally very reliable and require minimal attention. When they are due for checking and cleaning it is good practice to have them thoroughly sand-blasted, gapped and checked under pressure on the machine that most garages have installed. They can also be used as good indications of engine condition, particularly as regards the fuel mixture being used and the state of the pistons and cylinder bores. Check each plug as it is possible that one cylinder condition is different from the rest. Plugs come in different types to suit the particular type of engine. A 'hot' plug is for engines which run at lower temperatures than normal and a 'cold' plug is for the hotter running engines. If plugs of the wrong rating are fitted they can either damage the engine or fail to operate properly. Under normal running conditions, a correctly rated plug in a properly tuned engine will have a light deposit of a brownish colour on the electrodes. A dry black sooty deposit indicates an over-rich fuel mixture. An oily blackish deposit indicates worn bores or valve guides. A dry, hard, whitish deposit indicates too weak a fuel mixture. If plugs of the wrong heat range are fitted, they will have similar symptoms to a weak mixture together with burnt electrodes (plug too hot) or to an over-rich mixture caked somewhat thicker (plug too cold). Do not try and economise by using plugs beyond 10 000 miles. Unless the engine remains in exceptionally good tune, reductions in performance and fuel economy will outweigh the cost of a new set.

2 The HT leads and their connections at both ends should always be clean and dry and, as far as possible, neatly arranged away from each other and nearby metallic parts which could cause premature shorting in weak insulation. The metal connections at the ends should be a firm and secure fit and free from any signs of corrosive deposits. If any lead shows signs of cracking or chafing of the insulation, it should be renewed. Remember that radio interference suppression is required when renewing any leads.

## 22 Fault diagnosis – ignition system

There are two main symptoms indicating ignition faults. Either the engine will not start, or it is difficult to start and then misfires. If the misfire is regular, the fault is most probably in the secondary, or high tension circuit. If the misfire is intermittent, the fault could be in either the high or low tension circuits. If the car stops suddenly or will not start at all, it is likely that the fault is in the low tension circuit. Loss of power and overheating (apart from carburation or emission control system faults – see Chapter 3), are normally due to faults in the distributor or incorrect ignition timing.

### Engine fails to start

1 If the engine fails to start and the car was running normally when it was last used, first check there is fuel in the petrol tank. If it turns over normally on the starter motor and the battery is evidently well charged, then the fault may be in either the high or low tension circuits. First check the HT circuit. Note: *If the battery is known to be fully charged, the ignition light comes on, and the starter motor fails to turn the engine, check the tightness of the leads on the battery terminals and the secureness of the earth lead at its connection to the body. It is quite common for the leads to have worked loose, even if they look and feel secure. If one of the battery terminal posts gets very hot when trying to work the starter motor, this is a sure indication of a faulty connection to that terminal.*

2 One of the most common reasons for bad starting is wet or damp spark plug leads and distributor. Remove the distributor cap. If condensation is visible internally, dry the cap with a rag and also wipe over the leads. Refit the cap.

3 If the engine still fails to start, check that current is reaching the

plugs, by disconnecting each plug lead in turn at the spark plug end, and holding the end of the cable about $\frac{3}{16}$ in (5 mm) away from the cylinder block. Spin the engine on the starter motor.

4 Sparking between the end of the cable and the block should be fairly strong with a regular blue spark. (Hold the lead with rubber to avoid electric shock). If current is reaching the plugs, remove them and clean and regap them as specified.

5 If there is no spark at the plug leads take off the HT lead from the centre of the distributor cap and hold it to the block as before. Spin the engine on the starter once more. A rapid succession of blue sparks between the end of the lead and the block indicate that the coil is in order and that the distributor cap is cracked, the rotor arm faulty, or the carbon brush in the top of the distributor cap is not making good contact with the spring on the rotor arm. Possibly, the points are in bad condition.

6 If there are no sparks from the end of the lead from the coil, check the connections at the coil end of the lead. If in order, start checking the low tension circuit.

## Engine misfires

7 If the engine misfires regularly, run it at a fast idling speed. Pull off each of the plug caps in turn and listen to the note of the engine. Hold the plug cap in a dry cloth or with a rubber glove as additional protection against a shock from the HT supply.

8 No difference in engine running will be noticed when the lead from the defective circuit is removed. Removing the lead from one of the good cylinders will accentuate the misfire.

9 Remove the plug lead from the end of the defective plug and hold it about $\frac{3}{16}$ in (5 mm) away from the block. Re-start the engine. If the sparking is fairly strong and regular the fault must lie in the spark plug.

10 The plug may be loose, the insulation may be cracked, or the points may have burnt away giving too wide a gap for the spark to jump. Worse still, one of the points may have broken off. Either renew the plug, or clean it. Reset the gap, and then test it.

11 If there is no spark at the end of the plug lead, or if it is weak and intermittent, check the ignition lead from the distributor to the plug. If the insulation is cracked or perished, renew the lead. Check the connections at the distributor cap.

12 If there is still no spark, examine the distributor cap carefully for tracking. This can be recognised by a very thin black line running between an electrode and some other part of the distributor. These lines are paths which now conduct electricity across the cap thus letting it run to earth. The only answer is a new distributor cap.

13 Apart from the ignition being incorrect, other causes of misfiring have already been dealt with under the Section dealing with the failure of the engine to start. These are:

(a) *The coil may be faulty giving an intermittent misfire*
(b) *There may be a damaged lead or loose connection in the low tension circuit*
(c) *The condenser may be short circuiting*
(d) *There may be a mechanical fault in the distributor*

# Chapter 5 Clutch

## Contents

Clutch – inspection and renovation ............................................... 8
Clutch master cylinder – removal, dismantling, reassembly and refitting ............................................................................................ 5
Clutch operating cylinder – removal, dismantling, reassembly and refitting ................................................................................... 4
Clutch operating lever and thrust release bearing – dismantling, inspection and reassembly ...................................................... 10
Clutch pedal – removal and refitting .......................................... 6
Clutch – removal ............................................................................ 7
Clutch – refitting ........................................................................... 9
Fault diagnosis – clutch .............................................................. 11
General description ......................................................................... 1
Hydraulic system – bleeding ...................................................... 3
Routine maintenance ..................................................................... 2

## Specifications

| | |
|---|---|
| **Type** ............................................................................................ | Borg and Beck or Laycock, diaphragm spring, hydraulically operated |

**Driven plate**

| | |
|---|---|
| Diameter ...................................................................................... | 7.5 in (19 cm); Hunter GLS 8.5 (21.6 cm) |
| Number of springs ..................................................................... | Four |
| Colour of springs: | |
|     Single carb models ............................................................. | Light grey |
|     Twin carb models ............................................................... | Two orange/violet and two white/light green |

**Clutch assembly**

| | |
|---|---|
| Adjustment .................................................................................. | On pedal only |
| Thrust bearing ............................................................................ | Carbon ring |

| | |
|---|---|
| **Master cylinder bore** ............................................................... | 0.625 in (15.875 mm) |

| | |
|---|---|
| **Slave cylinder bore** ................................................................. | 1.125 in (28.575 mm) |

**Torque wrench setting**

| | lbf ft | Nm |
|---|---|---|
| Clutch to flywheel bolts .......................................................... | 16 | 21 |

## 1 General description

All models have a diaphragm spring, single plate, hydraulically operated clutch. The cover assembly incorporating the diaphragm spring and pressure plate, is bolted to the flywheel, sandwiching the friction disc between them. The friction disc has a splined hub which engages with the splined input shaft of the gearbox. The friction material on both sides of the plate is gripped by the cover and flywheel surfaces in much the same way as brake shoes grip the drums. When the clutch pedal is depressed, the pressure plate is pulled off by the diaphragm spring.

The centre section of the friction plate is spring cushioned against the outer part to take up any shock and help ensure a smooth drive take-up.

The diaphragm spring is mounted on shouldered stubs between two fulcrum rings and is attached to both pressure plate and cover by tangentially positioned straps. When pressure is applied to the centre of the diaphragm, the outer edge moves in the opposite direction, drawing the pressure plate with it.

The friction disc between the pressure plate and flywheel is free floating along the input shaft splines and as it gets thinner with wear so the pressure plate automatically moves forward to take it up under the pressure of the diaphragm spring. The additional travel of the operating lever is compensated for by the hydraulic clutch piston moving fractionally further along the cylinder in the rest position. The pressure is applied to the centre of the diaphragm by a carbon faced thrust ring pivot mounted at the end of the operating lever. No

adjustments are necessary.

The Laycock clutch fitted to some models differs from the Borg and Beck clutch in the manner by which the diaphragm is coupled to the pressure plate. With Borg and Beck clutches, drive is transmitted via straps which are riveted to the pressure plate and clipped to the diaphragm. The pressure plate on the Laycock clutch has lugs which locate through a driving plate and which houses the diaphragm. In all other respects the clutch and actuating mechanisms are similar, and the procedure for removal, inspection, renovation and refitting is the same.

## 2 Routine Maintenace

Every 5000 miles or three months (minimum) check the level of the fluid in the reservoir (check the brake fluid reservoir too!). If the level is a little bit down, top it up. If the level is well down there must be a reason – probably a leak. Trace the pipe to both ends for signs of leakage. Keep the reservoir cap clean and the air vent hole clear. Lubricate the pedal cross-shaft bushes with a few drops of engine oil.

## 3 Hydraulic system – bleeding

1 The need for bleeding the cylinders and fluid line arises when air gets into it. Air gets in whenever a joint or seal leaks, or when dismantling takes place. Bleeding is simply the process of venting the air out again.

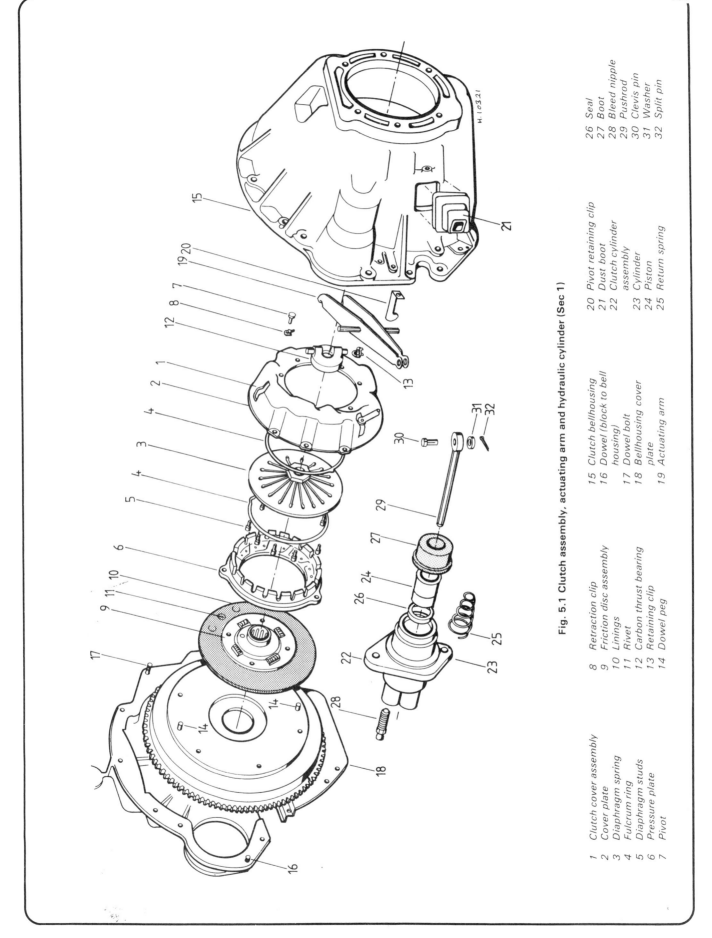

Fig. 5.1 Clutch assembly, actuating arm and hydraulic cylinder (Sec 1)

1 Clutch cover assembly
2 Cover plate
3 Diaphragm spring
4 Fulcrum ring
5 Diaphragm studs
6 Pressure plate
7 Pivot

8 Retraction clip
9 Friction disc assembly
10 Linings
11 Rivet
12 Carbon thrust bearing
13 Retaining clip
14 Dowel peg

15 Clutch bellhousing
16 Dowel (block to bell housing)
17 Dowel bolt
18 Bellhousing cover plate
19 Actuating arm

20 Pivot retaining clip
21 Dust boot
22 Clutch cylinder assembly
23 Cylinder
24 Piston
25 Return spring

26 Seal
27 Boot
28 Bleed nipple
29 Pushrod
30 Clevis pin
31 Washer
32 Split pin

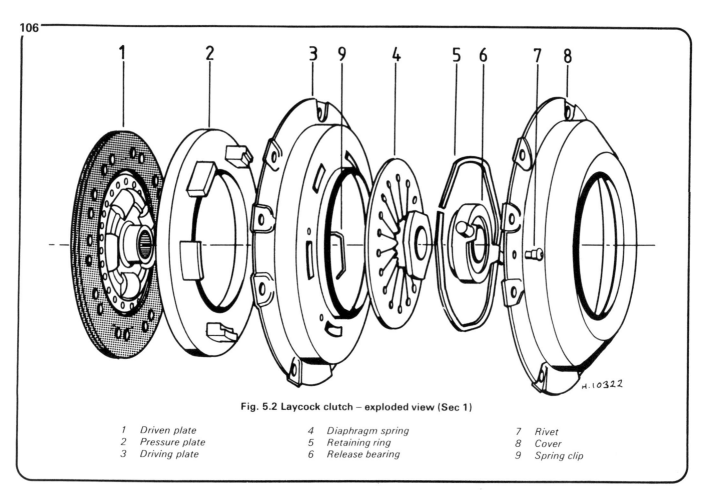

**Fig. 5.2 Laycock clutch – exploded view (Sec 1)**

| | | | | | |
|---|---|---|---|---|---|
| 1 | Driven plate | 4 | Diaphragm spring | 7 | Rivet |
| 2 | Pressure plate | 5 | Retaining ring | 8 | Cover |
| 3 | Driving plate | 6 | Release bearing | 9 | Spring clip |

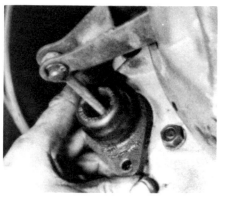

4.1 Removing the clutch cylinder from the bellhousing flange

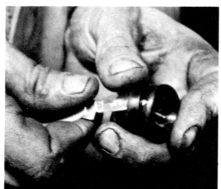

4.3a Removing the clutch cylinder piston seal

4.3b Fitting a replacement clutch cylinder seal

4.4a Reassembling the piston into the clutch cylinder

4.4b Refitting the clutch cylinder boot

4.5 Refitting the clutch cylinder to the bellhousing flange

2    Make sure the reservoir is filled. Obtain a piece of $\frac{3}{16}$ in bore diameter rubber tube about two to three feet long and a clean jam jar. A small quantity of fresh, clean hydraulic fluid is also necessary.

3    Detach the cap (if fitted) on the bleed nipple at the clutch cylinder and clean up the nipple and surrounding area. Unscrew the nipple three quarters of a turn and fit the tube over it. Put about $\frac{1}{2}$ in (1 cm) of fluid in the jar and put the other end of the pipe in it. The jar can be placed on the ground under the car.

4    The clutch pedal should then be depressed quickly and released slowly until no more air bubbles come from the pipe. Quick pedal action carries the air along rather than leaving it behind. Keep the reservoir topped up.

5    When the air bubbles stop, tighten the nipple at the end of a downstroke.

6    Check that the operation of the clutch is satisfactory. Even though there may be no exterior leaks it is possible that the movement of the pushrod from the clutch cylinder is inadequate because fluid is leaking internally past the seals in the master cylinder. If this is the case, it is best to renew all seals in both cylinders.

## 4    Clutch operating cylinder – removal, dismantling, reassembly and refitting

1    The clutch cylinder is fixed to the rear left-hand side of the clutch bellhousing flange by two bolts. If it is to be removed for overhaul, first seal the cap of the fluid reservoir with a piece of plastic film (to minimise fluid loss) and undo the pipe where it joins the cylinder. Then remove the two mounting bolts, disengage the pushrod from the piston inside the rubber boot, and lift the unit out. (If the cylinder is merely being moved out of the way for gearbox renewal the pipe need not be detached) (photo).

2    Remove the rubber boot. If a little air pressure is applied to the fluid inlet it will force the piston out of the cylinder – or it may be possible to shake it out. If the piston is seized, removal may be difficult. Soak the assembly in methylated spirit and if this does not release it, buy a new unit. The cylinder bore will almost certainly be damaged anyway. Remove the spring (if fitted).

3    The seal may be removed from the piston by levering it off out of the groove. Note that the feathered side of the seal faces into the cylinder, so a new seal must be fitted the same way onto the piston. Pistons vary. Some have a flat end into the cylinder, others have two concave ends and the inner end is the one to which the seal groove is nearest. Thoroughly clean the cylinder and piston with methylated spirit or clean hydraulic fluid and fit a new seal by stretching it over the piston into the groove, using the fingers only. The lip faces *into* the cylinder (photos).

4    Refit the spring (wide end first) and piston into the cylinder, using a little fluid to lubricate the walls, and make sure the lip of the seal does not get turned back. Refit the rubber boot so it locks into the outer groove. It is a good idea to smear a little rubber grease (*not* ordinary grease) around the end of the piston under the boot (photos).

5    Refitting is a reversal of the removal procedure. Make sure the unit is fitted on the rear side of the bellhousing flange – it is possible to put it on the front! (photo).

6    Bleed the system as described in the previous section.

## 5    Clutch master cylinder – removal, dismantling, reassembly and refitting

1    The master cylinder and fluid reservoir are a single unit and indications of something wrong with it occur when the pedal travels down without operating the clutch efficiently (assuming, of course, that the system has been bled and there are no leaks).

2    To remove the unit from the car, first seal the cap with a piece of film to reduce fluid wastage whilst dismantling the pipes. Alternatively, the fluid may be pumped out from the clutch cylinder bleed nipple by opening the nipple and depressing the pedal several times.

3    From inside the car, remove the split pin and clevis pin which attaches the pushrod assembly to the clutch pedal. It will be necessary to remove the parcel tray for this which is held by a screw at each end and plastic buttons to the side panels. When the pushrod is free, remove the spring retainer collar and return spring.

4    From the engine compartment, undo the hydraulic union of the pipe outlet from the cylinder and pull the pipe out and to one side.

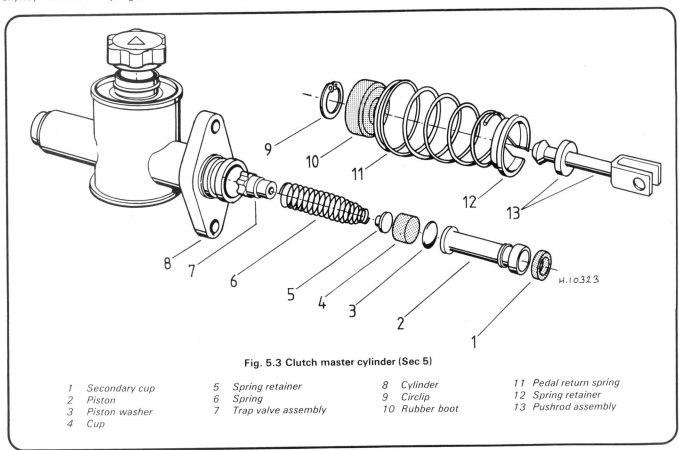

**Fig. 5.3 Clutch master cylinder (Sec 5)**

| | | | |
|---|---|---|---|
| 1    Secondary cup | 5    Spring retainer | 8    Cylinder | 11    Pedal return spring |
| 2    Piston | 6    Spring | 9    Circlip | 12    Spring retainer |
| 3    Piston washer | 7    Trap valve assembly | 10    Rubber boot | 13    Pushrod assembly |
| 4    Cup | | | |

Undo the two bolts holding the whole unit to the vertical face of the bulkhead and take it out.

5    To dismantle the assembly, first remove the rubber boot, then with a pair of contracting circlip pliers, remove the circlip from the internal bore of the cylinder. The piston assembly may then be drawn out. The trap valve can be ejected by blowing through the cylinder outlet orifice.

6    Thoroughly clean all the component parts, the cylinder and orifices with methylated spirit or clean hydraulic fluid.

7    Reassembly is the reverse of the dismantling process, using a new trap valve and seal cups as necessary. A complete repair kit will include everything required. Before fitting new seals, however, examine the cylinder bore for any signs of pitting, ridging or scoring. Any such signs mean that the cylinder is unserviceable and should be renewed. This normally means renewal of the whole assembly.

8    It is most important that the seals and washers are assembled into the cylinder in the correct order and the right way round. This order can be seen from the exploded drawing (Fig. 5.3). The main cup seal should have its lip facing the interior of the cylinder, and the dome washer between it and the piston should have the convex surface against the head of the piston. The secondary cup seal should be carefully fitted into the groove at the outer end of the piston, also with its lip facing forward into the cylinder.

9    Ensure the circlip is finally fitted securely into the groove and refit the rubber boot.

10   Refit the unit to the car in the opposite order to removal and refill the reservoir with fresh fluid of the correct specification. It is false economy to re-use the old fluid. Bleed the system as described in Section 3 and then check the clutch movement is satisfactory and no leaks are apparent.

---

## 6   Clutch pedal – removal and refitting

1    It may be necessary to remove the pedal if the bush and cross-shaft are worn so much that operation is affected.

2    To detach either of the two control pedals it is necessary first to withdraw the whole assembly.

3    First remove both brake and clutch master cylinders from the car.

4    Remove the front parcel tray and detach the steering column steady bracket. Remove the four nuts inside the car, holding the mounting plate to the bulkhead. The whole lot can then be lifted out from the engine compartment. Take out the split pin from the cross-shaft and the pedals may be removed. Renew the shaft or pedal as necessary. When refitting the pedals and cross-shaft make sure the wave washer is correctly placed between the clutch pedal boss and the mounting plate on the cross-shaft.

5    The assembly is refitted in reverse order of removal.

---

## 7   Clutch – removal

1    If it is necessary to renew the friction plate or examine the clutch in any way it will be first of all necessary to remove the gearbox (see Chapter 6) in order to get at it. Once the gearbox is removed or the engine taken out, the succeeding operations are the same, although work is easier with the engine out when no pit or ramp is available. If the engine and gearbox have been removed from the car together, they will have to be separated.

2    Before removing the clutch cover bolts mark the position of the cover in relation to the flywheel so that it may be put back the same way.

3    Slacken off the cover retaining bolts half a turn at a time, in a diagonal fashion, evenly so as to relieve the diaphragm spring pressure without distorting it.

4    When the bolts are removed, the friction plate inside will be released and the cover can be pulled off the locating dowel pegs.

---

## 8   Clutch – inspection and renovation

1    Unfortunately, it is not possible to inspect the clutch without going to the considerable trouble of removing the assembly. Consequently, either one waits for trouble to develop, or alternatively a check and overhaul is carried out after a certain period of use, even though no faults are evident. Wear of the clutch friction plate depends a great deal on how the car has been driven. Habitual clutch slipping will

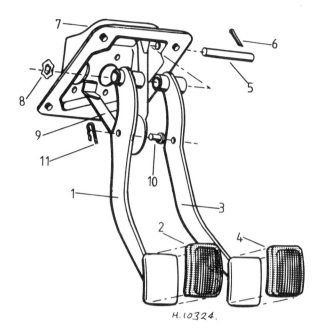

H.10324.

**Fig. 5.4 Clutch pedal and mounting assembly (Sec 6)**

| | |
|---|---|
| 1   *Clutch pedal* | 7    *Mounting plate* |
| 2   *Pedal pad* | 8    *Wave washer* |
| 3   *Brake pedal* | 9    *Steering steady bracket* |
| 4   *Pedal pad* | 10   *Clevis pin* |
| 5   *Pedal cross-shaft* | 11   *Split pin* |
| 6   *Cotter pin* | |

obviously cause rapid wear. If trouble is awaited, action must be taken immediately it occurs; otherwise further, more costly wear could occur. Trouble usually comes in the form of slipping, when the engine speeds up and the car does not; or squealing, denoting that the friction material is worn to the rivets; or juddering denoting all sorts of things (see Fault Diagnosis). Wear on the carbon thrust release ring which presses onto the centre of the diaphragm every time the clutch is operated could also cause squealing if the wear was extreme. If the clutch is not examined when wear is apparent, the faces of the flywheel and pressure plate may be severely scored and call for costly renewal.

2    Having decided to dismantle the clutch, first examine the faces of the flywheel and the pressure plate. If these are smooth and shiny, or only very lightly scored, a new friction disc will suffice to regain satisactory performance. If there is severe scoring, be prepared to buy a new pressure plate assembly and/or flywheel. It is possible to skim the face of the flywheel but engineering advice should be sought. If a new flywheel is obtained it will have to be matched to balance the same as the original. If you hurriedly put the badly scored surfaces back together with a new friction plate you will achieve short-lived results only. After a few thousand miles the same old trouble will recur and judder will always be present in some form or another.

3    The friction plate lining <u>surface</u> should be at least $\frac{1}{32}$ in (0.8 mm) above the heads of the rivets, otherwise the disc is not really worth putting back. If the friction lining material show signs of chipping or breaking up or has black areas caused by oil contamination it should also be renewed. Oil contamination will be confirmed by signs of oil which may be visible on the flywheel or in the bellhousing (in the gearbox). Consideration must be given to curing any such leaks before refitting the clutch assembly. Linings can be obtained for fitting the existing clutch discs but it is hardly worth it. With a new assembly you know the splines and the disc itself are in good condition.

4    No attempt should be made to recondition the clutch cover assembly. If any defects are found, a complete replacement assembly (which will have been correctly balanced during manufacture) must be fitted.

## 9 Clutch – refitting

1   If the original cover is being re-used, line up the marks made before removal, and support the friction plate on one finger between cover and flywheel so that the larger boss faces the flywheel. Friction discs are normally marked 'This side to flywheel'. Lubricate the splines with a waterproof grease (photo).

2   Locate the cover on the dowel pegs in the flywheel, then place all the cover bolts in position and screw them up lightly by hand.

3   It is necessary to line up the centre of the friction disc with the exact centre of the flywheel. This is easily done if a piece of shouldered bar can be placed in the counter bore at the flywheel centre with the larger diameter supporting the friction disc. If you do not have such a thing, the disc may be lined up by eye if the engine is out of the car. For the man flat on his back on a cold concrete floor with his eyes full of grime it is certainly worthwhile making up some sort of centralising tool from a piece of broom handle or tube to get reasonably accurate positioning. If this is not done great difficulty (and possible damage to the gearbox input shaft) may be experienced when the time comes to refit the gearbox to the engine (photo).

4   With the friction plate centralised, the cover bolts should be tightened diagonally, evenly and progressively so the diaphragm spring will not be distorted. Remove the centralising tool. Before refitting the gearbox to the engine do not forget to check the clutch thrust release bearing and operating mechanism.

5   Refit the gearbox (see Chapter 6) and bleed the hydraulic system if it has been disturbed.

## 10 Clutch operating lever and thrust release bearing – dismantling, inspection and reassembly

1   When the clutch pedal is depressed the hydraulic clutch cylinder piston actuates the lever which pivots in the bellhousing and forces a carbon faced thrust ring or bearing against the steel boss at the centre of the diaphragm spring. In time the carbon ring will wear away, and if this condition is allied to a well worn friction plate, difficulty may be experienced in disengaging the clutch due to the limit of piston travel being reached before the diaphragm has been depressed sufficiently. A new carbon thrust ring face projects 0.25 in approximately from the housing and should be renewed if it is significantly less than this (photo).

2   To renew the release bearing, the clutch bellhousing and gearbox must be separated from the engine. The bearing is held to the actuating arm by two spring steel clips which, when released, allow it to be drawn off over the gearbox input shaft. Refitting is a reversal of the removal procedure. Should the release arm require removal, the pivot pin clip holding it in position may be released by undoing the nut on the outside of the bellhousing. Once, again, do *not* undo this without first separating the engine and gearbox. You will not be able to get it back (photos).

9.1 Refitting the clutch plate and cover

9.3 Aligning the friction disc and refitting the bolts

10.1 Comparison of worn and unworn clutch thrust bearings

10.2a Removing the clutch thrust bearing

10.2b Removing the clutch actuating arm

## 11  Fault diagnosis – clutch

| Symptom | Reason(s) |
|---|---|
| Judder when taking up the drive | Loose engine mountings<br>Worn (or oil contaminated) clutch plate friction linings<br>Worn splines on clutch plate hub, or on gearbox input shaft<br>Worn crankshaft spigot bush (pilot bearing) |
| Clutch slip | Damaged or distorted pressure plate assembly<br>Clutch plate linings worn or oil contaminated |
| Noise on depressing clutch pedal | Dry, worn or damaged clutch release bearing<br>Excessive play in input shaft splines |
| Noise as clutch pedal is released | Distorted clutch plate<br>Broken or weak clutch plate hub cushion coil springs<br>Distorted or worn input shaft<br>Release bearing loose |
| Difficulty in disengaging clutch for gear change | Fault in master cylinder or slave cylinder<br>Air in hydraulic system<br>Gearbox driveshaft splines worn, damaged or in need of lubrication |

# Chapter 6 Manual gearbox, overdrive and automatic transmission

## Contents

Automatic transmission – full throttle adjustment .......................... 30
Automatic transmission downshift cable – adjustment ................. 29
Automatic transmission – fluid level ............................................... 28
Automatic transmission – general description ............................... 27
Automatic transmission – removal and refitting ........................... 33
Automatic transmission selector lever linkage – adjustment ........ 31
Automatic transmission – starter inhibitor/reversing light switch . 32
Fault diagnosis – automatic transmission ...................................... 34
Fault diagnosis – manual gearbox .................................................. 10
Fault diagnosis – type 'D' overdrive .............................................. 17
Fault diagnosis – type 'J' overdrive ............................................... 26
Manual gearbox – reassembly .......................................................... 9
Manual gearbox – dismantling .......................................................... 4
Manual gearbox – examination of main assemblies ....................... 5
Manual gearbox – general description ............................................. 1
Manual gearbox input shaft bearing – removal and refitting ........ 6
Manual gearbox mainshaft – dismantling and reassembly ......... 7
Manual gearbox rear cover – removal and refitting of bush and oil seal ...................................................................................... 8
Manual gearbox – removal and refitting ......................................... 3

Manual gearbox – routine maintenance ........................................... 2
Type 'D' overdrive – dismantling, overhaul and reassembly ......... 13
Type 'D' overdrive – general description ....................................... 11
Type 'D' overdrive operating lever – adjustment ......................... 14
Type 'D' overdrive relief valve, non-return valve and operating valve – removal, inspection and refitting ...................................... 15
Type 'D' overdrive – removal and refitting .................................... 12
Type 'D' overdrive – routine maintenance ...................................... 16
Type 'J' overdrive – dismantling, overhaul and reassembly ......... 20
Type 'J' overdrive – general description ........................................ 18
Type 'J' overdrive pressure filter – removal and refitting ............ 24
Type 'J' overdrive pump non-return valve – removal and refitting ............................................................................................ 23
Type 'J' overdrive relief valve and dashpot – removal and refitting ............................................................................................ 22
Type 'J' overdrive – removal and refitting ...................................... 19
Type 'J' overdrive – routine maintenance ....................................... 25
Type 'J' overdrive solenoid control valve – removal and refitting ............................................................................................ 21

## Specifications

### Manual gearbox and overdrive

**Type** ...................................................................................... Four forward speeds, all synchromesh and reverse

### Ratios

| | Standard | Close ratio |
|---|---|---|
| Top | 1.000 : 1 | 1.000 : 1 |
| Third | 1.392 : 1 | 1.296 :1 |
| Second | 2.140 : 1 | 1.993 : 1 |
| First | 3.353 : 1 | 3.122 : 1 |
| Reverse | 3.569 : 1 | 3.323 : 1 |

### Overdrive (where fitted)

| | 'D' type | 'J' type |
|---|---|---|
| Ratio | 0.803 : 1 | 0.797 : 1 |

### Capacities

| | |
|---|---|
| Standard | 3.5 pints (4.2 US pints, 1.9 litres) |
| With 'D' type overdrive | 4.5 pints (5.4 US pints, 2.5 litres) |
| With 'J' type overdrive | 5 pints (6 US pints, 2.8 litres) |

### Automatic transmission

**Type** ...................................................................................... Borg Warner Model 35 (3-speed) or Model 45 (4-speed)

### Fluid capacity (from dry)

| | |
|---|---|
| Model 35 | 11.25 pints (13.5 US pints, 6.4 litres) |
| Model 45 | 10.5 pints (12.6 US pints, 6.1 litres) |

## Transmission gear ratios

| | Model 35 | Model 45 |
|---|---|---|
| 1st | 2.39 : 1 | 3.00 : 1 |
| 2nd | 1.45 : 1 | 1.94 : 1 |
| 3rd | 1.00 : 1 | 1.35 : 1 |
| 4th | — | 1.00 : 1 |
| Reverse | 2.09 : 1 | 4.69 : 1 |

*The above ratios are multiplied by the torque converter ratio given below:*

| | |
|---|---|
| 2.00 : 1 | Model 35, L, D, N, R, P selections |
| 2.00 : 1 | Model 35, 1, 2, D, N, R, P selections – early models |
| 2.4 : 1 | Model 35, 1, 2, D, N, R, P selections – certain later models |
| 2.3 : 1 | Model 35, 1, 2, D, N, R, P selections – certain later models |
| 2.00 : 1 | Model 45 |

## Shift speeds

*The shift speeds given below are typical for the models in the Hunter range. Where shift speeds are occurring a long way outside those given, a dealer should be consulted for further information*

### Early models (BW 35)

| *Throttle position* | *'D' selected* | *mph* | *km/hr* |
|---|---|---|---|
| Light | 1 to 2 | 3 to 7 | 5 to 11 |
| Light | 2 to 3 | 5 to 10 | 8 to 16 |
| Full | 1 to 2 | 22 to 27 | 35 to 43 |
| Full | 2 to 3 | 34 to 44 | 55 to 70 |
| Forced | 1 to 2 | 33 to 40 | 53 to 64 |
| Forced | 2 to 3 | 50 to 60 | 80 to 96 |
| Kickdown | 3 to 2 | 47 to 56 | 76 to 90 |
| Kickdown | 3 to 1 | 26 to 33 | 42 to 53 |

### Later models (BW 35)

| *Throttle position* | *'D' selected* | *'I' selected* | *mph* | *km/hr* |
|---|---|---|---|---|
| Light throttle | 1 to 2 | – | 7 to 12 | 11 to 19 |
| Light throttle | 2 to 3 | – | 11 to 16 | 18 to 25 |
| Forced throttle | 1 to 2 | – | 32 to 41 | 51 to 66 |
| Forced throttle | 2 to 3 | – | 60 to 68 | 96 to 109 |
| Kickdown | 3 to 2 | – | 52 to 65 | 83 to 104 |
| Kickdown | 2 to 1 | – | 21 to 33 | 34 to 53 |
| Zero throttle | – | 2 to 1 | 7 to 10 | 11 to 16 |

### BW 45

| *Throttle position* | *Gear change* | *mph* | *km/hr* |
|---|---|---|---|
| Light throttle | 1 to 2 | 6 to 9 | 9 to 14 |
| Light throttle | 2 to 3 | 8 to 13 | 13 to 21 |
| Light throttle | 3 to 4 | 13 to 20 | 21 to 32 |
| Forced throttle | 1 to 2 | 24 to 28 | 39 to 45 |
| Forced throttle | 2 to 3 | 40 to 47 | 65 to 76 |
| Forced throttle | 3 to 4 | 58 to 68 | 94 to 110 |
| Kickdown | 4 to 3 | 65 to 52 | 105 to 84 |
| Kickdown | 3 to 2, 4 to 2 | 38 to 30 | 61 to 49 |
| Kickdown | 2 to 1, 4 to 1 | 21 to 17 | 34 to 27 |
| Zero throttle | 3 to 1 | 3 to 0 | 5 to 0 |

*Torque wrench settings*

### Manual gearbox

| | lbf ft | Nm |
|---|---|---|
| Clutch housing studs in gearbox casing | 12 | 16 |
| Front cover studs in geaarbox casing | 8 | 11 |
| Rear cover studs in gearbox casing | 12 | 16 |
| Clutch housing to gearbox casing – nuts | 34 | 45 |
| Front cover to gearbox casing – nuts | 13 | 18 |
| Rear cover to overdrive adaptor – nuts | 13 | 18 |
| Mainshaft rear bearing – nut | 80 | 108 |
| Synchro hub | 80 | 108 |
| Drain and filler plugs | 37 | 50 |
| Reverse gear idler spindle | 9 | 12 |
| Top cover to gearbox casing – bolts | 4 | 5 |
| Speedometer adaptor to end cover – bolts | 4 | 5 |
| Clutch withdrawal lever clip – bolt | 4 | 5 |
| Layshaft spindle locking plate – screw | 4 | 5 |
| Rear cover to gearbox casing – bolt | 13 | 18 |

### Overdrive 'D' Type

| | lbf ft | Nm |
|---|---|---|
| Nuts, overdrive to adaptor plate | 13 | 18 |
| Plug, pump valve | 12 to 15 | 16 to 21 |
| Plug, relief valve | 12 to 15 | 16 to 21 |
| Plug, drain | 12 to 15 | 16 to 21 |

## Overdrive 'J' type

| | lbf ft | Nm |
|---|---|---|
| Nuts, overdrive to adaptor plate | 13 | 18 |
| Nuts, rear case to main case | 13 | 18 |
| Nuts, bridge piece | 7 | 9 |
| Ring nut, output shaft | 50 to 60 | 69 to 83 |
| Plug, pressure take-off | 9 to 15 | 12 to 21 |
| Plug, dashpot | 16 | 22 |
| Plug, pump | 16 | 22 |
| Plug, filter | 16 | 22 |
| Sump setscrews | 7 | 9 |
| Solenoid | 30 to 40 | 41 to 54 |

## Automatic transmission

| | lbf ft | Nm |
|---|---|---|
| Converter to drive disc | 32 | 43 |
| Drive disc to crankshaft | 40 | 54 |
| Transmission case to converter: | | |
| (BW 35) | 9 | 12 |
| (BW 45-M10) | 28 | 38 |
| (BW 45-M12) | 38 | 51 |
| Sump to transmission: | | |
| (BW 35) | 9 | 12 |
| (BW 45) | 5.4 | 7 |
| Inhibitor switch: | | |
| (BW 35) | 7 | 9 |
| (BW 45) | 3.6 | 5 |
| Sump drain plug | 12 | 16 |

## 1 Manual gearbox – general description

The gearbox is a constant mesh four forward and one reverse speed unit with synchromesh fitted on all four forward speeds. The input shaft and mainshaft are mounted in the casing on ball bearings and locate into each other on needle rollers. The laygear cluster revolves on needle roller bearings on the fixed layshaft; endfloat is controlled by a thrust washer at each end fitted between the casing and the laygear. With the exception of reverse, all gears are helically cut. Gear selection is by three forks running on three separate rails and the forks are held in their neutral and selection positions by spring loaded detent balls housed in each fork, which engage in grooves in the rails. The selector lever operates the forks through a remote control which permits a short, positive action lever to be used. Reverse gear selection position is achieved by overcoming a spring-loaded plunger which bears on the base of the gear shift lever at the end of the remote control housing.

## 2 Manual gearbox – routine maintenance

1 The oil level in the gearbox should be checked every 5000 miles. No routine oil changes are recommended for the unit. If contamination has occurred, however, this should be done immediately.
2 To check the oil level in the gearbox the car should be stood on level ground and the filler and level plug, which is mounted on the right-hand side of the gearbox casing, removed. A quantity of the correct specification oil should be added until it overflows from the filler hole. In cold weather it may be necessary to wait a little time for this to be seen. Do not overfill the box in such instances otherwise additional internal pressure will be built up when running which may burst oil seals or at least force oil past them.
3 To drain and replenish the gearbox oil, first run the car for sufficient time to enable the warmth of the engine to transmit to the gearbox and allow the oil to thin down a little. Then stand the car on level ground and remove both the filler and drain plugs. Allow at least fifteen minutes to drain and then refit the drain plug, preferably with a new washer, and refill with the correct oil to the level plug hole.

## 3 Manual gearbox – removal and refitting

1 The gearbox may be removed together with the engine, in which case the instructions are given in Chapter 1.
2 If the gearbox is being removed on its own, time spent on initial preparation work in raising and supporting the car will be amply repaid later. Ideally, of course, the car would be raised on a hoist or ramp or

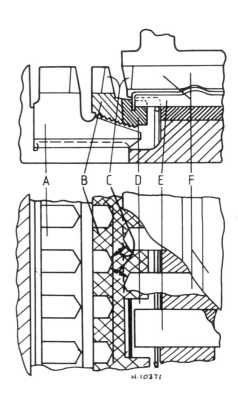

H·10371

**Fig. 6.1 Synchro hub – cross-section to show operation (Sec 1)**

| | | | |
|---|---|---|---|
| A | Gear wheel dogs | D | Baulk ring cut-outs |
| B | Baulk rings | E | Blocker bars |
| C | Sliding sleeve and baulk ring dog teeth faces | F | Sliding sleeve |

put over a pit, but as most owners will not have this facility, they must certainly acquire a set of four chassis stands to support the car as high as possible safely. The maximum possible clearance between the car and the ground should be obtained to provide the easiest possible access and manoeuvring space for two people when the gearbox is eventually lowered to the ground.
3 Disconnect the battery leads, drain the cooling system and drain the oil from the gearbox. Disconnect the top radiator hose from the engine so that when the engine is tilted, it will not be strained.

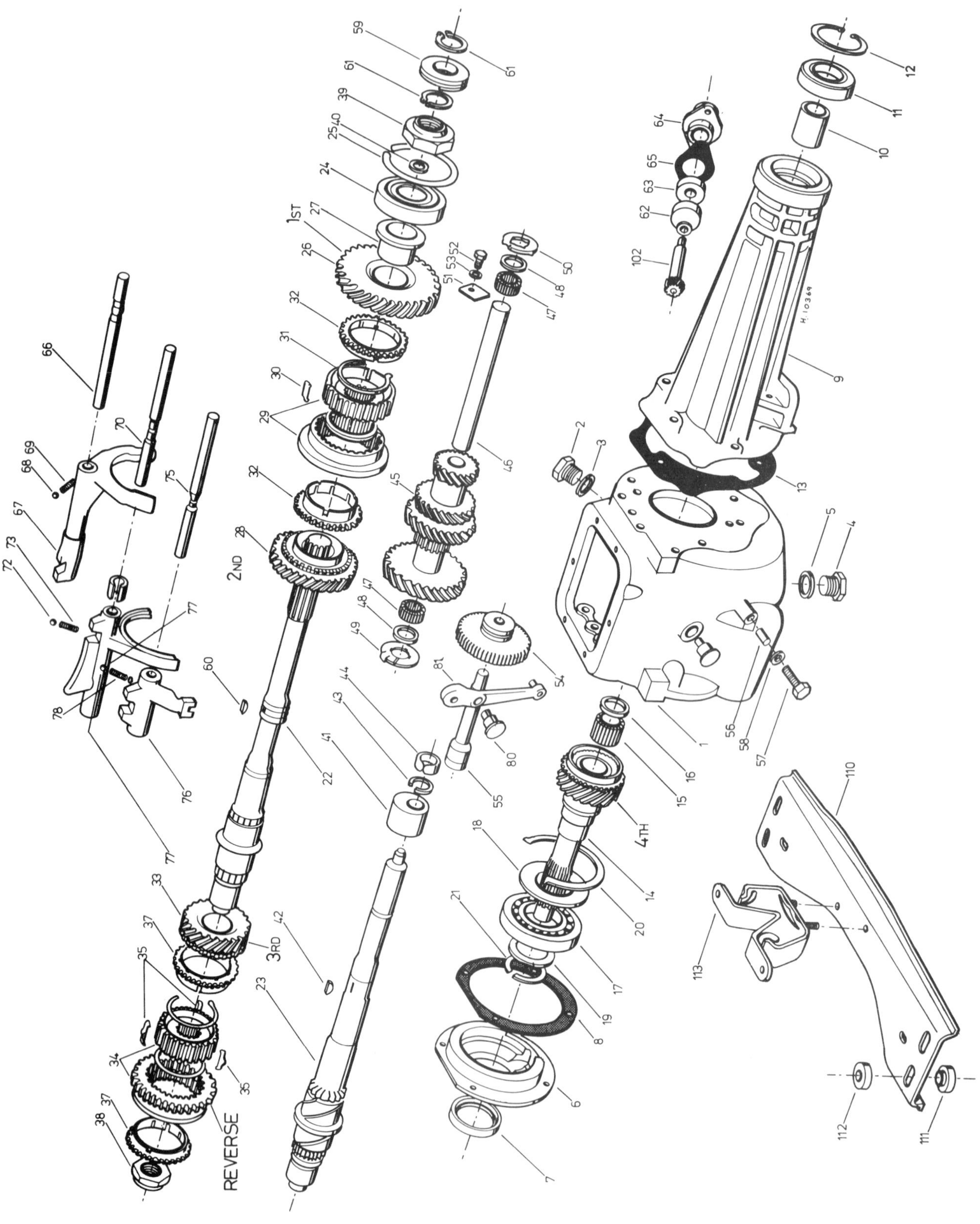
1ST
2ND
3RD
4TH
REVERSE
H.10369

Fig. 6.2 Gearbox – exploded view (Sec 1)

| | | | | |
|---|---|---|---|---|
| 1 Casing | 27 Boss | 48 Retaining ring | 69 Detent spring | 92 Spring washer |
| 2 Filler level plug | 28 2nd gear | 49 Thrust washer (front) | 70 Selector rail 3rd/4th gear | 93 Reverse stop plunger |
| 3 Washer | 29 Synchro-hub assembly 1st/2nd gear | 50 Thrust washer (rear) | 71 Selector fork 3rd/4th gear | 94 Spring |
| 4 Drain plug | 30 Blocker bar | 51 Locking plate | 72 Ball | 95 Rubber sleeve |
| 5 Washer | 31 Retaining clip | 52 Bolt | 73 Detent spring | 96 Retainer |
| 6 Front cover | 32 Baulk ring | 53 Washer | 74 Spacer sleeve | 97 Closing plate |
| 7 Oil seal | 33 3rd gear | 54 Reverse idler gear | 75 Selector rail reverse | 98 Plug (reverse light switch hole) |
| 8 Gasket | 34 Synchro-hub assembly 3rd/4th gear | 55 Reverse idler gear shaft | 76 Selector fork reverse | 99 Washer |
| 9 Rear extension cover | 35 Blocker clip | 56 Locking pin | 77 Ball | 100 Plug (overdrive switch hole) |
| 10 Bush | 36 Retaining clip | 57 Screw | 78 Detent spring | 101 Washer |
| 11 Oil seal | 37 Baulk ring | 58 Washer | 79 Shim | 102 Speedometer driving pinion |
| 12 Circlip | 38 Nut (mainshaft front) | 59 Speedometer drive wheel | 80 Reverse lever pivot pin | 103 Gear change lever |
| 13 Gasket | 39 Nut (mainshaft rear) | 60 Woodruff key | 81 Reverse lever | 104 Knob |
| 14 Input shaft | 40 Lockwasher | 61 Circlip | 82 Top cover | 105 Locknut |
| 15 Needle rollers | 41 Cam (overdrive oil pump) | 62 Speedometer pinion bearing | 83 Oil shield | 106 Spring |
| 16 Spacer | 42 Woodruff key | 63 Seal | 84 Gasket | 107 Disc |
| 17 Bearing | 43 Circlip | 64 Cable adaptor | 85 Change shaft | 108 Retaining cap |
| 18 Oil seal | 44 Retaining ring | 65 Gasket | 86 Damper pad | 109 Grommet |
| 19 Spacer ring | 45 Laygear | 66 Selector rail 1st/2nd gear | 87 Spring | 110 Rear mounting crossmember |
| 20 Circlip | 46 Layshaft | 67 Selector fork 1st/2nd gear | 88 Selector lever | 111 Flexible insulator |
| 21 Circlip | 47 Needle rollers | 68 Ball | 89 Locking screw | 112 Rubber collar |
| 22 Mainshaft | | | 90 Selector safety catch | 113 Flexible mounting |
| 23 Overdrive mainshaft | | | 91 Washer | |
| 24 Bearing (mainshaft) | | | | |
| 25 Circlip | | | | |
| 26 1st gear | | | | |

4   Remove the four bolts securing the rear of the propeller shaft to the pinion flange. It is important to mark the pinion flanges before separating them in order that they may be refitted in the same relationship. Lower the propeller shaft and withdraw it from the gearbox, removing the centre bearing mounting at the same time (where applicable).

5   Unscrew the knob from the gear lever and take out the screws securing the front of the console panel. Pull out the ashtray and remove the two screws inside holding the rear of the console. Lift off the console and disconnect any switch wires, noting their connections and colours (photo).

6   Slide the rubber boot from the base up the lever and take it off.

7   Four setscrews holding the spring retaining cap onto the top of the remote change casing will now be visible and should be removed. This will release the gear lever assembly which can be lifted straight up out of the box (photos).

8   If a reversing light or overdrive is fitted, the connecting wire should be detached.

9   It is necessary to detach the centre track rod of steering gear from the drop arm and slave arm connections. This is so that the bellhousing is not obstructed when the gearbox is drawn back. The centre track rod will still be connected to the outer track rods but it will be possible to drop it the necessary three to four inches. For details of disconnecting the balljoint pins, refer to Chapter 11.

10  On models fitted with steel sumps, remove the two brace rods which bolt to the bellhousing and sump flange.

11  Remove the clutch hydraulic cylinder mounting bolts and move the cylinder to one side. The hydraulic system need not be disturbed.

12  For steel sump models, remove the bottom bolts in the bellhousing (which secure the cover plate) and take off the cover plate. On aluminium sump models, the bolts hold the sump casting itself to the bellhousing.

13  Remove the starter motor bolts and draw it forward, clear of the housing. It may rest alongside the engine if tied with a piece of string to hold it in place.

14  Detach the speedometer drive cable from the rear extension cover by unscrewing the knurled union nut (photo).

15  So that the gearbox may be drawn off the engine, the engine must be tilted backwards and this is achieved when the rear supporting crossmember is removed. Before removing this however, the engine must be supported on a jack which will keep the degree of tilt under control. The head of the jack should be placed under the rear edge of the crankcase on the sump mounting flange (steel sumps) if possible, or otherwise as near the rear of the sump as possible. Put a piece of wood between the jack and sump to spread the load. This latter method applies anyway to engines with aluminium sumps. The crossmember may then be removed by undoing the four rubber bushed mounting bolts – two at each end (photo).

16  Carefully, lower the jack so the engine tilts sufficiently to enable the gearbox to come off when the remainder of the bellhousing bolts are removed. Watch the front of the engine to see the sump does not foul the anti-roll bar, although when sufficiently tilted, the engine may be chocked with wood against the anti-roll bar.

17  The remainder of the bolts holding the bellhousing to the engine may now be removed and the gearbox should be free to move (photo).

18  Two people at least are needed to support the weight of the gearbox. If they are lying underneath the car it is a wise precaution to place some soft padding such as sacks underneath the gearbox. Then, if the weight is suddenly too much it will not be damaged if it falls a bit quickly! Whatever else may happen do *not* tilt the gearbox or heave it from side to side whilst it is still mated to the clutch assembly. This could cause strain and damage to the gearbox input shaft or clutch cover (photo).

19  Refitting the gearbox is a reversal of the removal procedure but the following points should be borne in mind:

   *(a)   The clutch friction disc must be centred properly if the clutch assembly has been disturbed*
   *(b)   Do not tilt the gearbox in an effort to refit it*
   *(c)   The propeller shaft should be refitted so the mating flanges line up in the same position*
   *(d)   Do not forget to refill the gearbox with oil*

3.5 Removing console

3.7a Removing gear lever retaining cap

3.7b Lifting out the gear lever

3.14 Withdrawing the speedometer drive cable

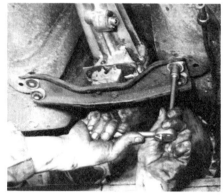

3.15 Removing rear supporting crossmember

3.17 Removing bellhousing bolts

3.18 Removing gearbox

4.2 Removing the gearbox top cover

4.3 Separating the bellhousing from the gearbox

4.4a Removing the speedometer drive mechanism

4.4b The speedometer drive mechanism removed

4.4c Removing the gearbox extension

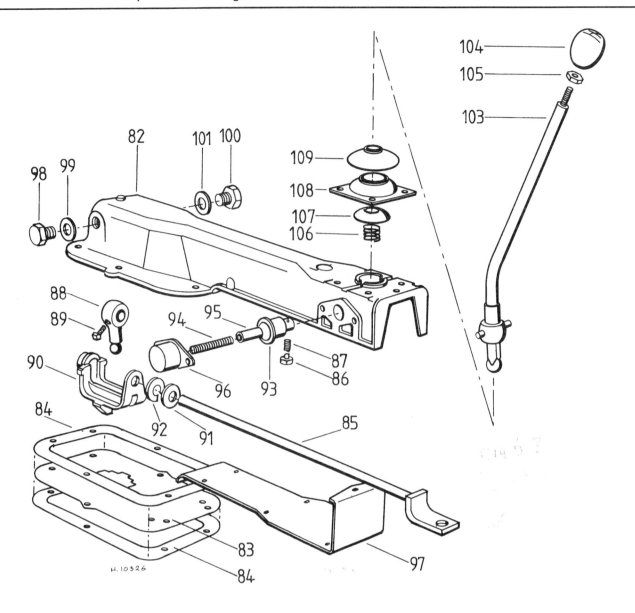

Fig. 6.3 Gearbox top cover and gearshift – exploded view. For key refer to Fig. 6.2 (Sec 1)

## 4  Manual gearbox – dismantling

1  Before any dismantling is begun, clean off the gearbox exterior thoroughly with paraffin or a proprietary solvent. This will minimise the possibility of dirt being transferred to the interior.

2  Remove the top cover (which incorporates the remote change mechanism) by undoing the six bolts which hold it to the top of the gearbox casing. The oil shield plate underneath should then be lifted off (photo).

3  The clutch thrust release bearing and arm should now be detached as described in Chapter 5. Separate the bellhousing from the gearbox casing by undoing the six bolts and washers inside the housing (photo).

4  Remove the mainshaft extension cover. To do this, first remove the two setscrews holding the speedometer drivegear mechanism to the side of the cover. With these removed, the assembly may be drawn out. Undo the bolts holding the extension cover to the rear of the gear casing and draw it off. The mounting crossmember may be separated from it, but this is not essential (photos).

5  The selector rails and forks are next to be dismantled. The first thing to note is that the rails must be driven out from the front toward the rear. Dummy selector rails should be made from the $\frac{7}{16}$ in (11 mm)

diameter rod. These are used to retain the detent balls and springs in the selector forks when the rail proper is driven out. Otherwise, the balls could fly out and be lost. Three shafts are needed, two being 2.9 in (73.6 mm) long and one 4.95 in (125.7 mm) long. On some models the 3rd/4th selector fork (the one on the centre rail) has a long integral boss instead of a spacer tube. For these, two long and one short dummy rail are required. Using the dummy shafts, drive out the selector rails from the front of the casing starting with the reverse selector rail (the left one). Leave the dummies in position after the rails have been driven out and then lift out the selector forks.

6  Next remove the layshaft so that the laygear cluster may be lowered to the bottom of the box. A dummy shaft will be needed for reassembly so it is best to use it also for dismantling. It should be made from 0.75 in (18 mm) diameter bar or tube and be 6.5 in (165 mm) long. A piece of electrical conduit pipe was used on the occasion when the photographs were taken. Ensure, however, that the burrs and sharp edges are removed, and that the dummy is clean. Remove the bolt and washer holding the locking plate into the groove at the rear of the casing. Using the dummy layshaft, drive the layshaft out from the front of the box. Provided the dummy shaft has not been made too long it will fit flush with the ends of the laygear and permit it to drop the inch or so to the bottom of the casing.

7  If the four nuts (or setscrews) holding the front cover to the casing

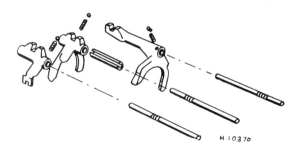

Fig. 6.4 Gearbox selector arrangement (later type) (Sec 4)

4.8 Removing the mainshaft nut

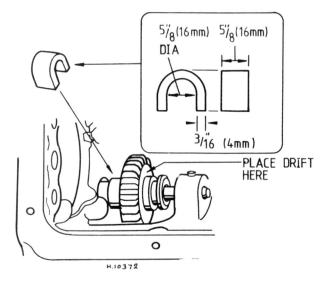

Fig. 6.5 Reverse idler gear – details of spacer required when drifting out the shaft (Sec 4)

are now taken out the input shaft, bearing and front cover can all be withdrawn from the casing. The counter bore end of the input shaft houses twenty three needle rollers and a spacer ring and these should be taken out now and kept in a suitable container where they will not be lost. The baulk ring on the 3rd/4th synchro hub for 4th gear will now be free to lift off the end of the mainshaft assembly. The position of the ring should be noted before removal, so the cut-outs will relate to the same hub blocker bars on refitting.

8    The mainshaft assembly is removed through the front of the casing. First remove the two circlips which hold the nylon worm gear for the speedometer in position. Then use the jaw of a large open-ended spanner and a hammer to drive the gear off the shoulder of the shaft rearwards. Remove and retain safely the Woodruff key. Later cars have a modified mainshaft and speedo wheel together with a retaining ring, which supersedes the two circlips and key. To remove the speedo wheel on later model gearboxes, tap the wheel and retaining ring forwards, using a piece of tubing as a drift, until it reaches the narrow portion of the mainshaft. Remove the retaining ring from the speedo wheel and then separately remove the wheel and retaining ring from the mainshaft. On overdrive models remove the oil pump cam, with key and circlips. To undo the mainshaft nut, the shaft will have to be held firm (photo). It can be locked in the box by engaging two gears at once, ie sliding the forward hub back on to 3rd gear and the rear hub on to either 1st or 2nd. Alternatively, the shaft can be gripped in the soft metal covered jaws of a vice but will be needed to support the weight of the casing if this is done. If a lockwasher is fitted bend back the tab, and with a suitably large spanner undo the nut and take it and the washer off the shaft. The front end of the mainshaft should now be supported with one hand and the shaft driven forward with a mallet through the rear bearing which will remain where it is. As soon as the shaft is free it can be fed through the front of the casing, but 1st gear and its centre bush will have to be slid off the back of the shaft as they are too large to go through the hole. Do not drop them! Reselect neutral. Identify all baulk rings to enable them to be refitted in their correct positions relative to their hubs and gears.
9    With the mainshaft assembly removed, lift up the laygear from the bottom of the box keeping it horizontal so the needle rollers in the ends do not fall out unintentionally. Take out also the two thrust washers located one at each end of the laygear, between it and the casing.
10   The mainshaft bearing can now be driven out of the casing from the inside using a suitable drift.
11   The reverse idler gear and operating lever do not normally need removal as they rarely cause trouble, being comparatively little used. However, if it is necessary a spacer will have to be made. Remove the operating lever and the screw and spindle locking pin from the side of the casing. Then make up a U-shaped spacer from some $\frac{3}{16}$ in flat strip. It should be $\frac{5}{8}$ in (16 mm) long and radiused to fit round the smaller diameter of the idler shaft. The gear can then butt the spacer up to the larger diameter shoulder at the front end of the shaft. Use a brass drift through the rear of the casing placed near the centre of the gear and drive the shaft forward out of the casing. The gearbox is now completely stripped into main assemblies.

## 5   Manual gearbox – examination of main assemblies

1    The correcting of operating faults, such as worn synchromesh or jumping out of gear, is normally routine. However, total operating quietness cannot be guaranteed unless everything is renewed.
2    Check the input shaft splines, by inserting it into a new clutch plate and testing for backlash. Examine the input shaft bearing for signs of sloppiness or roughness – it is usually the first component to wear. In any case, it is worthwhile fitting a new one while the box is stripped. Examine the mainshaft bearing similarly.
3    There are four baulk rings, one each side of the two synchroniser hub assemblies, but only one of these (for 4th gear) can be renewed without dismantling the mainshaft. The critical wear occurs in the three cut-outs where the blocker bars engage and is difficult to measure unless in comparison with a new one. As a general guide it is worthwhile renewing all four baulk rings, and certainly so if the synchromesh is at fault.
4    The hubs should be gripped (by hand) and twisted to see if the outer sliding sleeve moves rotationally in relation to the hub. If it does the splines between the hub and sleeve are worn and the whole hub assembly needs renewal.
5    All gears should be examined for signs of chipped teeth and extraordinary wear. They should be a smooth sliding fit on the shaft and not rock at all.
6    The nose of the mainshaft, which engages in the needle rollers in the counter bore of the input shaft, should be examined for signs of pitting or ridging. If such signs are apparent, the only cure is a new mainshaft. Examine the needle rollers also for signs of wear or pitting and renew them all if one looks bad.
7    The layshaft gears should be examined for chipping or extreme

wear. The shaft may show signs of wear at the ends where the gear runs on the needle roller bearings. If there is pitting or ridging, the layshaft should be renewed and new needle roller bearings fitted. The thrust washers at the ends of the laygear should be renewed as a matter of course. The selector mechanism, should also come in for careful examination. Examine the forks to see that they are not worn where they guide the hub sleeve. The 3rd/4th selector runs in a groove in the hub and there should be no play between hub groove and fork. The 1st/2nd selector fork is grooved to engage and land on the hub and here again there should be no play between the two. An impositive 'feel' in gear changing or jumping out of gear could be caused by insufficient pressure being exerted by the detent springs on the balls when engaged in the selector rail grooves. This can be tested by gripping the selector fork in a soft-jawed vice and temporarily refitting the appropriate rail. A suitable clamp and hook should be fitted to the end of the rail so that a pull scale can be attached. The force necessary to pull the rail groove across the ball should be between 25 and 35 lbf for forward gears and 40 and 45 lbf for reverse. The spring loading can be varied by adding or removing shims underneath the detent spring in the fork. This effectively tensions or relaxes the spring as necessary. If there are signs of wear on the rails or balls they should be renewed; as should any broken springs, of course.

8    Examine the gear casing for any signs of damage or cracks.

9    To summarize, if the gearbox is being dismantled it is worthwhile renewing the following items as a matter of course (the gaskets are essential):

*Input and mainshaft bearings (2)*
*Baulk rings (4)*
*Laygear thrust washers (2)*
*Gaskets including cover oil seals (set)*
*Circlips and mainshaft nuts*

10  If there are many other components in an obviously tired condition one must weigh up the advantages of renewing many parts (and ending up with a less than perfect gearbox) against obtaining a fully reconditioned unit on exchange.

---

### 6    Manual gearbox input shaft bearing – removal and refitting

1    The bearing is held into the front cover by a large internal circlip, the ends of which fit in a cut-out in the cover. Remove the circlip. If the edge of the cover is carefully supported between vice jaws, gear facing downwards, the shaft can be driven down with a mallet and the bearing and shaft together will come out of the cover. Remove the external circlips round the shaft in front of the bearing and the abutment washer behind it. Support the bearing on the vice jaws, making sure that the gear teeth are not fouling them and drive the shaft out downwards from the bearing. Remove the shield plate from behind the bearing. Refitting the bearing to the input shaft is a reversal of the removal method. Place the shield over the shaft first and then place the shaft into the bearing. Support the bearing on the inner race across the soft clad vice jaws and drive the shaft into it with a mallet. Do not close the vice jaws too far or they will catch the shoulder on the shaft. Make sure the bearing is driven on right up to the limit of the shoulder.

2    The abutment washer comes in one of two thicknesses, 0.054 to 0.056 in or 0.058 to 0.060 in and the larger of the two should be fitted, if it will go between the bearing and circlip. A new circlip should also be used.

3    It is wise to renew the front cover oil seal also before refitting the bearing and shaft. Drive out the old one from the inside using a suitable punch. Fit the new one in square so the flexible lip faces the bearing. The shaft and bearing may now be driven into the cover. One note of caution here: There are occasions when the lip of the oil seal stubbornly refuses to go onto the seal land on the shaft but sticks on the shoulder before reaching it, thus forcing the inner part of the seal back. This is no good as the seal will soon wear out and leak. To guide the lip of the seal onto the land a tube made up of flexible shim steel will be needed to put round inside the seal and over the shaft land. This can then be withdrawn after the bearing is fully home inside the front cover. Refit the large circlip locking the bearing and shaft into the cover, using a new clip.

---

### 7    Manual gearbox mainshaft – dismantling and reassembly

1    The difficult parts to shift on the mainshaft are the two synchro hub assemblies which are the only items now left to remove. They are a splined press fit onto the shaft, and have to be moved by pressure as opposed to striking. If no press equipment is handy, two long levers with lipped ends (tyre levers) are essential. It is best also to try and avoid dismantling them unless it is absolutely necessary. If they do happen to fly apart, it will be impossible to know where each blocker bar came from and how the splines were mated. It will not mean that the hub is useless but wear will be accelerated when unmatched surfaces come together on reassembly. Operations to dismantle and reassemble should be carried out carefully to ensure that undue loads and shocks are not applied to items such as gear teeth. Loads should be directed to areas where the mass of metal is greatest.

2    Grip the plain section of the tail end of the shaft in the padded jaws of a vice so the two hub assemblies are tilted upwards. To remove the front nut requires a large socket or tubular spanner. If none are available, cut a nick near one of the corners of the nut and undo it with a steel drift and hammer. The locking ring is peened into the groove but this will automatically come away when the nut turns. If this locking ring is seriously chewed up when the nut is removed, a new one should be obtained to ensure safe locking up when reassembled.

3    With the nut removed the two levers should be placed between the 2nd and 3rd gear wheels, where the dividing shoulder on the shaft is located. Leverage will force the 3rd gear and hub one way and/or the 2nd gear and hub the other. Further leverage can be then obtained

7.3a Removing the hub assemblies

7.3b Removing the hub assemblies

between the shoulder and the gear. Each hub assembly followed by the gear wheel, can then be taken off. The mainshaft is then completely stripped (photos).

4    If a hub assembly is suspected of being worn and is to be dismantled, first mark with a coloured wax crayon or a small dab of paint the relative positions of the hub and outer sleeve and each blocker bar to its groove in the hub. Slide the outer sleeve off the hub and the blocker bars and spring circlips will fall free. Then refit the sleeve on the hub. It should slide freely but with no other movement possible. The internal teeth on the sliding sleeve should have flat faces and be free from grooves or ridges. The blocker bars should be identical in length and top profile. The blocker bar circlips should not show signs of wear where they rest on the edges of the bars and the turned over end should not touch the inner face of the bar (see Fig. 6.6). If it does, carefully grind a little off. When reassembling the hub, fit the circlips so that when viewed from their own side the hooked end is at the anti-clockwise tail of the clip. Do not put both hooked ends into the same blocker bar. If a hub is badly worn the whole assembly should be renewed, bearing in mind, of course, the overall condition of the gearbox.

5    Reassemble the mainshaft by first clamping it in a vice by the plain section of the rear end, using soft jaws in the vice. 3rd gear should then be placed over the nose of the shaft. (3rd gear is the smallest of the three gears on the mainshaft – top gear is on the input shaft.) The helical tooth part of the gear abuts the shoulder on the shaft. Then place a baulk ring over the gear cone, making sure it is the right type. (The two rings on the 3rd/4th hub are different from those on the 1st/2nd hub.) The hub assembly is next put on with the selector fork groove of the outer sleeve towards the nose of the shaft. This will be a drive fit onto the splines and two things should be carefully watched. The hub assembly must be treated with care when fitting, so when driving it on with a drift, hit the centre of the boss only. At the same time keep an eye on the baulk ring to make sure the three cut-outs line up on the blocker bars of the hub when it is driven fully home. The large front nut should next be fitted. Strictly speaking, a new one should be used because the old self-locking ring will almost certainly line up with the used part once more against the groove. However, it is known for them to be re-used provided the locking ring is not severely disturbed on removal. The nut should be tightened to a torque of 80 lbf ft and the locking ring staked into the groove. If you have to tighten up using a hammer and drift, use a 2 lb hammer and take it as far as it will go (photos).

6    Remove the mainshaft from the vice and support it vertically in the jaws, tail end upwards clamping the nose between soft jaw plates. 2nd gear is fitted next (the middle size of the three), placed with the helical teeth abutting the shoulder. Place a baulk ring over the cone of the gearwheel. The 1st/2nd hub should now be driven on to the splines and this should be done with the drift against the centre hub only. Note also that the selector fork land of the outer sleeve is next to the 2nd gear wheel (photos).

## 8    Manual gearbox rear cover – removal and refitting of bush and oil seal

1    If wear is apparent in the rear bush, the simplest, but most expensive method of correcting this is to obtain an exchange cover. Replacement bushes are available, but these must be bored accurately when in position, both in respect of their finished size and of the squareness of the bore to the front face of the cover. The bush must also be positioned correctly; angularly, to ensure alignment of the bush oiling groove. It is therefore advised that a specialist machinist be consulted.

2    The rear cover oil seal should be renewed if the gearbox is dismantled and of course must be if it is obviously leaking. It is possible to do this job with the gearbox still in the car, after removing the propeller shaft. Remember to catch the oil, or drain the gearbox, as applicable. First take out the circlip which retains it (if fitted). There are three ways of getting the old seal out. If you can borrow a proper extractor tool, it can be drawn out easily with the gearbox on or off the car. If not, it can be driven out with a long drift against the inside of the seal provided, of course, that the rear cover is removed from the gearbox. This may also be done with the gearbox still in the car but will involve removal of the propeller shaft, speedometer drivegear and the rear support crossmember first. The third method is to cut the old seal away from the outside with a cold chisel. This method will require

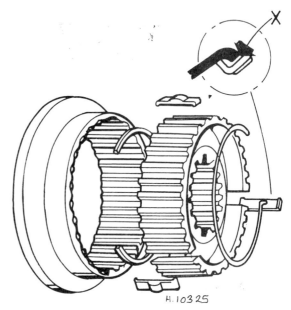

H.10325

**Fig. 6.6 Synchro hub – exploded view (Inset: Gap X should exist between the end of the clip and the bottom of the recess) (Sec 7)**

great care to avoid damaging the bore of the case where the seal fits. The new seal should be driven in firmly and square, open side inwards, with a suitably sized drift, such as an old piston (as was used in the photographs).

3    Remember to refill with oil.

## 9    Manual gearbox – reassembly

1    Before assembly begins, make sure every part is perfectly clean, including the interior of the casing, and that a supply of clean oil, grease and the necessary new parts and gaskets are available. A proprietary jointing compound should also be handy as all gaskets should be coated with it on fitting.

2    Check first that the endfloat of the laygear is correct. Place the two thrust washers in position so the pips fit the cut-outs in the casing. Put the laygear in position (without the shaft) between them and measure the gap between the end of the gear and the face of a thrust washer with a feeler gauge. It should be between 0.006 and 0.008 in (0.15 and 0.20 mm) and if necessary a front thrust washer of a different thickness may be obtained from a parts store.

3    Fit the mainshaft bearing into the casing. First the circlip should be fitted into the outer race and the bearing tapped square into the casing. The wider part of the race (the circlip is off centre) goes into the casing (photo).

4    Fit the reverse idler gear assembly so the flat on the smaller end of the shaft will engage with the pin in the interior supporting lug in the casing. Refit the operating lever with the pin in the groove of the gearwheel (photo).

5    The laygear should be prepared by fitting the twenty seven needle rollers into each end, holding them in position with thick grease. Put the spacer ring on top of the rollers and the dummy shaft into position in the gear. Put the cluster into the gearbox with the larger gear towards the front and let it rest on the bottom. At the same time, position the thrust washers at each end so they line up as near as possible with the layshaft holes in the casing. They should be fitted so the pips locate in the cut-outs in the casing, and if smeared with grease, will not move around. In subsequent operations, care should be taken not to disturb them. If they move too far out of line from the shaft holes, it may be impossible to position them again when the time arrives to fit the layshaft. And that is one of the last things to be done (photos).

6    The mainshaft can now be put into the casing from the front, tail end first. Get 1st gear with its centre boss and baulk ring ready and when the end of the mainshaft is inside the box, put the baulk ring on first, cut-out side towards the hub, followed by the gearwheel and

7.5a Mainshaft clamped in a vice

7.5b Refitting 3rd/4th gear hub assembly

7.5c Driving the 3rd/4th gear hub assembly home

7.5d Refitting the front mainshaft nut

7.6a Refitting 2nd gear and baulk ring

7.6b Refitting the 1st/2nd gear hub assembly

7.6c Driving the 1st/2nd gear hub assembly home

8.2a Removing circlip

8.2b Seal, partially driven out

8.2c Placing new seal in position

8.2d Driving the new seal home

9.3 Fitting the mainshaft bearing

9.4 Refitting the reverse idler gear assembly

9.5a Refitting the needle rollers in the laygear

9.5b Fitting the dummy shaft

9.5c Placing the laygear cluster in the gearbox

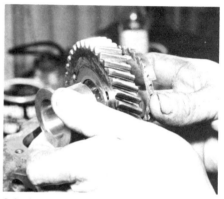
9.6a 1st gear, centre boss and baulk ring ready for fitting

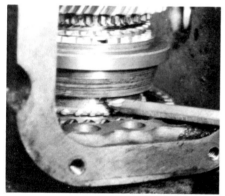
9.6b Mainshaft assembly refitted inside gearbox

9.7 Driving the mainshaft assembly home

9.9a Fit spacer ring to the mainshaft nose

9.9b Fit the remaining baulk ring to the 3rd/4th synchro hub

9.10a Fit the needle rollers

9.10b Assembled front cover and shaft

boss. The gearwheel cone side goes towards the baulk ring and the flange of the boss is towards the tail end of the shaft. The mainshaft can then be put through the bearing in the casing (photos).

7 The whole gearbox should now carefully be positioned over the vice jaws so the mainshaft bearing is supported by the jaws and the rear of the mainshaft points downwards. The shaft is then driven downwards with a mallet and at the same time an eye must be kept on the 1st/2nd synchro hub and 1st gear baulk ring. As the gap between the gear and rear bearing diminishes the baulk ring must be positioned so the three cut-outs line up with the blocker bars in the hub. If the fit of the shaft into the bearing is not too tight, the final positioning may be done more easily with the gearbox horizontal once again on the bench. (Beware the bearing is not inadvertently driven back out of the casing!) (photo).

8 The mainshaft locking nut can now be fitted. Fit the lockwasher and then run the nut up to it. Check once again that the 1st gear baulk ring is properly located and the bearing circlip fully up to the casing. Do not tighten the nut fully at this stage.

9 The gearbox is now ready to receive the input shaft assembly. Place the spacer ring over the nose of the mainshaft with the chamfered edge inwards, followed by the last of the four baulk rings which fits on to the 3rd/4th hub. The three cut-outs should engage with the blocker bars. A little dab of grease will help to hold it in position until the input shaft is fitted (photos).

10 The counter bore of the input shaft should be smeared with thick grease and the twenty three needle rollers put into position. Then place a new gasket in position on the cover, having smeared both sides with jointing compound to ensure an oil-tight seal. The assembly should then be located on the nose of the mainshaft engaging the front cover over the four studs in the casing. The flat on the front cover should be horizontal at the upper edge so the oil drain hole in the casing is at the lower edge. Refit the nuts and tighten them up fully (photos).

11 Fit the layshaft. Ensure that the thrust washers are in position and then carefully turn the box upside down so the laygear drops into mesh with the mainshaft gears and input shaft. Make final adjustments to the position of the thrust washers and insert the layshaft from the rear of the gear casing, plain end leading. Carefully, tap it through the

laygear driving the dummy shaft ahead. Do *not* pull the dummy shaft out ahead of the layshaft. If a single needle roller were to move out of position, it could be a problem to reposition it. As soon as the layshaft is home, line up the locking slot so the locking plate and bolt can be fitted and tightened (photos).

12 The mainshaft nut can now be tightened to 80 lbf ft. If a suitable torque wrench is not available, full force on a large adjustable spanner will be adequate. The mainshaft can be locked, whilst tightening the nut, by moving both synchro hubs on to two gears at the same time. Otherwise, the mainshaft should be manoeuvred so it can be clamped in the vice whilst the weight of the gearbox is still supported. Move the hubs to neutral when finished. Punch the lockwasher onto a flat of the nut when fully tightened. Give the mainshaft a spin to ensure that everything is revolving freely and smoothly (photos).

13 Refit the speedometer drivegear inner circlip and Woodruff key. Drive on the gear with an open-ended spanner jaw and fit the second circlip. To refit the later type speedo wheel, note the register at one end of the internal bore of the wheel. Fit the retaining ring followed by the wheel, with the register facing rearwards, over the splines of the mainshaft. Refit the retaining ring into the bore of the wheel until it contacts the register mark. Drive on the wheel assembly using tubing as a drift (photos).

14 The selectors are fitted next. Provided dummy rails have been used, no difficulty need be experienced. Fit the 3rd/4th selector fork in position (this is the one with the groove in the fork) then the 1st/2nd fork and finally the reverse selector, fitting the small forked arm over the pin on the reverse operating lever (photos).

15 The rails are fitted starting with the 1st/2nd gear selector rail. This is the one with the three detents nearest the end of the rail and should be tapped in from the rear of the casing with the long plain section leading. The dummy rail will be driven ahead (photo).

16 The 3rd/4th gear selector rail goes in the centre. This rail has three detents nearer the centre than the 1st/2nd rail and should be pushed in with the shorter plain section first. As soon as it is through the casing, fit the sleeve over the end (if there is one) and then continue driving it through the fork. Once again the dummy rail will be driven ahead of it (photo).

17 Insert the reverse selector rail (the one with only two detents). The

9.10c Front cover and shaft being secured to the front of the casing

9.11a Fitting the layshaft

9.11b Fitting the locking plate

9.12a Securing the mainshaft nut

9.12b Securing the mainshaft nut lockwasher

9.13a Fitting the speedometer drive inner circlip

9.13b Fitting the speedometer drive gear

9.13c Fitting the outer circlip

9.14a Fitting the 3rd/4th selector fork

9.14b Fitting the 1st/2nd selector fork

9.14c Fitting the reverse selector fork

9.15 Fitting the 1st/2nd selector rail

9.16 Fitting the 3rd/4th selector rail

9.17 Fitting the reverse selector rail

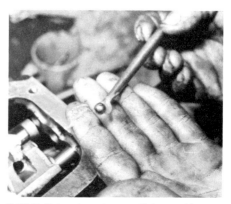

9.19 Refitting the selector rail detent shims springs and balls

9.20a Fitting the rear cover to the gearbox casing

9.20b Refitting rear cover bolts

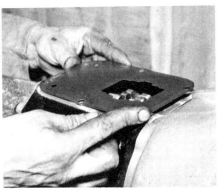

9.21a Refitting the splash shield

9.21b Refitting the top cover

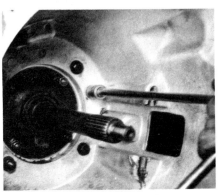

9.23 Refitting the clutch bellhousing

shorter plain section goes in first from the rear of the casing (photo).
18 When all rails are fitted, the ends should be flush with the casing. With the gears in neutral, the cut-outs in the tops of the forks should line up with each other.
19 For those who have decided not to use dummy rails, the appropriate shims and springs should be placed in the hole in the fork. The ball can then be held to the end of a suitable rod with a blob of grease and put into position and pressed down whilst the rail proper is moved forward to trap it. A steady hand and patience are needed here. It must also be remembered that if a ball, with grease attached, is dropped into the box it might stick in an awkward place and be very difficult to shake out. If this should happen remove the springs and shims from the forks before inverting the box. If necessary use a quantity of paraffin to flush it out (photo).

20 Fit a new gasket onto the mating face of the rear cover, having treated it with jointing compound on both sides, and offer up the cover to the casing. Refit the bolts and tighten them up (photos).
21 There are two gaskets for the top cover, one above and one below the splash shield. Treat both with jointing compound and fit them with the splash shield into position. Refit the top cover. Refit the top cover bolts and tighten them down evenly (photos).
22 It is a good idea at this stage to refit the gear lever into the top cover remote control extension so that the selection of gears can be checked. Check that the reverse stop plunger and spring are well greased and tight, and that the selector lever and screw are absolutely tight on the gearshift shaft.
23 Refit the clutch bellhousing and clutch operating lever and the thrust bearing (photo).

## 10 Fault diagnosis – manual gearbox

| Symptom | Reason(s) |
| --- | --- |
| Gear lever rattles or is loose | Wear on gear lever pivot ball and/or pins<br>Loose selector lever in top cover |
| Ineffective synchromesh | Worn baulk rings<br>Worn blocker bars<br>Worn or damaged synchromesh cones |
| Jumps out of gear | Ineffective detent springs<br>Wear on selector forks<br>Worn synchromesh dogs<br>Worn synchromesh hubs |
| Noise and/or vibration | Worn bearings<br>Worn or damaged gears<br>Insufficient or unsuitable oil |
| Noise and difficult gear engagement | Clutch fault<br>Selector mechanism fault |
| Gear selection not positive | Overall wear in selector mechanism |

## 11 Type 'D' overdrive – general description

1 The overdrive unit is attached to the extension on the rear of the gearbox by eight studs and nuts, and takes the form of a hydraulically operated epicyclic gear. Overdrive operates on third and fourth speeds to provide fast cruising at lower engine revolutions. The overdrive 'in-out' switch on the left of the steering wheel actuates a solenoid attached to the side of the overdrive unit. In turn the solenoid operates a valve which opens the hydraulic circuit which pushes the cone clutch into contact with the annulus when overdrive is engaged.
2 Attached to the end of the extended gearbox mainshaft are the inner components of a unidirectional clutch. The hydraulic pressure which enables the overdrive clutch to be engaged is provided by a

hydraulic pump operated by an eccentric cam on the mainshaft.
3 Behind the cam is a steady bearing with a plain phosphor-bronze bush carried in the main housing. Next to this is the sun wheel of the epicyclic gear which is carried on a Clevite bush. The planet carrier and unidirectional clutch come next and are mounted on splines cut in the mainshaft. The smaller diameter portion of the end of the mainshaft turns in a needle roller bearing fitted inside the larger diameter output shaft.
4 Two bearings mounted in the rear of the overdrive casing support the output shaft. A ball bearing housed in a flanged ring is held to the cone clutch member. A bolt at each of the four corners of the flange passes through one of the four clutch return springs by which the ring, together with the clutch cone, is held against the annulus.
5 The pressure of the springs prevents freewheeling on overrun, and

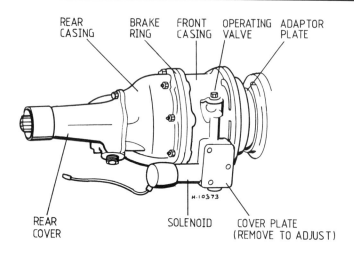

REAR CASING    BRAKE RING    FRONT CASING    OPERATING VALVE    ADAPTOR PLATE

REAR COVER    SOLENOID    COVER PLATE (REMOVE TO ADJUST)

H.10373

**Fig. 6.7 Type 'D' overdrive unit – general view (Sec 11)**

they are also strong enough to handle reverse torque. Also attached to the bolts are two bridge pieces which rest against two hydraulic operating pistons working in cylinders cast in the main casing.

6    The sunwheel and pinions are case hardened and the annulus heat treated. The pinions have needle roller bearings and run on case hardened pins. The gearteeth are helical. The outer ring of the unidirectional clutch is pressed into the annulus. The clutch is of the caged roller type and is loaded by a round wire lock type spring.

7    The overdrive unit works in the following way. Under normal running conditions with the overdrive switched out the cone clutch is held against the centre annulus by the four clutch return springs, so locking the sunwheel to the annulus. In this way the complete gear train rotates together as a solid unit giving direct drive.

8    On switching in the electrically operated solenoid, the centre rod moves inwards, operating the linkage mechanism which lifts a tube, so raising the ball valve off its seating against the pressure of the spring which normally holds the ball in place.

9    With the ball valve fitted, oil under pressure, is free to travel along the drillings in the casing to the two operating cylinders. The pistons are pushed forward against the two bridge pieces which move the clutch cone into contact with the cast iron brake ring sandwiched between the main and tail casings. This brings the sunwheel to rest and allows the annulus to overrun the unidirectional clutch and so give an increased speed to the output shaft.

10    When the overdrive is switched out, the rod in the centre of the solenoid moves outwards, allowing the valve tube to drop and the ball valve to return to its seat. Oil from the two cylinders is then free to return through the centre of the tube to the bottom of the overdrive casing. To ensure direct drive is re-engaged smoothly, the cylinders are emptied slowly because of a small restrictor jet in the base of the valve tube. The oil is then free to flow round in open circuit.

11    The oil for the hydraulic system is supplied by a pump which is pressed into the main housing and held by a grub screw. The pump supplies oil through a non-return valve to a relief valve, in which a piston moves back against a compression spring, until the correct pressure is obtained when a hole in the relief valve is uncovered. Excess oil from the relief valve is then led through drilled passages to an annular groove in the mainshaft steady bush. Radial holes in the shaft feed oil, through axial drillings, to the needle roller bearings, thrust washers and unidirectional clutch.

12    The overdrive is normally a very reliable unit and trouble is usually due to either the solenoid sticking, a fault in the hydraulic system due to dirt or insufficient oil, or incorrect solenoid operating lever adjustment.

**12 Type 'D' overdrive – removal and refitting**

1    It is not necessary to remove the overdrive from the car in order to attend to the following: the hydraulic lever setting; the relief valve; the non-return valve; the solenoid and the operating valve.

2    The overdrive unit can be removed from the car as a separate item if the gearbox does not require attention.

3    Remove the gearbox top cover and remote control assembly as described in Chapter 6, Section 4, paragraph 2. **Note**: *Carry out the operation in paragraph 4 first, if a pit is to be used.*

4    Place the car over a pit or raise it on axle stands to provide the maximum possible working space beneath.

5    Drain the oil from the overdrive unit and gearbox.

6    Remove the propeller shaft (see Chapter 7).

7    Unscrew the speedometer drive from the overdrive rear cover.

8    Disconnect the snap connectors to the overdrive solenoid.

9    Refer to the procedure given in Section 3 of Chapter 6, and lower the gearbox sufficiently to allow eventual withdrawal of the overdrive. **Note**: *There is no intention of removing the gearbox unless specifically required.*

10    Remove the eight nuts from the overdrive/gearbox retaining studs then carefully pull the overdrive off the end of the mainshaft.

11    To mate the overdrive and gearbox, start by placing the overdrive in an upright position and then line up the splines of the clutch and planet carrier by eye, turning them anticlockwise only, with the aid of a long thin screwdriver.

12    Under normal circumstances, if everything is in line, the gearbox mainshaft should enter the overdrive easily. If trouble is experienced, do not try and force the components together but separate them and re-align the components. Place the gearbox in top gear while refitting.

13    As the mainshaft is fed into the overdrive, gently rotate the input shaft to and fro to help 'feed-in' the mainshaft into the splines. At the same time, make certain that the lowest portion of the cam on the mainshaft will rest against the pump. Also take care, as the gearbox extension and overdrive come together, that the end of the mainshaft enters into the needle roller bearing in the tail shaft.

14    The remainder of the refitting procedure is a straightforward reversal of the removal sequence.

**13 Type 'D' overdrive – dismantling, overhaul and reassembly**

1    All numbers in brackets in this Section refer to Fig. 6.8: Unscrew the operating valve plug (54) and take out the spring (30), plunger (39) and ball (40).

2    Undo the nuts (26) from the bolts (19), then remove the two bridge pieces (25). The two operating pistons (52) can now be pulled out of their cylinders in the main casing assembly (71).

3    Cut the locking wire (if fitted) on the non-return relief valve plug (59), undo the plug and remove the spring (47) and ball (46). The non-return valve body (48) can then be unscrewed from the pump body (50). Undo the grub screw (45) and pull the pump body (50) from the casing (71).

4    Undo the eight nuts and spring washers a turn at a time from the studs (70) which hold the main casing assembly (71) to the rear casing (73). As the nuts are undone the pressure of the springs (28) will gradually be released. Take off the main casing (71) together with the brake ring (72) and pull the four clutch springs (28) off their guide bolts (19). Remove the clutch (18) together with the sunwheel assembly (17).

5    It is likely that the brake ring (72) will stick to the casing (71). To separate the ring, gently tap it on its flange with a soft-faced hammer.

6    To free the sunwheel (17) from the centre of the clutch assembly, (18) release the circlip (24) on the splined end of the sunwheel and push out the sunwheel (17).

7    Remove the large circlip (23) with a pair of circlip pliers, and pull the bearing housing (20), complete with thrust bearing (21), off the clutch assembly (18).

8    Lift out the planet carrier (16) from the annulus (7). Removal of the unidirectional roller clutch is not recommended, unless the rollers are thought to be chipped or worn, but if this is to be carried out, take off the circlip and brass retaining washer in front of the clutch.

9    As the inner member (11) is removed, the roller bearings (10) will fall out. Gather them together carefully. On no account should the outer bearing ring be removed as it is expanded into the annulus.

10    Renewal of roller bearing (9) calls for the use of special tools, and a main dealer should be consulted.

11    To remove the combined output shaft and annulus (7) from the rear casing, first undo the locking screw to free the speedometer pinion and bush (80), then remove the tailshaft casing (75) from the rear casing (73) by undoing the six retaining nuts. When sliding the tailshaft casing off take care not to damage the oil seal (78) and bush (76).

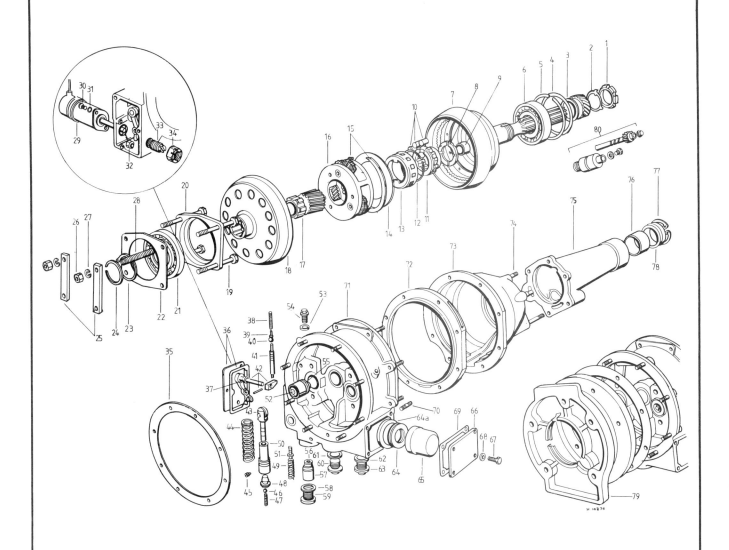

**Fig. 6.8 Type 'D' overdrive unit – exploded view (Sec 10)**

1   Locknut
2   Tabwasher
3   Speedometer wheel
4   Shim
5   Circlip
6   Rear bearing
7   Annulus
8   Thrust washer
9   Mainshaft bearing
10  Rollers ⎫
11  Ratchet ⎬ free
12  Circlip ⎪
13  Roller cage ⎭
14  Retaining plate
15  Circlip
16  Planet carrier with wheels
17  Sunwheel
18  Clutch cone
19  Bolt
20  Bearing housing
21  Bearing
22  Retainer plate

23  Circlip
24  Snap ring ⎫
25  Bridge plates ⎬ clutch
26  Nut         ⎪ release
27  Tab washer ⎭
28  Spring
29  Solenoid
30  Setscrew
31  Washer
32  Nut (solenoid to valve lever)
33  Stop pad ⎫ solenoid
         ⎬ and valve
34  Locknut ⎪ lever
         ⎭ adjustment
35  Joint ring
36  Valve lever cover
37  Sealing ring (operating shaft)
38  Spring ⎫
39  Plunger ⎬ operating
40  Ball   ⎭ valve

41  Operating valve
42  Operating lever assembly
43  Plunger
44  Spring
45  Pump body retaining screw
46  Ball
47  Spring
48  Valve body
49  Spring
50  Pump body
51  Plunger
52  Operating piston
53  Washer
54  Plug
55  Piston ring (rubber)
56  Relief valve body
57  Rubber ring
58  Washer
59  Plug
60  Cover plug
61  Washer

62  Washer
63  Drain plug
64  Ring magnets
64a Sealing ring
65  Filter
66  Filter cover plate
67  Setscrew
68  Washer
69  Filter cover plate joint
70  Stud (front to rear casing)
71  Front casing
72  Brake ring
73  Rear casing
74  Stud (rear casing to rear
     cover)
75  Rear cover
76  Bush
77  Circlip
78  Rear oil seal
79  Gearbox adaptor
80  Speedometer drive assembly

12   Remove any shims (4) between the tailshaft cover and the annulus main bearing (6). Remove the circlip (5) from round the bearing (6) and remove the annulus (7) and bearing (6) by driving them forward into the rear casing (73).

13   To remove the rear bearing (6), knock back the lockwasher (2), undo the locknut (1) and slide off the speedometer drive gear (3) and the bearing (6).

14   Thoroughly clean all parts and examine them carefully. Check the oil pump plunger and pin are not worn and the spring has now contracted. Examine the O-rings from the operating pistons and renew them if worn or hardened; also check the cylinder bores are free from score marks and wear. Check the bearings for roughness, and for looseness between the inner and outer races. Examine the splines for burrs and wear, and the rollers of the clutch for chips and flat spots.

15   Renew the clutch linings if they are burnt or worn, and examine the main and rear casings for cracks or other damage. Renew the steady bush if worn, and examine the gear teeth for cracks, chips and general wear. Examine the sealing balls for ridges which will prevent them seating properly. Check the free length of the springs.

16   Assembly of the unit can commence after any damaged or worn parts have been exchanged and new gaskets and seals obtained. Start by fitting the rear bearing (6) with its circlip groove to the rear over the output shaft. Drive the bearing against the locating shoulder behind the annulus, using a piece of pipe.

17   Fit the speedometer gear (3), the lockwasher (2) and the locknut (1). Now fit the annulus assembly (7) into the rear casing (73) and fit the circlip (5) into its groove in the bearing (6).

18   The bearing (6) is located in the tailshaft cover (75) and a shim or shims (4) is fitted into the recess in the cover to ensure a snug fit with a correct endfloat of the output shaft of 0.005 to 0.010 in (0.127 to 0.254 mm).

19   If a new bearing (6) is to be fitted, reshim as follows. Place two or three shims into the rear cover recess. Offer the cover up to the case, with clip and bearing already fitted. Check the gap between case and cover with feeler gauges. Remove the cover. Remove the shims and measure their sum thickness. The sum thickness of the shims, minus the gap measured, gives the shim thickness required.

20   Refit the tailshaft cover complete with shims, and secure it with the six nuts. Insert the speedometer drive and pinion (80) and secure it with its washer and locking screw.

21   Reassemble the components of the unidirectional clutch, holding the rollers (10) in place in the cage (13) with grease prior to fitting the inner member (11). Ensure that the circlip (12) is fitted in such a way that it pushes the rollers up the ramp on the inner member (11). Do not omit to refit the thrust bearing (8). Finally, fit the retaining plate (14) and circlip(15) in place. This job will be simplified if tool number L178 is available. See Fig. 6.9.

22   Turn each of the planet gearwheels so the line etched on one tooth of each of the gearwheels lines up with one of the three corresponding lines on the periphery of the planet carrier (see Fig. 6.10). Insert the sunwheel (17) into the carrier to keep the planet gearwheels in the correct positions, and carefully fit the complete sunwheel and carrier assembly to the annulus. When fitted, the sunwheel can be withdrawn. Note that the sunwheel can now be inserted or removed as frequently as required, but if the planet carrier is removed from the annulus, the

carrier gearwheels will have to be reset as described at the beginning of the paragraph.

23   Slide the splined end of the sunwheel (17) into the centre of the clutch assembly and secure the sunwheel with the circlip (24). If the thrust bearing was removed for renewal, press the new bearing (21) into its housing (20). Insert the four bolts (19) into the housing, threaded ends facing forwards, and fit the bearing and housing assembly over the centre of the clutch assembly (18). Lock the bearing and housing in place on the clutch with the bearing retaining circlip (23) which fits in a groove on the clutch.

24   Carefully, fit the clutch and sunwheel assembly to the planet carrier in the annulus. Refit the retainer plate (22) and clutch springs (28) over the bolts (19).

25   Coat the mating faces of the main casing (71) and rear casing (73) with jointing compound, and offer up the rear casing to the brake ring and front casing. Slide the four bolts (19) through their holes in the main casing and refit and tighten down a turn at a time, the nuts and washers which hold the casings together.

26   Fit the rubber O-rings (55) to the two operating pistons (52) and with the pistons generously lubricated with oil, slide them into their cylinders in the housing, so the spigoted ends face the front of the overdrive assembly. Slip the two bridge pieces (25) over the ends of the four bolts (19) and refit the nuts and washers (26, 27) and tighten them down.

27   Refit the oil pump body, smaller end first, into the centre hole at the bottom of the casing, making sure the oil inlet faces the rear. Gently tap it into position until the groove lines up with the grub screw hole. Fit and tighten the grub screw.

28   Refit the component parts of the relief valve, operating valve, and non-return valve in the order shown in Fig. 6.8 and do up the three plugs. Do not fit the operating lever cover plate until adjusted (see next Section) after fitting the unit to the car.

### 14 Type 'D' overdrive operating lever – adjustment

1   If the overdrive does not engage, or will not release when it is switched out, and providing the solenoid is not at fault, the trouble is likely to be that the operating lever is out of adjustment. Adjustment can be made without removing the overdrive.

2   Undo the three bolts and washers holding the solenoid cover plate in position, to give access to the operating lever and solenoid plunger.

3   Procure a short length of mild steel rod of $\frac{3}{16}$ in (4.76 mm) diameter. Switch the ignition on, put the car in top gear, and flick the actuating switch to the overdrive position.

4   If the rod can now be passed through the hole 'A' in the operating arm (see Fig. 6.11) into the hole in the casing, adjustment is correct.

5   If the solenoid does not move the arm far enough for the rod to be inserted, or if it moves the arm too far, the plunger must be adjusted. Switch off the ignition. Hold the solenoid plunger from turning by means of the two flats machined on its shank, and pressing the plunger tightly into the solenoid, screw the self-locking nut 'B' (Fig. 6.11) in or out until the test rod can be pushed fully home into the hole in the casing.

6   Operate the switch several times, checking with the test rod to

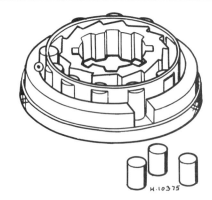

Fig. 6.9 Assembling the type 'D' unidirectional clutch using tool No L178 or L178A (Sec 13)

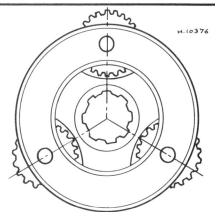

Fig. 6.10 Type 'D' overdrive unit – alignment of the planet gearwheels (Sec 13)

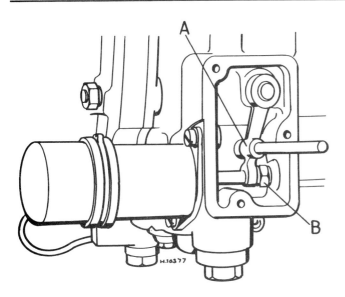

**Fig. 6.11 Type 'D' overdrive unit – checking the operating plunger adjustment (see text) (Sec 14)**

ensure adjustment is correct. Measure the current consumed by the solenoid which, with the operating arm correctly set, should be 2 amps. If a reading of about 17 amps is obtained this shows that the solenoid plunger is not moving sufficiently to switch to the holding coil from the operating coil. If very fine adjustment will not remedy this condition, fit a new solenoid and plunger.

## 15 Type 'D' overdrive relief valve, non-return valve and operating valve – removal, inspection and refitting

1   Access to the relief and non-return valves located in the bottom of the overdrive is gained after removing the engine steady rod and bracket from the rear crossmember. Drain the oil from the gearbox and overdrive.
2   Cut through the locking wire, unscrew the plugs and remove and clean the components. Note that the valve cap and non-return valve body are unscrewed from the pump, and that the relief valve body is removed with circlip pliers.
3   Examine the seatings for pits or chips, and the balls for wear and ridges. The steel ball in the non-return valve is very hard, and if the ball is undamaged and the seating is suspect, tap the ball firmly into its seat with a soft metal drift.
4   Reassembly is a straightforward reversal of the removal sequence. Do not omit to fit the copper washer on the relief valve between the cap and main casing, and hold the non-return valve ball to its spring with petroleum jelly during refitment.
5   Access to the operating valve can only be gained after removing the remote control assembly from inside the car. Undo the plug and check that the ball is lifted 1/32 in (0.79 mm) when the solenoid is actuated. Failure to move, points to a fault in the solenoid or operating arm.

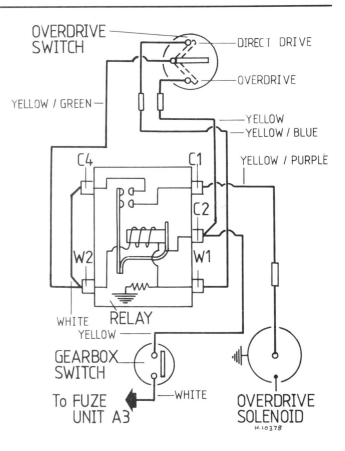

**Fig. 6.12 Type 'D' overdrive unit – circuit diagram (Sec 14)**

6   The ball can be removed with a magnet and the valve with a piece of $\frac{1}{8}$ in (3.1 mm) wire. Check the ball and seat and clean out the small hole in the side of the valve tube. Check if the oil pump is working by jacking the rear of the car off the ground and placing the car in top gear. Engage overdrive and with the engine running, watch and see if oil is being pumped into the valve chamber. Refitting is a reversal of the removal procedure.

## 16 Type 'D' overdrive – routine maintenance

1   With regard to topping up the oil level and renewal of the oil, the same service intervals and procedures apply as for the manual gearbox.
2   When the oil is to be renewed, the filter unit must be removed and cleaned. To do this unscrew the four retaining bolts then take off the cover plate and gasket. Clean the filter in paraffin and dry thoroughly, before reassembling. Ensure the three magnetic rings are fitted into the filter, followed by the large diameter sealing ring. This is to be fitted with its rubber face towards the filter.

## 17 Fault diagnosis – type 'D' overdrive

| Symptom | Reason(s) |
| --- | --- |
| Overdrive will not engage | Solenoid faulty |
| | Selector mechanism requires adjustment |
| | Oil level in unit too low |
| | Relief valve faulty |
| | Internal hydraulic leakage |
| | Operating valve faulty |
| | Non-return valve faulty |
| | Hydraulic pump faulty |
| | Damaged gears, bearings or moving parts |

| Symptom | Reason/s |
| --- | --- |
| Overdrive will not release<br>**Note**: *If this occurs immediate attention is required to preclude damage. Do **not** select reverse gear* | Wiring fault<br>Selector mechanism requires adjustment<br>Restrictor jet blocked in operating valve<br>Clutch sticking<br>Solenoid stop incorrectly adjusted<br>Damaged internal parts |
| Overdrive clutch slipping | Oil level in unit too low<br>Selector mechanism requires adjustment<br>Internal hydraulic leakage<br>Foreign matter in valves<br>Clutch linings worn or carbonised |
| Free wheeling on overrun or clutch slipping in reverse | Selector mechanism requires adjustment<br>Clutch linings worn or carbonised<br>Restrictor jet blocked in operating valve<br>Clutch springs broken<br>Solenoid stop incorrectly adjusted |

## 18 Type 'J' overdrive – general description

1 The type 'J' overdrive unit takes the form of a hydraulically operated epicyclic gear which operates on third and top gears to provide fast cruising at lower engine revolutions. The overdrive is engaged or disengaged by a driver-controlled switch which controls an electric solenoid mounted on the overdrive unit. A further switch called an inhibitor switch is included in the electrical circuit to prevent accidental engagement of overdrive in reverse, first or second gears.

2 The overdrive unit is designed to be engaged or disengaged when engine power is being transmitted through the power line without the use of the clutch pedal, at any throttle opening or road speed. It is important that the overdrive is not disengaged at high road speeds as this will cause excessively high engine speeds.

3 The overdrive gears are epicyclic and comprise a central sunwheel which is in mesh with three planet wheels. These three gears are also in mesh with an internally toothed annulus. The planet carrier is splined to the input shaft which is, in fact, the mainshaft of the manual gearbox. The annulus is an integral part of the output shaft.

4 When the overdrive is disengaged, the engine torque is transmitted from the input shaft to the inner member of an unidirectional clutch and then onto the outer member of the clutch, via rollers, which are driven up inclined faces, and wedge or lock the inner and outer members. The outer member of the clutch forms part of the combined annulus and the output shaft. Thus, as the gear train is not operative, the drive is direct through the overdrive unit.

5 Mounted on the externally splined extension shaft of the sungear is a cone clutch and this is pressed onto the annulus by a number of springs which press against the overdrive unit casing. The spring pressure is transmitted to the clutch member by a thrust ring and ball bearing, so causing the inner friction lining of the cone clutch to be in contact with the outer cone of the annulus and rotate with the annulus whilst the springs and thrust ring remain stationary.

6 As the sunwheel is splined to the clutch member, the whole gear train is locked together so permitting overrun and engine torque in reverse gear to be transmitted through the overdrive unit. Also, an additional load is imparted to the clutch during over-run and reverse conditions by the sunwheel, which, due to the special helix angle of the gear teeth, thrusts rearwards and has for its reaction member the cone clutch.

7 When the overdrive unit is engaged, the cone clutch takes up a new position, whereby it is no longer in contact with the annulus, but has moved forward, so that its outer friction lining is in contact with the brake ring which is part of the overdrive unit casing. The sunwheel to which the clutch is attached is now held still. The planet carrier rotates with the input shaft and the three planet wheels are caused to rotate about their own axis and drive the annulus at a greater speed than the input shaft. This is made possible because the unidirectional clutch outer member can overrun the inner member. Hydraulic pressure generated by a pump in the overdrive unit acts on two pistons when a small valve is opened and moves the cone clutch in a forward direction. The small valve is controlled by the solenoid which is operated by the driver using an electric switch. This hydraulic pressure is sufficient to overcome the spring pressure that holds the clutch member onto the annulus, and cause the clutch to engage with the brake ring and hold the sunwheel at rest. As the overdrive unit is attached to the rear of the gearbox, it is able to share the oil in the gearbox. The cam operated plunger pump draws the oil from the overdrive oil sump and, via drillings, passes it to the two operating piston chambers, the ball type operating valve and the pressure relief valve. Oil is also passed to various other parts of the overdrive unit for lubrication purposes.

8 When the driver moves the overdrive switch to the 'engaged' position, current passes to the solenoid and causes the operating valve to close. Pressure built up in the hydraulic system causes the two pistons to move against the action of the springs which hold the sliding member onto the annulus. Therefore, the sliding member is moved into contact with the brake ring.

9 Oil then continues to be pumped into the hydraulic operating system, so compressing the modulator springs that are inside the pistons, resulting in a cushioning effect by the progressive application of the load between the sliding member and the brake ring. As the sunwheel is now in a locked condition and the planet gears are free to revolve, the overdrive condition is in existence. Any further delivery of oil will open the pressure relief valve which will allow oil to pass to the various components for lubrication purposes and then return to the overdrive oil sump.

10 When the driver moves the overdrive switch to the 'disengaged' position, current will cease to flow to the solenoid and the operating valve ball will be unseated by hydraulic pressure so uncovering the exhaust port. The spring load on the sliding member will force oil to pass from the piston chambers whilst, at the same time, oil will continue to be pumped into the circuit, and, with the two circuits connected, allowing mixing of the two oil flows, causing action against each other, will control the movement of the sliding member. The sliding member is, therefore, disengaged from the brake ring and this time engaged with the annulus at a controlled rate. The oil flow will then pass through the exhaust port and provide lubrication for the various internal parts.

## 19 Type 'J' overdrive – removal and refitting

1 Before beginning the sequence to remove the overdrive unit it is necessary to drive the vehicle and engage overdrive and then disengage the overdrive with the clutch depressed. This will release the spline loading between the planet carrier and unidirectional clutch which can make removal difficult.

2 The procedure for removal of the type 'J' overdrive is similar to that for the type 'D' overdrive previously described, but in addition it is recommended that the battery earth lead is temporarily removed.

3 When refitting the overdrive, first rotate the gearbox mainshaft until the cam is at its lowest point which will coincide with the pump strap when the two units are fitted together.

4 Check the planet carrier retaining clip is in position on the

mainshaft and then, to prevent the mainshaft rotating, select 1st or reverse gear.

5   Fit a new gasket to the front face of the overdrive unit using a non-setting gasket cement.

6   Rotate the overdrive output shaft clockwise whilst applying slight forward pressure until the splines engage as the unit is being offered up to the gearbox. Ensure the pump strap slides onto the cam smoothly; do not use excessive force.

7   Should it be found that the overdrive unit will not push fully home onto the adaptor plate face but a gap of about $\frac{5}{8}$ in (16 mm) exists, it is an indication that the planet carrier and unidirectional clutch splines have become misaligned. Remove the overdrive unit again and rotate the inner member of the unidirectional clutch in an anti-clockwise direction, using a long shaft screwdriver.

8   Refit the eight nuts that secure the overdrive unit to the adaptor plate and tighten in a diagonal manner, to the correct torque figure.

9   The remainder of the refitting procedure is the reverse of the removal procedure.

10   Check the oil level.

## 20 Type 'J' overdrive – dismantling, overhaul and reassembly

1   Before dismantling the overdrive unit, it must be appreciated that special tools are required for certain operations. These are:

*Tool L354A, dowelled plug spanner. A tool of this type is not difficult to make, but beware of using a drift to attempt to remove the plugs if the tool is not available, since irreparable damage can occur*

*Tool L178 or 178A, for assembling unidirectional clutch. It may be possible to dispense with this tool if the clutch rollers are held in position with grease during assembly*

*Tool L401A. Removing tool for relief valve body and dashpot sleeve. It is not envisaged that this tool will be readily made*

2   Using a screwdriver or small chisel, bend back the tab washers that lock the four nuts securing the operating piston bridge pieces and undo the four nuts. Lift away the four nuts and tab washers followed by the two bridge pieces.

3   Undo and remove the six nuts that secure the main casing to the rear casing in a progressive manner as these two parts will be under the influence of the clutch return spring pressure. Note the position of the copper washers which fit on the two studs at the top of the casing. Note also the earth lead under the solenoid nut above the solenoid aperture.

4   The main casing, complete with brake ring and springs, can now be lifted from the main casing.

5   Lift out the sliding member assembly complete with the sunwheel followed by the planet carrier assembly. This should be done with care as it is easy to accidentally damage the oil catcher which is located under the planet carrier assembly.

6   To dismantle the main casing and brake ring, first tap the brake ring from its spigot in the main casing using a suitable drift.

7   Using a pair of pliers carefully remove the two operating pistons.

8   Undo and remove the six bolts and spring washers securing the sump to the main casing. Lift away the sump, gasket and suction filler.

9   Remove the relief valve and dashpot assembly as described in Section 22.

10   Remove the non-return valve as described in Section 23.

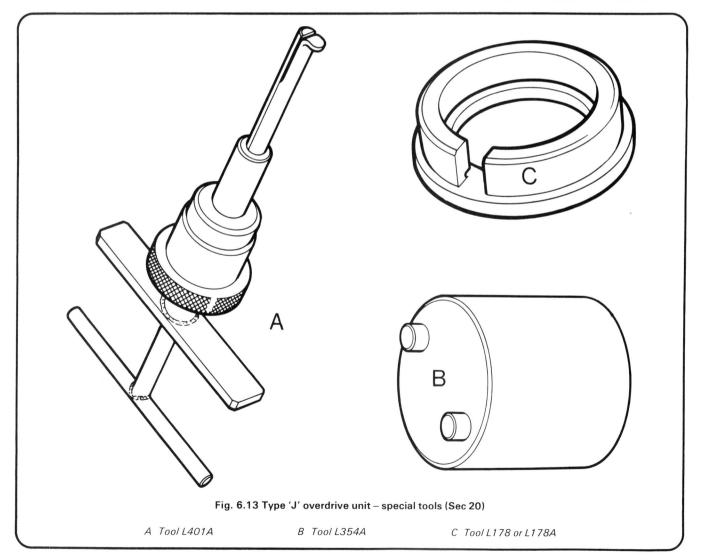

**Fig. 6.13 Type 'J' overdrive unit – special tools (Sec 20)**

*A Tool L401A*          *B Tool L354A*          *C Tool L178 or L178A*

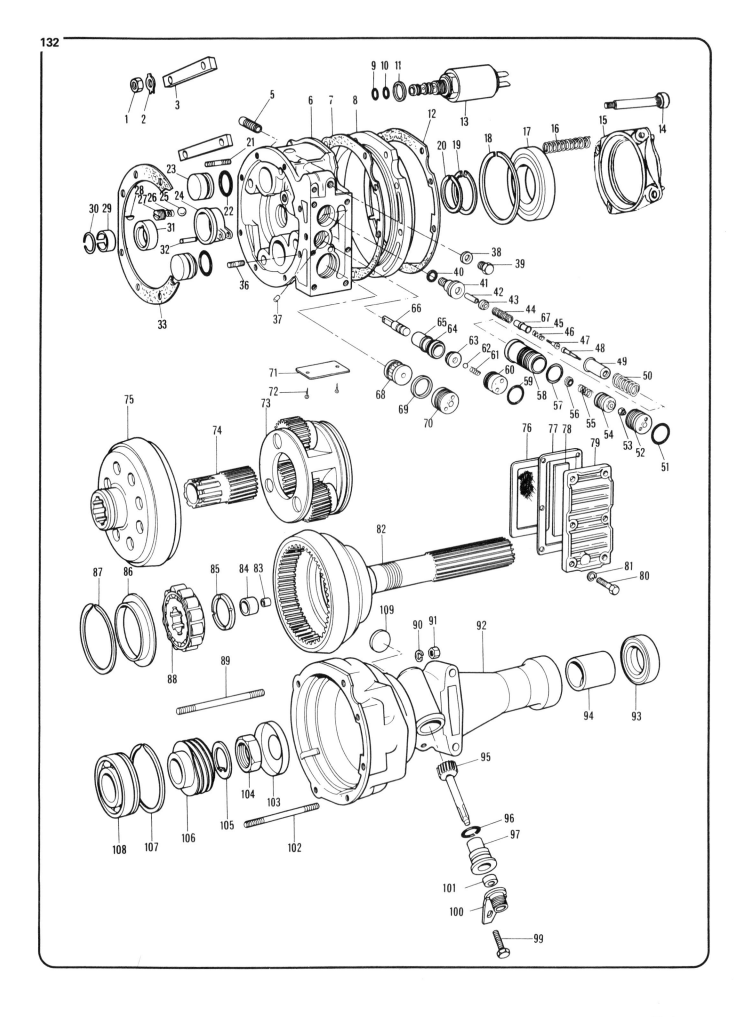

11 Remove the pressure filter as described in Section 24.
12 Remove the solenoid control valve, as described in Section 21.
13 With a screwdriver, carefully remove the circlip from the sunwheel extension and lift out the sunwheel.
14 Again, using a screwdriver, remove the circlip from its groove on the cone clutch hub and tap the clutch from the thrust ring bearing with a soft-faced hammer.
15 If necessary, the bearing may be removed from its housing using a vice and suitable packing. It will be necessary to remove the larger circlip which retains it before removal commences.
16 Using a screwdriver, remove the circlip which retains the unidirectional clutch. Lift away the oil thrower.
17 Place tool number L178A over the now exposed unidirectional clutch and lift the inner member, complete with rollers, into the special tool. Lift away the bronze thrust washer.
18 Withdraw the speedometer driven gear and bearing.
19 To remove the annulus, first drive a centre punch into the welch plug located at the top of the rear casing and lever it out.
20 Using a pair of circlip pliers expand the circlip which secures the annulus bearing.
21 Place the rear casing vertically over supports and with a light blow from a soft-faced mallet on the end of the annulus, drive the annulus complete with bearing downwards from the rear casing.
22 Undo and remove the nut that secures the speedometer driving gear and with the aid of a universal puller withdraw the ball race.
23 The overdrive unit is now fully dismantled and may be inspected for wear.
24 Inspect the teeth and cone surface of the annulus for wear. Check that the unidirectional clutch rollers are not chipped and the inner and outer members are free from damage.
25 Examine the spring and cage for distortion. Check the lubrication port at the rear of the annulus is clear.
26 Inspect the rear casing bush and oil seal for wear or damage.
27 Examine the clutch linings on the sliding member for signs of excessive wear or overheating. Should there be signs of these conditions, the whole sliding member assembly must be renewed. It is not possible to fit new linings as these are precision machined after bonding.
28 Make sure the ball race rotates smoothly, as this can be a source of noise when the car is running in direct gear.
29 Inspect the clutch return springs for any signs of distortion, damage or loss of springiness.
30 Check the sunwheel teeth for signs of wear or damage.
31 Inspect the main casing for cracks or damage. Examine the operating cylinder bores for scores or wear. Check the operating pistons for wear and renew the sealing rings if there are any signs of damage.
32 Check the pump plunger assembly and ensure the strap is a good fit on the mainshaft cam and that there is no excess play between the plunger and strap.
33 Should the pump plunger assembly be worn or damaged, this must be renewed as a complete assembly.
34 With the non-return valve assembly clean, inspect the ball and valve seat and also the O-rings for signs of damage.
35 Check the relief valve and dashpot assembly for wear. The pistons must move freely in their respective housings. Ensure that the rings are in good order.
36 Do not dismantle the dashpot and relief valve piston assemblies otherwise the pre-determined spring pressures will be disturbed.
37 Finally, examine the O-rings on the solenoid valve for damage, which, if evident, should be renewed, together with the sealing washers.
38 Clean the sump filter in petrol and if any particles are stuck in the gauze, rub with an old toothbrush. Wipe the magnetic plug free of any metallic particles.
39 Reassembly of the unit can commence after any damage or worn parts have been renewed and new gaskets and seals obtained. Do not use jointing compound during assembly.
40 Fit a new annulus ball-race and then position the speedometer driving gear so the plain portion is facing the ball-race. Secure with the nut and a new locking washer. Tighten the nut to the correct torque figure.
41 Place the ball-race circlip in the rear casing and expand using a pair of circlip pliers.
42 Press the annulus through the circlip and into the casing until the bearing is fully home and the circlip is located in its groove. This must

**Fig. 6.14 Type 'J' overdrive unit – exploded view (Sec 20)**

| | | | |
|---|---|---|---|
| 1 | Nut | 55 | Double dashpot spring |
| 2 | Tab washer | 56 | Spring retainer |
| 3 | Bridge piece | 57 | O-ring |
| 5 | Breather | 58 | Dashpot sleeve |
| 6 | Main case | 59 | O-ring |
| 7 | Gasket | 60 | Pump plug |
| 8 | Brake ring | 61 | Non-return valve spring |
| 9 | O-ring | 62 | Steel ball |
| 10 | O-ring | 63 | Non-return valve seat |
| 11 | Washer | 64 | O-ring |
| 12 | Gasket | 65 | Pump body |
| 13 | Solenoid | 66 | Pump plunger |
| 14 | Thrust pin | 67 | Packing washer |
| 15 | Thrust ring | 68 | Pressure filter |
| 16 | Clutch return spring | 69 | Pressure filter washer |
| 17 | Thrust ball race | 70 | Pressure filter plug |
| 18 | Retaining circlip | 71 | Nameplate |
| 19 | Circlip for sliding member | 72 | Securing screw |
| 20 | Circlip for sunwheel | 73 | Planet carrier assembly |
| 21 | Stud | 74 | Sunwheel |
| 22 | O-ring | 75 | Clutch sliding member |
| 23 | Operating piston | 76 | Sump filter |
| 24 | Pump strap | 77 | Sump gasket |
| 25 | Steel ball | 78 | Sump gasket |
| 26 | Lubrication relief valve spring | 79 | Sump |
| 27 | Lubrication relief valve plug | 80 | Sump setscrews |
| 28 | Woodruff key | 81 | Shakeproof washer |
| 29 | Spring ring for mainshaft | 82 | Annulus |
| 30 | Circlip | 83 | Restrictor plug |
| 31 | Cam | 84 | Mainshaft support bush |
| 32 | Pump pin | 85 | Thrust washer |
| 33 | Gasket | 86 | Oil thrower |
| 36 | Stud | 87 | Circlip |
| 37 | Restrictor plug | 88 | Freewheel assembly |
| 38 | Washer | 89 | Stud |
| 39 | Pressure topping plug | 90 | Shakeproof washer |
| 40 | O-ring | 91 | Nut |
| 41 | Relief valve body | 92 | Rear case |
| 42 | Relief valve spindle | 93 | Oil seal |
| 43 | Relief valve spring plate | 94 | Bearing bush |
| 44 | Relief valve spring | 95 | Speedo driven gear |
| 45 | Relief valve spring cup | 96 | O-ring |
| 46 | Residual spring | 97 | Speedo bearing |
| 47 | Relief valve spindle | 99 | Setscrew |
| 48 | Dashpot spring | 101 | Oil seal |
| 49 | Dashpot spring cup | 102 | Stud |
| 50 | Dashpot spring | 103 | Weir |
| 51 | O-ring | 104 | Locking nut |
| 52 | Dashpot plug | 106 | Speedo driving gear |
| 53 | Dashpot piston locknut | 107 | Annulus ball race circlip |
| 54 | Dashpot piston | 108 | Annulus front ball race |
| | | 109 | Welch washer |

be done carefully so the rear bush and oil seal are not damaged.

43   Fit a new welch plug and secure by striking lightly in the centre with a suitable size flat-faced punch.

44   Next, position the spring and inner member of the unidirectional clutch in the cage, locating the spring so the cage is spring-loaded in an anticlockwise direction when viewed from the front.

45   Place this assembly onto tool L178A with the open side of the cage uppermost and feed the clutch in, in a clockwise direction, until all the rollers are in place. Refit the bronze thrust washer in the recess in the annulus.

46   Transfer the unidirectional clutch assembly from the special tool into its outer member in the annulus.

47   Refit the oil thrower and secure with the circlip. Check that the clutch rotates in an anti-clockwise direction only.

48   To assemble the clutch sliding member assembly, fit the ball-race into its housing and secure with the large circlip.

49   Place this assembly onto the hub of the cone clutch and fit the circlip into its groove.

50   Insert the sunwheel into the hub and refit the circlip onto the sunwheel extension.

51   Lightly smear the operating pistons with oil and refit to the main casing.

52   Place a new gasket into the main casing and fit the brake ring, ensuring it is fully home on its spigot location.

53   Reassemble and refit the relief valve and dashpot assembly, as detailed in Section 22.

54   Reassemble and refit the non-return valve, as detailed in Section 23.

55   Reassemble and refit the pressure filter, as described in Section 24.

56   Refit the overdrive sump, suction filter and gasket and secure with the six bolts and spring washers.

57   Refit the solenoid control valve and tighten firmly, using an open-ended spanner.

58   Mount the rear casing assembly vertically in a bench vice and insert the planet carrier assembly. The gears may be meshed in any position.

59   Place the sliding member assembly, complete with clutch non-return springs, onto the cone of the annulus, at the same time engaging the sunwheel with the planet gears. Fit the brake ring into its spigot in the tail casing using a new joint washer on both sides.

60   Position the main casing assembly onto the thrust housing pins, at the same time entering the studs in the brake ring.

61   Fit the two operating piston bridge pieces and secure with the four nuts and new tab washers.

62   Fit the six nuts which secure the rear and main casing assemblies, ensuring that the two copper washers are correctly located on the two top studs. It will be observed that as the nuts are tightened the clutch return spring pressure will be felt.

## 21 Type 'J' overdrive solenoid control valve – removal and refitting

1   Disconnect the battery earth.

2   Disconnect the two terminals at the rear of the solenoid noting which way round the cables are fitted.

3   Using a 1 in (25 mm) AF open-ended spanner, unscrew the assembly. Do not use a wrench around the cylindrical body of the solenoid valve otherwise it will be severely damaged.

4   To test the solenoid, connect into a circuit using a 12 volt battery and ammeter. The solenoid should require approximately 2 amps.

5   Check that the plunger in the valve moves forwards when the solenoid is energised and is returned to its direct drive position by spring pressure when de-energised.

6   It should be noted that this type of solenoid does not operate with a 'click' as observed in other types of overdrive.

7   Inspect the O-rings on the solenoid valve for damage and, if necessary, renew them together with the sealing washer.

8   If it is necessary to clean the operating valve, immerse this part of the solenoid valve only, in paraffin until the valve is clean.

9   The solenoid and operating valve constitute a self-contained unit sealed by the factory. If it proves to be faulty, it must be renewed complete.

10   Refitting is the reverse of the removal sequence.

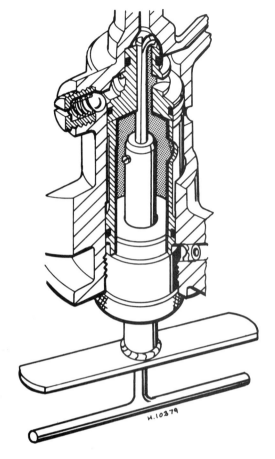

Fig. 6.15 Type 'J' overdrive unit – using tool L401A to remove the relief valve and dashpot body (Sec 22)

## 22 Type 'J' overdrive relief valve and dashpot – removal and refitting

1   A special tool, L354A, is essential for removing the relief valve plug. If the vehicle has been used recently, take care to avoid burns from hot oil.

2   Remove the six bolts and spring washers securing the overdrive sump gauze filter, and lift away the cover, joint and filter.

3   Take out the dashpot assembly, residual spring, and relief valve.

4   The relief valve piston assembly may now be withdrawn by carefully pulling it out with a pair of pliers.

5   Insert special tool L401A into the relief valve body centre, and withdraw it complete with the dashpot sleeve. Take care not to damage the valve bore.

6   Do not attempt to dismantle the dashpot and relief valve piston assemblies, otherwise the predetermined spring pressures will be disturbed.

7   Inspect the pistons and ensure that they move freely in their respective housings. Make sure the O-rings are not damaged.

8   Before assembly, make sure all components are clean and lightly oiled.

9   Insert the relief body in the bore and, using the relief valve outer sleeve, push fully home.

10   It should be noted that the end with the O-ring is nearest the outside of the main casing.

11   Next, position the relief valve spring and piston into the dashpot cut taking care that both ends of the residual pressure spring are correctly located. Carefully position these components in the relief valve outer sleeve, at the same time engaging the relief valve piston in its housing. Fit the base plug and tighten flush with the main housing to the correct torque figure.

12   Refit the filter, gasket and sump and secure with the six bolts and spring washers.

## 23 Type 'J' overdrive pump non-return valve – removal and refitting

1    A special tool, L354A, is essential for removing the pump plug. If the vehicle has been used recently, take care to avoid burns from hot oil.

2    Undo and remove the six bolts and spring washers securing the overdrive sump and gauze filter. Lift away the sump, gasket and gauze filter.

3    Using tool L354A, remove the pump plug, taking care not to lose the non-return spring and ball. The pump valve seat can now be lifted away.

4    The pump body will be held in position by its O-ring. Should it be necessary to remove this, rotate the propeller shaft until the pump plunger is at the top of its stroke.

5    Next, carefully withdraw the pump body by hooking a piece of wire into the now exposed inlet port.

6    Carefully clean and then inspect the non-return valve ball and valve seat and make sure that the O-rings are not damaged. Fit new O-rings if necessary.

7    To refit the non-return valve assembly, first place the spring in the non-return valve plug, then position the ball on the spring.

8    The non-return valve seat can now be located on the ball and the complete assembly screwed into the main case using tool L354A. Tighten to the correct torque setting.

9    Refit the suction filter, sump gasket and sump and secure with the six bolts and spring washers.

## 24 Type 'J' overdrive pressure filter – removal and refitting

1    For removal a special tool, L354A, is necessary to remove the pump plug. If the vehicle has been used recently, take care to avoid burns from hot oil which will be released.

2    Undo and remove the six bolts and spring washers securing the overdrive sump and gauze filter. Lift away the sump, gasket and gauze filter.

3    Using tool L354A, remove the pressure filter base plug.

4    The filter element will come away with the plug. Note the aluminium washer which locates on the shoulder in the filter bore.

5    Remove any dirt and thoroughly wash the element in petrol or paraffin.

6    Refitting is the reverse sequence to removal. Always fit a new aluminium washer. Tighten the plug to the specified torque wrench setting.

## 25 Type 'J' overdrive – routine maintenance

1    With regard to topping-up the oil level and renewal of the oil, the same service intervals and procedures apply as for the manual gearbox.

2    When renewing the oil, remove and clean the sump filter as detailed in Section 24.

3    When renewing the oil, remove and clean the pressure filter as detailed in Section 24.

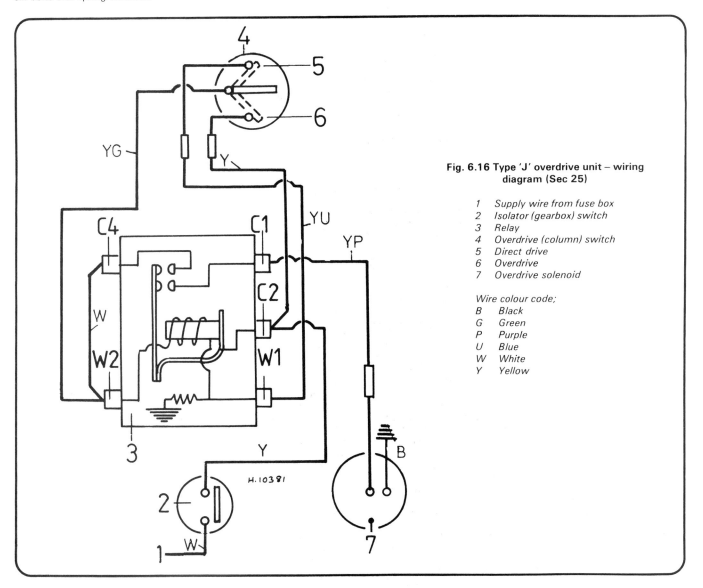

Fig. 6.16 Type 'J' overdrive unit – wiring diagram (Sec 25)

1    Supply wire from fuse box
2    Isolator (gearbox) switch
3    Relay
4    Overdrive (column) switch
5    Direct drive
6    Overdrive
7    Overdrive solenoid

Wire colour code;
B    Black
G    Green
P    Purple
U    Blue
W    White
Y    Yellow

## 26  Fault diagnosis – type 'J' overdrive

| Symptom | Reason(s) |
|---|---|
| Overdrive will not engage | Low oil level<br>Electrical wiring fault<br>Solenoid faulty<br>Filters blocked<br>Pump non-return valve faulty<br>Sticking piston in relief valve<br>Control orifice between solenoid and dashpot blocked. (To remove any blockage, compressed air only should be used; do not probe the orifice with wire) |
| Overdrive will not release<br>**Note**: *If this occurs immediate attention is required to preclude damage, do* **not** *select reverse gear* | Closed circuit in electrical system<br>Solenoid control valve plunger seized<br>Sticking piston in relief valve<br>Control orifice between solenoid and dashpot blocked. (To remove any blockage, compressed air only should be used; do not probe the orifice with wire)<br>Cone clutch sticking (tap brake ring with a soft-faced mallet) |
| Overdrive clutch slipping | Clutch linings faulty<br>Cone clutch movement obstructed – see also items listed under 'overdrive will not engage' |
| Overdrive disengagement slow and/or free-wheeling on overrun and/or reverse gear slipping | Sticking piston in relief valve<br>Solenoid sticking<br>Control orifice between solenoid and dashpot blocked (to remove any blockage, compressed air only should be used; do not probe the orifice with wire) |

## 27  Automatic transmission – general description

1    An optional fitment on models in the Hunter range is the Borg Warner automatic transmission. Until 1974, this was the Model 35 three-speed transmission which has been used on a wide range of British cars, but for 1974 models the Model 45 four-speed unit was made available.

2    The automatic transmission comprises two main components, namely, a three-element hydrokinetic torque converter capable of torque multiplication at an infinitely variable ratio between 2.0 : 1 and 1.0 : 1, and a torque/speed responsive, hydraulically operated planetary gearbox.

3    The Model 35 gearbox comprises a planetary gearset providing three forward gears and one reverse; the Model 45 is similar in operating principle but provides four forward gears and one reverse.

4    Early Model 35 transmissions use a selector with five positions, these being, L, D, N, R and P. Later Model 35 transmissions use a selector with six positions, these being 1, 2, D, N, R and P.

5    Model 45 transmissions use a selector with six positions, these being 2/1, 3, D, N, R and P.

6    Due to the complexity of the automatic transmission unit, if any malfunction is suspected, or if overhaul is required, the job should be entrusted to a main dealer or automatic transmission specialist. The contents of the following Sections are for general guidance and for servicing information.

## 28  Automatic transmission – fluid level

### Model 35 transmission

1    Run the car for about 5 miles (8 km), then select P and allow the engine to idle for about two minutes.

2    With the engine still idling and P selected, remove the transmission fluid dipstick, wipe it clean and then re-insert it in the dipstick/filler tube.

3    Withdraw the dipstick again, check the fluid level and, if necessary, top-up to the 'HIGH' mark. Do not overfill.

4    If it becomes necessary to check the level with the transmission cold, the fluid level should be $\frac{3}{8}$ in (9.5 mm) below the 'HIGH' mark with the engine idling and P selected. At the first opportunity the level should be re-checked when hot.

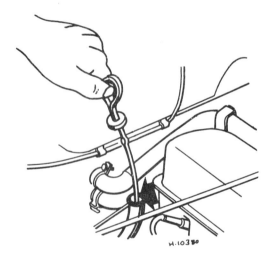

Fig. 6.17 Automatic transmission – checking the fluid level
(Sec 28)

### Model 45 transmission

5    Run the engine at a fast idle for about five minutes, select each driving range in turn, then switch off the engine with P still selected.

6    Remove the transmission fluid dipstick, wipe it clean and re-insert it.

7    Withdraw the dipstick again after approximately thirty seconds, check the fluid level and, if necessary, top-up to the 'FULL' mark on the dipstick. If the procedure was started with a cold engine, the 'WARM' side of the dipstick should be used. If the procedure was started with a hot engine (having run at least 5 miles – 8 km) the 'HOT' side of the dipstick should be used.

## 29  Automatic transmission downshift cable – adjustment

**Note**: The following procedure is given as a guide to adjustment only, and is not suitable where a replacement downshift cable has been fitted (because the cable stop is not crimped in position), where an existing cable stop is loose or damaged, or where a replacement engine, carburettor or transmission has been fitted. In any of these instances, adjustment should be made by a Talbot dealer, since transmission pressure checks will have to be made.

1 Adjust the outer cable so that the stop is 0.03 to 0.06 in (0.76 to 1.55 mm) clear of the abutment for Model 35 transmissions or 0.01 to 0.02 in (0.25 to 0.50 mm) for Model 45 transmissions.
2 Adjustment is by slackening the locknut(s) at the abutment bracket and repositioning the outer cable.

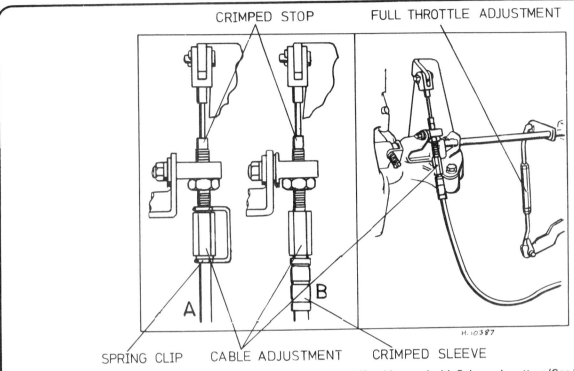

Fig. 6.18 Automatic transmission type BW35 – downshift cables used with Solex carburettors (Sec 29)

*A Early cables*          *B Later cables*

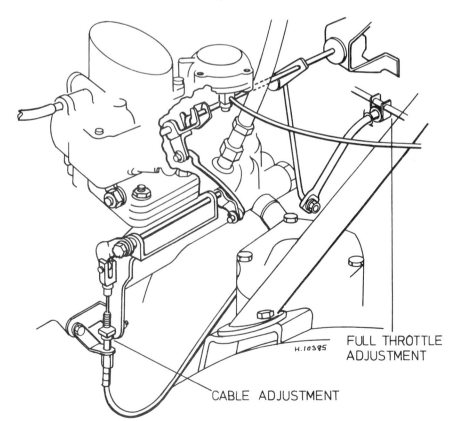

Fig. 6.19 Automatic transmission type BW35 – alternative downshift cable arrangement (Sec 29)

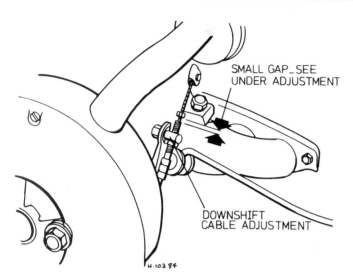

Fig. 6.20 Automatic transmission type BW35 – downshift cable arrangement with Stromberg CDS carburettor (Sec 29)

## 30 Automatic transmission accelerator linkage – full throttle adjustment

1    This adjustment should be set so that when the accelerator pedal is depressed to within 1 in (25 mm) of the floor covering, the downshift valve cam passes over the hard spot (detent). The carburettor butterfly should be $\frac{7}{8}$ open at this point.
2    When the accelerator pedal is depressed to the forced throttle position on Model 45 transmissions, there must be 1.75 in (44 mm) travel of the downshift cable. If this is not occurring, do not alter the downshift cable setting, but check the throttle linkage and cable settings.

## 31 Automatic transmission selector lever linkage – adjustment

### Model 35, cable operated, early type

1    Disconnect the cable at the transmission end from beneath the car.
2    Place the selector lever at N, and the transmission lever in the N position (move it fully forward to P then back two clicks to N).
3    Set the adjuster at the lower end of the cable to the mid position, then adjust the upper end so that the cable can be connected to the transmission lever (see Fig. 6.24).
4    Check the operation of the lever in all its positions.

### Model 35, rod operated, early type

5    Remove the cover plate on the right-hand side of the floor tunnel for access to the adjustment nuts.
6    Referring to Fig. 6.26, check, that if the lever (5) has a nut (6) at its lower end, this nut is tight.
7    Disconnect the adjustable rod (4) from the lever (5) and put the lever to the D position (move it fully backwards to P then forward three clicks to D).
8    Put the selector lever (1) at D, then adjust the rod (4) so that when it is reconnected to the transmission lever, the centre of the pin (2) is central in the slot of the lever (3) into which the pin engages, when the selector lever (1) is moved to the right. The rod adjustment (4) has a right- and left-hand thread.
9    Support the rod and tighten the locknuts. Move the selector lever to L to reach the rear locknut.
10   Check the operation of the lever in all its positions.

### Model 35, rod operated, later type

11   Referring to Fig. 6.27, loosen the nut (1). Place the selector lever to D position.
12   Move the lever (3) at the front end of the connecting rod (2) fully rearwards to the P position, then forward three clicks to D.

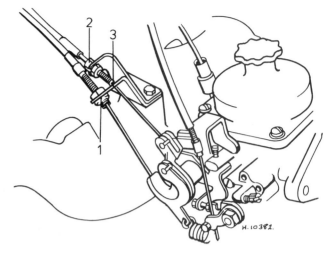

Fig. 6.21 Automatic transmission type BW45 – single carburettor throttle and downshift cable adjustments (Sec 29)

> 1   Throttle cable adjustment
> 2   Downshift cable adjustment
> 3   Clearance at crimped stop

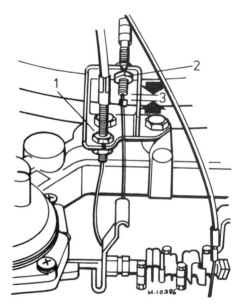

Fig. 6.22 Automatic transmission type BW45 – twin carburettor throttle and downshift cable adjustment (Sec 29)

> 1   Throttle cable adjustment
> 2   Downshift cable adjustment
> 3   Clearance at crimped stop

13   Hold the selector lever fully backwards in D and tighten the nut (1).
14   Check the operation of the lever in all its positions.

### Model 35, cable operated, later type

15   Referring to Fig. 6.28, place the selector lever (5) at D, then remove the clevis (2) from the lever (1).
16   Slacken the cable clamp bolts (3), then move the lever (1) fully forwards to P and then three clicks backwards to D.
17   Reconnect the clevis, then push the outer cable forward to take up any cable slackness. Tighten the clamp bolts to position the clamp in the elongated holes.

### Model 45

18   Place the selector lever at P, then loosen the self-locking nuts securing the transmission lever to the selector rod (Fig. 6.29).

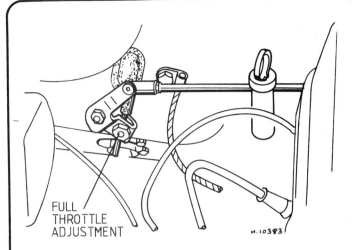

Fig. 6.23 Automatic transmission type BW35 – full throttle adjustment (Sec 29)

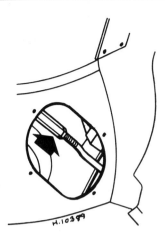

Fig. 6.25 Automatic transmission type BW35 – selector rod adjustment position – early type (Sec 31)

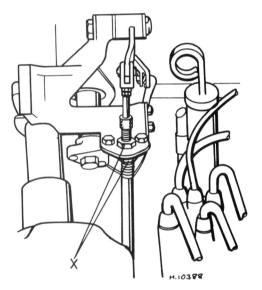

Fig. 6.24 Automatic transmission type BW35 – selector cable adjustment position (X) – early cable type (Sec 31)

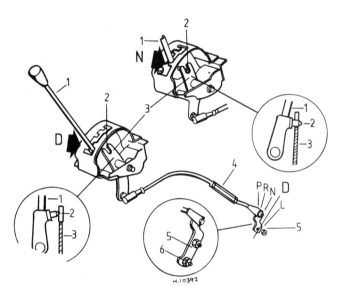

Fig. 6.26 Automatic transmission type BW35 – selector rod layout – early type – see text (Sec 31)

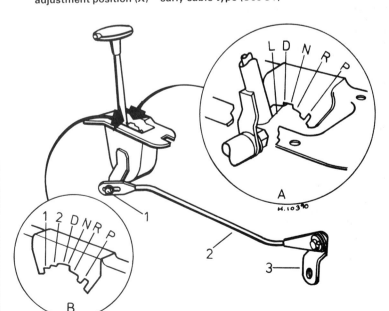

Fig. 6.27 Automatic transmission type BW35 – selector rod arrangements – later type – see text (Sec 31)

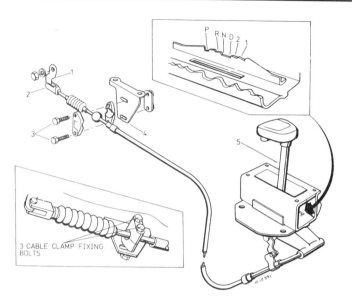

Fig. 6.28 Automatic transmission type BW35 – selector linkage adjustment – later cable type – see text (Sec 31)

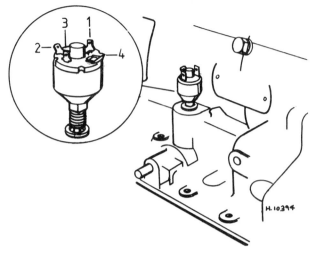

Fig. 6.30 Starter inhibitor switch – vertical type (note terminal numbers) (Sec 32)

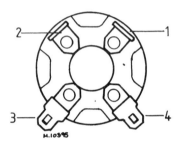

Fig. 6.31 Wiring connections BW35 – early switch (Sec 32)

*Terminals 1 and 2 – inhibitor*
*Terminals 3 and 4 – reversing light*

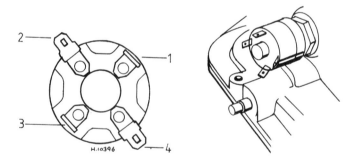

Fig. 6.32 Wiring connections BW35 – later switch, mounted vertically or horizontally (Sec 32)

*Terminals 1 and 3 – inhibitor*
*Terminals 2 and 4 – reversing light*

## 32 Automatic transmission – starter inhibitor/reversing light switch

### Model 35

1   Remove the existing switch by unscrewing, after removing the electrical connections. (Note the terminal numbers and refer to the table at the end of this section, to ensure that they are refitted correctly, since different types of switch have been used. The latest type of switch can be used to replace the earlier types, whether mounted vertically or horizontally).

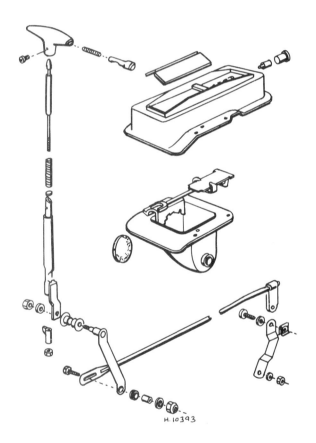

Fig. 6.29 Automatic transmission type BW45 – selector lever linkage (Sec 31)

19   Move the external lever on the transmission fully rearwards into its detent, then support the rod lightly and tighten the self-locking nut.
20   Check the operation of the lever in all its positions, and ensure that the key start only occurs with the selector lever in N or P.

2    Select P, then ensure that the washer is on the replacement switch. Apply a little non-setting gasket sealant on the switch screw threads, then screw the switch into the transmission. Use a spanner of about 4 in (10 cm) in length and tighten until just tight to avoid stripping the switch threads.

3    Fit the electrical leads and check that the engine will only start with N or P selected. Also check that the reverse lights operate with R selected.

**Wiring connections – inhibitor**

| | |
|---|---|
| *Early switch* | *Terminals 1 and 2 (adjacent)* |
| *Later switch, vertical or horizontal mounting* | *Terminals 1 and 3 (opposite)* |

**Wiring connections – reverse light**

| | |
|---|---|
| *Early switch* | *Terminals 3 and 4 (adjacent)* |
| *Later switch. vertical or horizontal mounting* | *Terminals 2 and 4 (opposite)* |

*Model 45*

4    Identify the switch wires, then remove them from the switch.

5    Remove the single retaining screw, then slide the switch off the cross-shaft.

6    Refitting is the reverse of the removal procedure.

## 33 Automatic transmission – removal and refitting

This operation is detailed in Chapter 1 of this Manual.

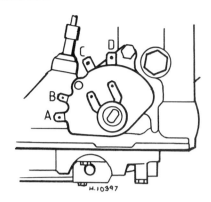

**Fig. 6.33 Wiring connections BW45 (Sec 32)**

*A – Green*            *C – White/red*
*B – Green/brown*      *D – White/red*

## 34 Fault diagnosis – automatic transmission

1    Fault finding on automatic transmissions is not easily translated into do-it-yourself terms and will inevitably require the use of special knowledge and equipment for rectification.

2    In the event of troubles occurring it is best to consult a main dealer or an automatic transmission specialist.

# Chapter 7 Propeller shaft

## Contents

General description ........................................................... 1
Routine maintenance ....................................................... 2
Single-piece propeller shaft – removal and refitting ...................... 3
Two-piece propeller shaft centre bearing – removal and

refitting ......................................................................... 5
Two-piece propeller shaft – removal and refitting ......................... 4
Universal joints – dismantling, and fitting new bearings ............... 7
Universal joints and splines – inspection and repair ..................... 6

## Specifications

**Type** ........................................................................... Tubular, single piece, with or without bonded rubber damper. Alternatively, divided type with rubber-mounted centre bearing

**Universal joints** ........................................................ Sealed needle roller bearings

### Torque wrench settings
*Propeller shaft (split)*

| | lbf ft | Nm |
|---|---|---|
| Coupling to front shaft nut ........................................... | 90 | 122 |
| Propeller shaft front to propeller shaft rear ........................... | 17 | 23 |
| Centre bearing to brackets ........................................... | 12 | 16 |

## 1 General description

1 Engine power is transferred from the engine to the rear axle and wheels through the gearbox and a rotating propeller shaft.
2 Variations of dimension between the engine/gearbox unit and the rear axle are compensated for by the splined sleeve at the forward end. Misalignment between the centrelines of the gearbox output shaft and the rear axle are absorbed by the universal joints at each end of the shaft.
3 The splines are lubricated from the gearbox and the universal joints are pre-packed with grease on assembly and should need no further attention.

## 2 Routine maintenance

No specific maintenance is necessary. Examine the universal joints from time to time for signs of wear.

## 3 Single-piece propeller shaft – removal and refitting

1 Jack up the rear of the car or position it over a pit or ramp. If jacked up, support the body side members with proper stands.
2 If the rear wheels are off the ground it will be necessary to apply the handbrake or engage a gear whilst undoing the pinion flange bolts. Otherwise the propeller shaft will turn.
3 Mark the relationship of the two flanges to each other with a file notch or punch mark and then undo the four nuts and bolts. Before removing the last one, make sure the propeller shaft will not drop on your head and also place a container under the rear end of the gearbox extension cover to catch any oil drips (photo).
4 Move the shaft forward a little to disengage the flange register, then lower it and draw the front end from the gearbox. Do not let the sleeve or its internal splines get damaged or contaminated with grit in any way (photo).
5 Refitting is a reversal of the removal procedure. Make sure the sleeve end is a good fit on the splines with no backlash (if there is any it may mean renewal of both the sleeve and gearbox mainshaft). The oil seal in the gearbox rear cover should be in good condition (see

Chapter 6). The mating marks of the flanges should be lined up to their previous positions.

## 4 Two-piece propeller shaft – removal and refitting

1 As the two-piece shaft with its centre bearing is rather an unwieldy object, it is better to remove the rear portion of the shaft first.
2 Jack up the rear of the car, or position the rear of the car over a pit or ramp.
3 If the rear wheels are off the ground, place the car in gear and put the handbrake on, to ensure the propeller shaft does not turn when an attempt is made to loosen the four nuts securing the propeller shaft to the rear axle.
4 The propeller shaft is carefully balanced to fine limits and it is important for it to be refitted in exactly the same position as it was prior to removal. Scratch a mark on the propeller shaft and rear axle flanges and on the flanges at the front end of the rear portion, to ensure accurate mating when the time comes to reassemble.
5 Unscrew the four self-locking nuts, bolts and securing washers which hold the flanges together at either end, and lower the rear portion from the car.
6 Place a can or tray under the rear of the gearbox or overdrive extension to catch any oil that may leak out when the front of the propeller shaft is drawn out.
7 Undo the bolts holding the centre bearing assembly to its mounting bracket and draw it to the rear, complete with the front portion of the propeller shaft.
8 Refitting the propeller shaft is a reversal of the above procedure. Make sure that the mating marks made on the rear portion line up correctly.

## 5 Two-piece propeller shaft centre bearing – removal and refitting

1 Mark the coupling and the front half of the propeller shaft to ensure the shaft goes onto the same splines in the rear coupling on reassembly.
2 Undo the self-locking nut holding the front portion of the propeller shaft in the rear coupling, then withdraw the shaft and remove the

3.3 Removing propeller shaft flange bolts

3.4 Disengaging propeller shaft from gearbox extension

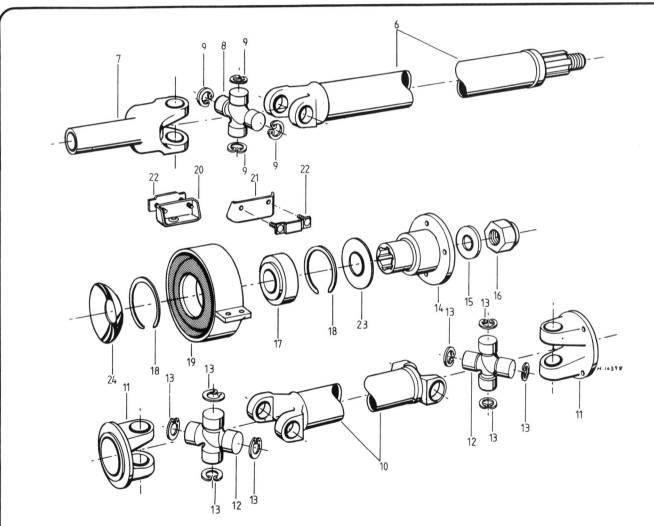

Fig. 7.1 Two-piece propeller shaft and centre bearing assembly – exploded view (Sec 4)

| | | | | | | | |
|---|---|---|---|---|---|---|---|
| 6 | Front portion shaft | 11 | Flange | 16 | Self-locking nut | 21 | Bracket |
| 7 | Sleeve and yoke | 12 | Spider | 17 | Centre bearing | 22 | Plate and studs |
| 8 | Spider | 13 | Circlips | 18 | Circlip | 23 | Dust shield |
| 9 | Circlips | 14 | Coupling | 19 | Bearing housing | 24 | Water shield |
| 10 | Rear portion shaft | 15 | Washer | 20 | Bracket | | |

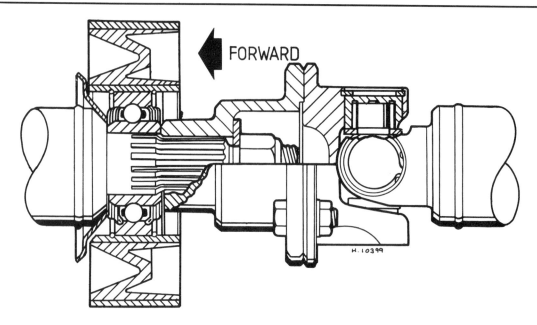

**Fig. 7.2 Centre bearing assembly – sectional view (Sec 5)**

water shield from the front of the bearing housing and the dust seal from the rear.

3   Remove the circlips from their grooves in the bearing housing from either side of the bearing; then press out the bearing.

4   To refit the bearing, fit one of the circlips in its groove, press the bearing up to it, then fit the other circlip to lock it in position. Both sides of the bearing should now be packed with a waterproof sealing compound.

5   Reassembly from now on is a direct reversal of the removal procedure. The points which follow should be checked, to confirm that assembly is correct.

6   The centre bearing rubber must be facing in the direction indicated in Fig. 7.2.

7   The single bolt fixing of the centre bearing mounting must be on the right-hand side of the vehicle.

8   Correctly preload the bonded support by positioning the centre bearing so that a gap is left between the front and rear shaft flanges of 0.180 to 0.200 in (4.50 to 5.10 mm) in the static unladen condition. Then fit the bolts to secure the flanges. If necessary, the correct preload may be achieved by elongating the bolt holes in the appropriate direction.

9   Ensure the three yokes welded to the propeller shafts are all in line.

10  Ensure that flange marks, made before dismantling, coincide when assembly is complete.

---

### 6   Universal joints and splines – inspection and repair

1   Wear in the needle roller bearings is indicated by vibration or 'clunks' in the transmission, particularly when the drive is being taken up or when going to overrun. Backlash in the rear axle has the same effect so check that too if symptoms occur.

2   It is easy to check the needle roller bearings whilst the propeller shaft is still in position. Try to turn the shaft with one hand and grip the flange or sleeve on the other side of the joint with the other hand. There should be no movement between the two. If there is any, the bearings will need renewal.

3   The splines of the sliding sleeve should be a smooth sliding fit on the gearbox mainshaft and no trace of rotational backlash should be apparent. If there is any serious backlash the repair could be costly as both the gearbox mainshaft and the sleeve may need renewal

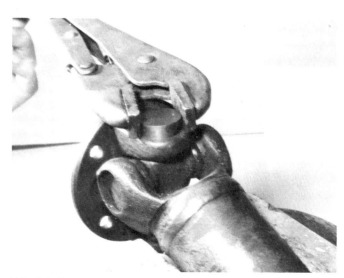

7.2a Gripping and removing a cup

7.2b Joint being separated

7.3a Universal joint kit

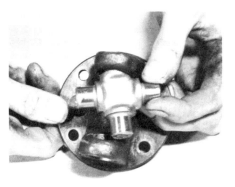

7.3b Entering the spider in flanges

7.3c Starting a cup in a flange

7.3d Pressing a cup into position

7.3e Spider entered in yokes on the propeller shaft, and a cup being pressed in

7.3f Checking for freedom of movement before finally fitting all the circlips

(although a new sleeve only may suffice). Any significant signs of ridging on the outer surface of the sleeve may be the cause of oil leaks from the rear of the gearbox and a new seal may not be sufficient to rectify the trouble. Much depends on the degree of wear apparent and the owner will have to decide whether a new sleeve is worthwhile.

## 7   Universal joints – dismantling, and fitting new bearings

1   Clean away all traces of dirt from the whole assembly. Mark the yokes to facilitate reassembly. Remove the circlips which hold each set of needle roller bearings in position. If the circlip is tight, tap the face of the bearing cup inside it which may be jamming it in its groove.
2   The bearing should come out if the edges of the yoke ears are tapped with a mallet. If, however, they are very tight it should be possible to shift them, pressing them between the jaws of a vice using two distance pieces. Two different size socket spanners are ideal and it will be possible to force one out sufficiently far to enable it to be gripped by another suitable tool (pliers or vice again) and drawn out. Take care not to damage the yokes. If the bearings are seized up or worn so badly that the holes in the yokes are oval then a new yoke will be needed – and if this is on the propeller shaft then that will have to be acquired too as the whole assembly is balanced.
3   New bearings will be supplied with new seals and circlips. Make sure the needles are correctly in positon, and the cup $\frac{1}{3}$ full of grease. Put the gaskets and retainers on the four journals of the spider. Reassemble to the marks made when dismantling. Press each cup through the yoke onto the spider journal. Fit all four on one joint before putting the circlips in position and make sure everything moves freely (photos).

# Chapter 8  Rear axle

## Contents

Differential carrier − removal and refitting ........................................ 4
Differential, crownwheel and pinion − overhaul ............................. 5
Fault diagnosis − rear axle ................................................................ 7
General description ............................................................................. 1

Halfshafts, bearings and oil seals − removal and refitting ............. 3
Rear axle − removal and refitting ...................................................... 6
Routine maintenance ......................................................................... 2

## Specifications

**Type** ............................................................................................ Semi-floating, hypoid bevel gears

### Bearings
Pinion .............................................................................................. Taper roller
Differential crownwheel assembly ............................................... Taper roller
Hub ................................................................................................... Ball

### Adjustment
Hypoid bevel pinion ........................................................................ Shims
Differential assembly ..................................................................... Shims
Crownwheel to pinion (backlash) .................................................. 0.005 to 0.009 in (0.127 to 0.229 mm)

### Number of teeth

|  | 4.22:1 | 3.89:1 | 3.70:1 |
|---|---|---|---|
| Crownwheel | 38 | 35 | 37 |
| Pinion | 9 | 9 | 10 |

*All engines except Holbay*
**Final drive ratios** ........................................................

### Overall ratios

|  | 4.22:1 | | 3.89:1 | | 3.70:1 | |
|---|---|---|---|---|---|---|
|  | Standard gearbox | Close ratio gearbox | Standard gearbox | Close ratio gearbox | Standard gearbox | Close ratio gearbox |
| Top (overdrive) | − | 3.39 | 3.12 | 3.12 | − | − |
| Top | 4.22 | 4.22 | 3.89 | 3.89 | 3.70 | 3.70 |
| Third (overdrive) | − | 4.39 | 4.35 | 4.05 | − | − |
| Third | 5.87 | 5.47 | 5.41 | 5.04 | 5.15 | 4.80 |
| Second | 9.04 | 8.42 | 8.32 | 7.75 | 7.92 | 7.37 |
| First | 14.16 | 13.18 | 13.04 | 12.14 | 12.41 | 11.55 |
| Reverse | 15.07 | 14.03 | 13.88 | 12.92 | 13.20 | 12.30 |

*Holbay engine*
**Final drive ratios** ........................................................

### Overall ratios

|  | 3.70:1 | 3.89:1 |
|---|---|---|
| Top (overdrive) | − | 3.10:1 |
| Top | 3.70:1 | 3.89:1 |
| Third (overdrive) | − | 4.02:1 |
| Third | 4.79:1 | 5.04:1 |
| Second | 7.37:1 | 7.75:1 |
| First | 11.55:1 | 12.14:1 |
| Reverse | 12.29:1 | 12.92:1 |

**Fluid Capacity** ......................................................................... 1.75 pints (2.1 US pints, 1 litre)

### Torque wrench settings

|  | lbf ft | Nm |
|---|---|---|
| Pinion nut | 110 | 149 |
| Axleshaft nut | 190 | 258 |
| Crownwheel bolts | 47 | 64 |
| Differential bearing cap nuts | 52 | 71 |
| Differential housing to casing | 11 | 15 |

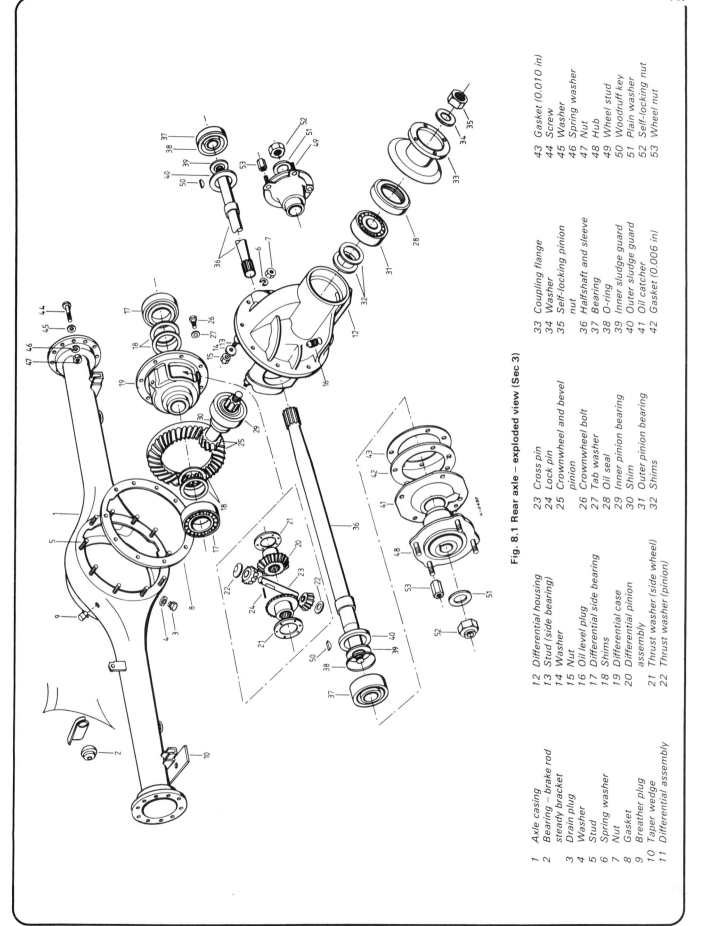

**Fig. 8.1 Rear axle – exploded view (Sec 3)**

1 Axle casing
2 Bearing – brake rod steady bracket
3 Drain plug
4 Washer
5 Stud
6 Spring washer
7 Nut
8 Gasket
9 Breather plug
10 Taper wedge
11 Differential assembly

12 Differential housing
13 Stud (side bearing)
14 Washer
15 Nut
16 Oil level plug
17 Differential side bearing
18 Shims
19 Differential case
20 Differential pinion assembly
21 Thrust washer (side wheel)
22 Thrust washer (pinion)

23 Cross pin
24 Lock pin
25 Crownwheel and bevel pinion
26 Crownwheel bolt
27 Tab washer
28 Oil seal
29 Inner pinion bearing
30 Shim
31 Outer pinion bearing
32 Shims

33 Coupling flange
34 Washer
35 Self-locking pinion nut
36 Halfshaft and sleeve
37 Bearing
38 O-ring
39 Inner sludge guard
40 Outer sludge guard
41 Oil catcher
42 Gasket (0.006 in)

43 Gasket (0.010 in)
44 Screw
45 Washer
46 Spring washer
47 Nut
48 Hub
49 Wheel stud
50 Woodruff key
51 Plain washer
52 Self-locking nut
53 Wheel nut

## 1  General description

The rear axle is of the semi-floating type incorporating a hypoid crownwheel and pinion with a two-pinion differential. The crownwheel and pinion and differential are mounted as an assembly in the differential carrier, and this is bolted to the front of the banjo type axle housing. This means that the axle does not have to be disturbed in order to remove and examine the differential and final drive.

## 2  Routine maintenance

1  Every 5000 miles remove the level plug located in the right-hand horizontal web of the differential casing. The oil should be level with the bottom of the threads in the hole and in order to see this the use of a hand mirror will help. Top-up with the recommended oil as required.
2  The rear axle is described by the manufacturer as 'fitted for life', and oil changes are not normally necessary. If oil contamination has occurred, however, the level/filler plug and the drain plug should be removed, preferably after a run, and the oil allowed to drain out. Refill with the correct oil to the height of the level plug, after first refitting the drain plug. Refit the level plug.
3  Check the breather plug is clear when checking the oil level.

## 3  Halfshafts, bearings and oil seals – removal and refitting

1  The halfshafts may be withdrawn without disturbing the differential gear. They are removed in order to renew the bearings or oil seals, or if the differential is to be removed. Read the whole of this Section before starting work.
2  Jack up the car at the rear and support it firmly on proper stands. Remove the rear wheels, free the handbrake and remove the brake drums (see Chapter 9).
3  Remove the clevis pin from the handbrake linkage and disconnect the hydraulic brake pipe from the wheel cylinder (see Chapter 9).
4  Remove the nuts and bolts securing the oil catcher plate and brake backplate to the axle casing flange. The halfshaft hub, bearing and backplate are now held in position as an assembly by the fit of the outer race of the bearing into the axle casing. Ideally the use of a proper impact hammer removal tool is needed to draw the assembly out. This consists of a flange which bolts to the wheel studs and to which is fitted a long shaft extension with a sliding weight on it. The sliding weight is hit against a flange at the extremity of the shaft and this draws the axle out. Whatever you do, this principle – of attaching a suitable bracket and striking point to the wheel studs – must be followed. *No part of the axle assembly itself must be struck.* A sustained pull is also quite ineffective and will probably only result in heaving the car off the stands. So get something suitable organised in advance or you will be wasting your time. One possibility is to use an old wheel rim bolted to the studs and then strike it from the inside with something suitably heavy. the success or otherwise of this method depends on access and the ability to get a good swing at it. Whatever method is used the car should be firmly supported.
5  It is essential that proper facilities are also available if the bearing/oil seal is to be renewed. The bearing has to be drawn off the outer end of the shaft. First, therefore, the hub has to be removed. It is held by a nut on to a keyed taper at the end of the shaft. A proper puller to get this off is essential otherwise the end of the shaft may be damaged. The bearing may then be pulled off, also using a suitable tool which can bear on the end of the shaft and pull against the inner race of the bearing. A keen owner may be able to make up a suitable puller, but the time and effort involved should be weighed against the advantage of handing the shaft to someone with the necessary equipment for fitting a new bearing.
6  Behind the bearing is a very tight fitting sleeve round the shaft. This serves to grip the bearing inner race against the hub. When the bearing is removed, therefore, the sleeve has to be moved about $\frac{1}{32}$ in (1 mm) towards the outer end of the shaft so that when a new bearing is pressed on, the hub will finally be drawn up against the bearing and the bearing will force the sleeve back. The force needed will be sufficient to grip the inner race of the bearing. It will be seen, therefore, that to attempt this work with nothing more than a hammer, chisel and hope will be almost certainly doomed to failure.
7  When fitting the new bearing (having first moved the sleeve into

position on the shaft) make sure the inner sludge guard is fitted to the shaft first, and the oil seal, which is incorporated in the bearing, faces inwards. The bearing should be pressed on until the sludge plate is just held between the inner race and sleeve on the shaft – no further. Then put the backplate and dust cover in position followed by the hub. When the hub is drawn on with the nut the bearing will be finally moved into position as required. Tighten the nut to the torque figure quoted in the Specifications.
8  When refitting the halfshaft, the splines at the inner end should first pick up the splines in the differential side gears. Then enter the bearing into the axle casing recess until the outer edge of the race is nearly flush with the casing. Then bolt up the back plate evenly, which will draw the bearing completely into position.
9  Reconnect the hydraulic pipe and handbrake linkage, refit the brake drum and bleed the brakes.

## 4  Differential carrier – removal and refitting

1  Jack up the car and support it on stands as for halfshaft removal. Drain the oil from the back axle by removing the drain plug. The halfshaft should then be removed sufficiently far for the inner ends to disengage from the differential side pinions. The propeller shaft should then be dismantled from the rear axle pinion flange. It is not necessary to draw it out from the gearbox provided it can be conveniently rested out of the way on one side.
2  Undo the ten nuts and washers holding the differential carrier to the casing. The whole unit can then be drawn forward off the studs and taken out.
3  When refitting the assembly ensure the mating faces are perfectly clean and free from burrs. A new gasket coated with sealing compound should also be used. Otherwise, refitting is a reversal of the removal operation.

## 5  Differential, crownwheel and pinion – overhaul

1  At some point in the life of a rear axle, an owner is faced with the need to cure either a severe backlash or an unacceptable whine or noise level. Such symptoms usually indicate worn bearings coupled with worn gears to a varying degree. Due to the fact that rebuilding and setting up a differential assembly is a specialised job, calling for training and experience, any owner contemplating such work should first seriously consider the relative economics of obtaining parts and rebuilding (with the possibility of an unsuccessful result) compared with obtaining a complete assembly. The work of overhauling the unit must definitely be considered to be outside the scope of the average owner.
2  If the pinion oil seal is leaking, a new one may be fitted after first removing the pinion nut and flange. The old seal may be dug out with a pointed tool, taking care not to damage the casing. A new one should be sealed on refitting with compound on the outside and pressed on the inner lip. These oil seals rarely fail and if one does then it is likely that the pinion bearings have also failed. In such cases the fitting of a new seal would be a waste of time.

## 6  Rear axle – removal and refitting

1  Removal of the rear axle should be a rare occurrence and the most likely reason is if the differential unit is faulty. Possibly a replacement assembly obtained from a breaker is being fitted complete, rather than just the differential assembly.
2  Jack up the rear of the car and support the body under the side frame, allowing the axle and springs to hang free. Remove the wheels.
3  Disconnect the propeller shaft (see Chapter 7) and the dampers at their lower mountings only (see Chapter 11).
4  Disconnect the handbrake linkage at both hubs and from the bracket on the axle casing. Also disconnect the hydraulic flexible brake hose coupling at the union with the rigid pipe (not at the three way connector) (see Chapter 9). Protect the ends of the fluid lines from dirt.
5  Remove all the U-bolts clamping the axle to the springs and then withdraw the axle from one side between the springs and the body.
6  When refitting the axle, make sure it is correctly located with the correct spring seats and clamps in position (see Chapter 11) and tighten the U-bolt nuts to the correct torque figure. Reconnect the handbrake linkage and hydraulic lines and bleed the hydraulic system.

## 7 Fault diagnosis – rear axle

| Symptom | Reason(s) |
| --- | --- |
| Vibration | Worn axleshaft bearing<br>Loose pinion flange bolts<br>Roadwheels out of balance<br>Propeller shaft out of balance |
| Noise on turns | Worn differential gears<br>Worn or incorrectly adjusted crownwheel and pinion |
| 'Clunk' on acceleration or deceleration | Excessive backlash in differential gears<br>Worn axleshaft splines<br>Worn propeller shaft joints<br>Loose pinion flange bolts |

# Chapter 9 Braking system

## Contents

Brake drums and shoes – removal, inspection and refitting ......... 5
Brake pedal – removal and refitting ....................................... 14
Disc calliper – removal, inspection, repair and refitting ................. 9
Disc pads – removal, inspection and refitting .......................... 3
Discs – removal, inspection and refitting ................................. 4
Dual braking system – general description ........................ 16
Dual hydraulic system – bleeding ........................................ 19
Fault diagnosis – braking system ........................................ 20
General description ........................................................ 1
Handbrake – adjustment and cable renewal ........................... 6
Hydraulic fluid pipes – removal, inspection and refitting .............. 7

Hydraulic system – bleeding ............................................. 13
Hydraulic wheel cylinders (rear) – inspection and repair .............. 8
Master cylinder (single circuit system) – dismantling, overhaul
and reassembly ........................................................... 11
Master cylinder (single circuit system) – removal and refitting .... 10
Pressure failure switch – overhaul ....................................... 18
Routine maintenance ...................................................... 2
Servo unit – removal, overhaul and refitting ........................... 12
Stop light switch ........................................................... 15
Tandem master cylinder and pressure failure switch – removal,
overhaul and refitting ..................................................... 17

## Specifications

### Brake diameters
Front disc ................................................................... 9.6 in (24.4 cm)
Rear drum .................................................................. 9.0 in (22.9 cm)

### Rear cylinder bore
Non-servo cars and cars fitted with accessory servo kit ....................... 0.75 in (19.05 mm)
Servo-assisted cars:
    Up to 7 Series ........................................................ 0.75 in (19.05 mm)
    7 Series onwards .................................................... 0.625 in (15.88 mm)

### Master cylinder bore ........................................... 0.75 in (19.05 mm)

### Calliper cylinder bore ......................................... 2.125 in (53.975 mm)

### Maximum disc run-out ......................................... 0.004 in (0.10 mm)

### Servo (if fitted) ................................................... Lockheed type 6

### Torque wrench settings

|  | lbf ft | Nm |
| --- | --- | --- |
| Disc to hub | 32 | 43 |
| Calliper to stub axle carrier | 60 | 81 |
| Backplate to axle casing | 18 | 24 |
| Bleed screws: |  |  |
|   Front | 9 | 12 |
|   Rear | 2 | 3 |
| Union nuts (male and female) | 8 | 11 |

## 1 General description

All models are fitted with Lockheed disc brakes at the front and drum brakes and shoes at the rear. All are hydraulically operated by the foot pedal and the independent handbrake operates the rear drum brakes only by an independent mechanical linkage. No adjustment to the brakes is necessary as the pistons for the disc pads move forward automatically (without retracting) as the pads wear. The hydraulic fluid in the system is automatically increased from the reservoir as the capacity increases when the pistons move forward. The rear brake shoes are automatically adjusted by a mechanical ratchet which restricts retraction as the linings wear.

The retraction of the pistons which force the pads against the discs is a frictional reaction and is governed only by the minute distortion of the fluid seal in the bore of the cylinder. The rear shoes however are spring retracted and the override ratchet device holds them closer to the drums as the linings wear. The ratchet is operated and takes up as needed each time the brakes are applied.

## 2 Routine maintenance

1 Every week, remove the hydraulic fluid reservoir cap, having made sure it is clean. Check the level of the fluid which should be just below the bottom of the filler neck. Check also that the vent hole in the cap is clear. Any need for regular topping-up, regardless of quantity, should be viewed with suspicion and the whole hydraulic system carefully checked for signs of leakage.
2 Every 5000 miles the brake pads and shoes should be examined to check the thickness of friction lining material remaining. Rear shoe linings should be renewed when the material has almost reached the level of the rivet heads. If the rivets ever rub on the drums they will cause scoring and reduced braking efficiency. The disc pads should be

renewed when minimum thickness is $\frac{1}{8}$ in (3 mm). If one pad shows signs of wear more than another they may be changed over to the other side of the disc (on some earlier models only). At the same time as friction material is examined the hydraulic pipes and unions should be examined for any signs of damage or corrosion. Brake lining wear varies according to driving style but no set of disc pads should be expected to last more than 15 000 miles. The rear brake shoe linings will probably last half as long again. Make sure the handbrake functions properly at all times.

3   Every 10 000 miles remove the air filter from the servo unit (if fitted) and clean or renew it.

4   Every 25 000 miles it is good policy to renew all hydraulic cylinder seals as a matter of routine, together with the fluid and flexible hoses. Any repair work in the interval should also, of course, be taken into account.

5   If you have just acquired a secondhand car, it is strongly recommended that all brake drums, pads, shoes and discs are thoroughly examined for condition and wear immediately. Even though braking efficiency may be excellent the friction materials could be nearing the end of their useful life and it is as well to know this without delay. Similarly, the hydraulic cylinders, pipes and connections should be carefully examined for leaks or chafing. Faults should be rectified immediately. It should be remembered that in the UK, three year old or older vehicles are subject to annual safety tests. Apart from safety, which is paramount, defects in the system, even though they may not yet affect stopping power, will possibly cause the vehicle to fail the test.

## 3   Disc pads – removal, inspection and refitting

1   If the brake pads have worn down to a friction material thickness of $\frac{1}{8}$ in (3 mm) they should be renewed as soon as possible. If one pad is worn on one side of the disc more than the other (this often happens – the inner pad wears faster) it was in order in some early models to change them over; provided, of course, neither has reached the minimum permissible thickness. However, later models and replacement pads are 'handed'. The pads are identified by a rectangular cut-away portion in the trailing edge of the plate. These pads cannot be moved to the other side of the same disc although they can be moved to the same position on the other disc. In order to check pad thickness, jack up the car and remove the wheel. The edge of the pad will then be visible in the calliper which is mounted on the forward side of the disc.

2   To remove the pads, depress the steady springs to relieve the pressure on the split pins and draw out the split pins. If the pads are then rotated upwards a little they can be eased out of the calliper.

3   When fitting new pads it will be necessary to ease the pistons back into their bores to accommodate the thicker material. First examine the fluid reservoir, because when the pistons move back the level will rise and it should not be allowed to overflow. Then move the pistons back by exerting steady pressure with a flat blade between piston head and disc. At the same time check that the anti-squeal cut-out portion of the piston crown is across the line of disc rotation on the lead inside, ie upwards in this instance. If it is not, rotate the piston

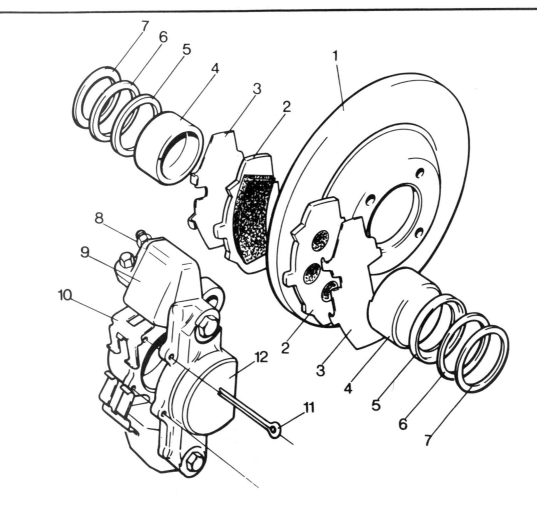

Fig. 9.1 Disc brake – exploded view (earlier models with shims) (Sec 3)

| | | | |
|---|---|---|---|
| 1   Disc | 4   Pistons | 7   Fluid seals | 10   Steady springs |
| 2   Brake pads | 5   Dust seal retainer | 8   Bleed nipple | 11   Split pins |
| 3   Anti-squeal shims | 6   Dust seals | 9   Inner half of calliper | 12   Outer half of calliper |

carefully until it is. Where the later type pads are fitted, without shims, the cut-out of the piston should be approximately angled at 25° from a line across the direction of disc travel.

4    When the gap is wide enough for the pads to go in, lead in the top edge first then hold the front lug and rotate the pad downwards so that it fits snugly in position. The shim plates (if used) should be slipped in between the pads and the pistons. (Note that later models and new pads have no shims). Place the steady springs in position with the longer legs facing each other and refit the split pins, spreading the ends a little to keep them in position.

5    Operate the brake pedal until firm pressure is felt. Then rotate the wheel to ensure that no binding is taking place (although the pads may

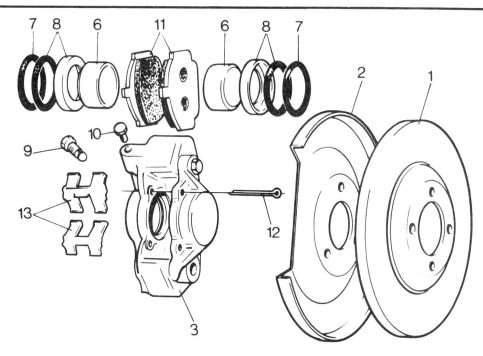

**Fig. 9.2 Disc brake – exploded view (later models without shims) (Sec 3)**

| | | | |
|---|---|---|---|
| 1  Disc | 6  Piston | 9  Bleed nipple | 12  Split pin |
| 2  Splash shield | 7  Fluid seal | 10  Plug | 13  Steady springs |
| 3  Calliper body | 8  Dust seal and retainer | 11  Pads | |

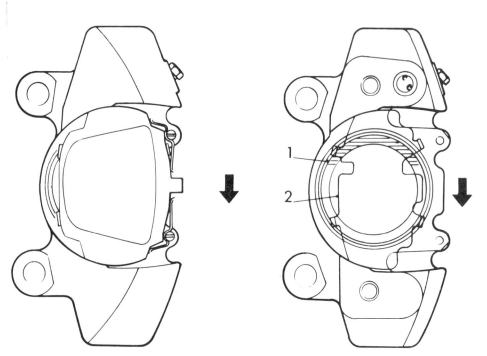

**Fig. 9.3 Calliper – section showing locations of pad, shim and piston cut-out (early models) (Sec 3)**

1    Cut-out                    2    Shim

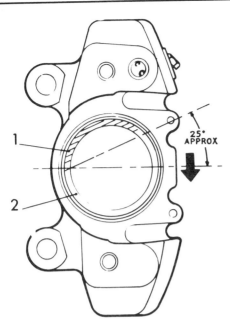

**Fig. 9.4 Calliper – section showing locations of pad and piston cut-out when new type pads are fitted to early models (Sec 3)**

*1   Piston cut-out*                     *2   Contact of piston to pad*

noticeably just touch the disc). Always fit new pads of the correct specification and if a different type must be used make sure it applies to both front wheels.

## 4   Discs – removal, inspection and refitting

1   Brake discs rarely give trouble but very severe use in unusually wet or dirty conditions may cause distortion or scoring. If it does not run true the performance of the brakes can be seriously affected. The amount of 'out-of-true' or run-out should not exceed 0.004 in (0.10 mm).
2   To check the discs, jack up the car and first make sure the hub bearing is in good condition. It may be necessary to tighten the bearing nut to eliminate any play which could exist due to the castellations of the nut and split pin position.
3   If a dial gauge micrometer is mounted against the surface of the disc while turning it, the amount of run-out can be measured. After checking, re-adjust the hub bearing (see Chapter 11). If the disc is heavily scored or damaged it should be renewed.
4   A damaged disc should only be reground as a last resort if no replacement is available. It will cost about the same if done properly. A maximum of 0.010 in (0.25 mm) may be removed from each side, each side must be ground off equally, and the maximum run-out between mounting and rubbing faces is 0.002 in (0.05 mm). Rubbing faces must be parallel to 0.001 in (0.025 mm). After grinding, the dimensions given in Fig. 9.5 should apply.
5   To remove a disc, first take off the calliper assembly (it is not necessary to disturb the hydraulics) as described in Section 9. Then remove the hub (and disc with it) as described in Chapter 11 for renewal of front wheel bearings.
6   The disc may then be removed from the hub by undoing the four bolts and washers.

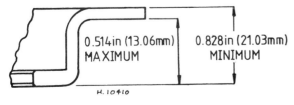

**Fig. 9.5 Brake disc – permissible machining dimensions (Sec 4)**

7   Fitting a disc is the reverse procedure, being careful to ensure that the mating faces of the disc and hub are perfectly clean and free from burrs or high spots. Wash off the protective coating from a new disc. Tighten the bolts evenly to the specified torque.
8   Refit the hub, adjust the bearing and refit the calliper. If the previous pads are being used allow time for bedding in before full braking efficiency is achieved.

## 5   Brake drums and shoes – removal, inspection and refitting

1   Jack up the car and remove the roadwheel. Block the front wheels and release the handbrake.
2   The drum is located over the four wheel studs and is positioned by a single countersunk screw into the hub which should be removed. The drum may then be pulled straight off the studs. If it seems stuck fast it will be due to binding at the roots of the wheel studs. A little easing fluid and a tap with a mallet on the edge should shift it. Do not hit the drum with a hammer as it is brittle and could easily fracture. It sometimes happens that very badly scored and worn drums can 'mesh' their grooves into the surface of the brake linings to such an extent that the drum cannot be pulled off; the automatic adjuster being inaccessible for release. On later models the mechanism can be reached and released by drilling a $\frac{5}{16}$ in hole at a radius of 2.55 in – opposite the locating screw. This is really rather a waste of time if the drum is to be renewed anyway. If you cannot actually break the drum to pieces with a hammer without risk of damaging the hub then cut it off – or cut nicks in it and try splitting it with a cold chisel. **Note:** *Wear eye protecting glasses when carrying out this operation.* If you cut into the shoes inside as well it does not matter as they are going to need renewal too.
3   With the drum removed, brush out any dust and examine the rubbing surface for any signs of pitting or deep scoring. The surface should be smooth and bright but minor hairline scores are of no consequence and could have been caused by grit or brake shoes with linings just worn to the rivets. A drum that is obviously badly worn should be renewed. A perfectly satisfactory replacement can often be obtained from a breakers yard. It is no economy having drums skimmed on a lathe (unless you can have it done for nothing). Also, as the radius is altered if the rubbing surfaces are machined out, standard shoes will not match properly until a lot of bedding in has taken place and re-radiused the linings.
4   The brake shoes should be examined next. There should be no signs of contamination by oil and the linings should be above the heads of the rivets. If the level is close (less than $\frac{1}{32}$ in) it is worth changing them. If there are signs of oil contamination they should be renewed, and the source of oil leakage found before it ruins the new ones as well.
5   To remove the shoes (having, of course, removed the drum) first detach the steady posts from the centre of each shoe. This can be done by holding the head with one pair of pliers and rotating the dished, slotted washer 90° so it unlocks from the post and comes off with the spring behind it.
6   Next note which holes the pull-off springs fit into in the shoes. Then lift the heel of each brake shoe (the end not on the hydraulic piston) against spring tension out of its slot on the backplate. This will relieve some of the tension and the other ends of the shoes can be similarly lifted out at the cylinder end. Take care that the piston does not come out. It can be retained adequately with a rubber band.
7   Ensure the wheel cylinder moves freely in the backplate slot. Remove, clean and check the outer piston. Lightly lubricate the slots in the tappet, wheel cylinder body and fixed abutment with high melting point grease. Lightly lubricate the tappet threads, adjuster wheel threads and body with molybdenum disulphide grease. Ensure the hydraulic piston moves freely and there are no fluid leaks. Be careful not to let the piston come right out of the cylinder or it will be necessary to bleed the brakes after it is put back.
8   To refit the shoes, first arrange them as shown in the drawing with the retractor springs hooked into the correct holes. The tappet should be screwed fully into the adjuster wheel, and then out again by two and a half turns. When the shoes are in position the adjuster wheel can be rotated to expand the shoes just far enough to allow the drum to be refitted. Refit the steady pins, springs and lockwashers. Centralise the shoes so that the drum will go on easily.
9   When the drum has been refitted operate the brakes to check that they do not bind. It is possible for light binding to occur initially, in which case they should be checked again after a few miles motoring.

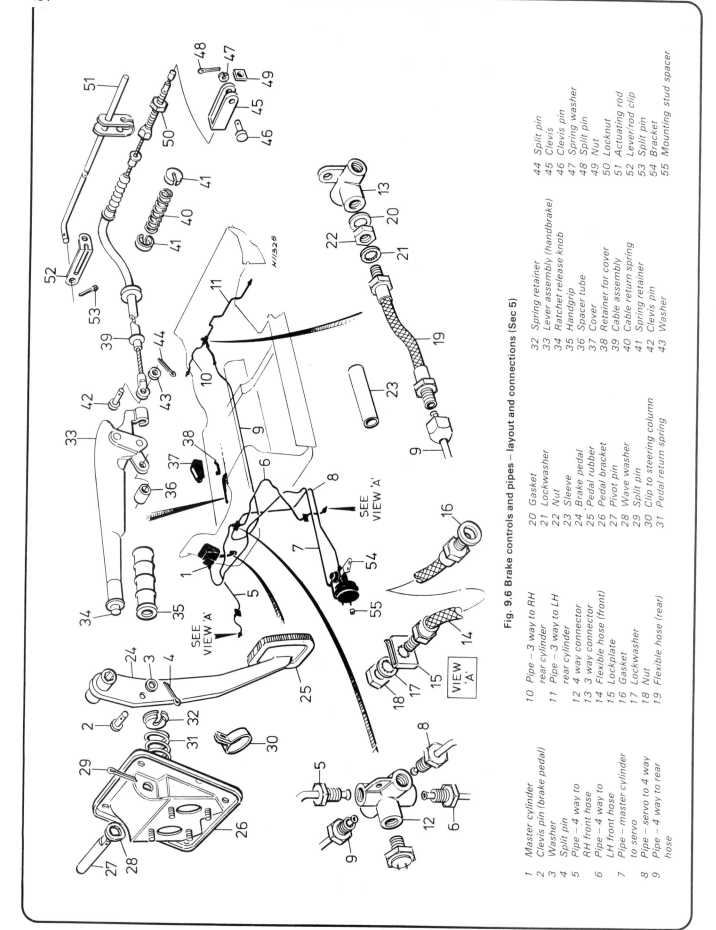

**Fig. 9.6 Brake controls and pipes – layout and connections (Sec 5)**

1 Master cylinder
2 Clevis pin (brake pedal)
3 Washer
4 Split pin
5 Pipe – 4 way to RH front hose
6 Pipe – 4 way to LH front hose
7 Pipe – master cylinder to servo
8 Pipe – servo to 4 way
9 Pipe – 4 way to rear hose
10 Pipe – 3 way to RH rear cylinder
11 Pipe – 3 way to LH rear cylinder
12 4 way connector
13 3 way connector
14 Flexible hose (front)
15 Lockplate
16 Gasket
17 Lockwasher
18 Nut
19 Flexible hose (rear)
20 Gasket
21 Lockwasher
22 Nut
23 Sleeve
24 Brake pedal
25 Pedal rubber
26 Pedal bracket
27 Pivot pin
28 Wave washer
29 Split pin
30 Clip to steering column
31 Pedal return spring
32 Spring retainer
33 Lever assembly (handbrake)
34 Ratchet release knob
35 Handgrip
36 Spacer tube
37 Cover
38 Retainer for cover
39 Cable assembly
40 Cable return spring
41 Spring retainer
42 Clevis pin
43 Washer
44 Split pin
45 Clevis
46 Clevis pin
47 Spring washer
48 Split pin
49 Nut
50 Locknut
51 Actuating rod
52 Lever/rod clip
53 Split pin
54 Bracket
55 Mounting stud spacer

## 6  Handbrake – adjustment and cable renewal

1    There is rarely any need to touch the handbrake as the automatic adjustment of the rear brake shoes also adjusts the handbrake operation. The only need for adjustment is when the cable stretches unduly or after fitting a new one. The principle of operation is simple. The inner cable runs to one wheel and the reaction of the outer cable when tension is applied is transferred to the other wheel by a rod. The mounting is on the differential cover of the rear axle. The end of the inner cable is connected to the brake wheel lever by a clevis on an adjuster screw. By slackening the locknut the adjuster can be screwed into the clevis, thus shortening the cable and taking up any excessive handbrake lever travel.

2    Due to the rear brake shoes being self-adjusting, care must be taken to avoid over-tensioning of the handbrake cable otherwise the brakes may bind on. When adjustments are being carried out, therefore, the following procedure ensures this cannot happen. First jack up the rear wheels so they are both off the ground together. Make sure the front wheels are securely chocked. Set the handbrake lever off and then lift it one notch on the ratchet. Slacken the cable adjuster and pump the foot brake to make sure the automatic adjustment is fully taken up. Make sure also that the wheel cylinders are sliding freely in the backplate (on early models) and return to rest normally after pulling on the operating lever. Then disconnect the clevis from the lever by removing the clevis pin, and alter the screwed adjuster until it can be refitted without moving the lever or without pulling on the cable to give any tension. Refit the clevis. After operating the hand lever a few times to settle the linkage the lever should travel six to eight notches before the brakes are fully on.

3    To fit a new cable it is first necessary to remove the handbrake lever. This is attached to the door sill by two bolts. Remove these, taking care to keep the distance pieces safely as they are essential to correct positioning. The end of the cable is then accessible and can be detached by removing the clevis pin. The other end is detached similarly and the outer cable is released from the brake rod by compressing the spring and releasing the spring retainers from round the cable. Refitting is a reversal of this process and the handbrake should be adjusted as previously described.

## 7  Hydraulic fluid pipes – removal, inspection and refitting

1    Periodically and certainly well in advance of the DoE test if due, all brake pipes, connections and unions should be completely and carefully examined. Fig 9.6 shows the composition of all such pipes and unions in the system.

2    Examine first all the unions for signs of leaks. Then look at the flexible hoses for signs of fraying, chafing and leaks. This is a preliminary inspection of the flexible hoses. Exterior condition does not necessarily indicate interior condition which will be considered later.

3    The steel pipes must be examined equally carefully. They must be thoroughly cleaned and examined for signs of dents or other percussive damage, rust and corrosion. Rust and corrosion should be scraped off and, if the depth of pitting in the pipes is significant, they will need renewal. This is most likely in those areas underneath the car body and along the rear axle where the pipes are exposed to the full force of road and weather conditions.

4    If any section of pipe is to be removed, first of all take off the fluid reservoir cap, line it with a piece of polythene film to make it airtight and screw it back on. This will minimise the amount of fluid dripping out of the system when the pipes are removed.

5    Rigid pipe removal is usually quite straightforward. The unions at

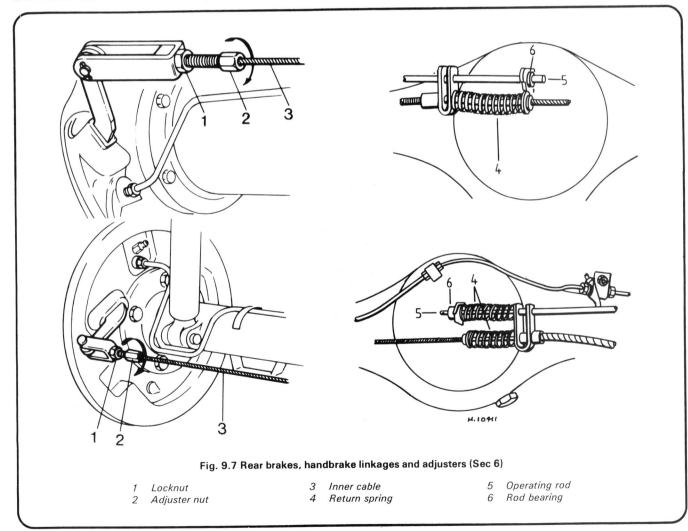

**Fig. 9.7 Rear brakes, handbrake linkages and adjusters (Sec 6)**

| | | | | | |
|---|---|---|---|---|---|
| 1 | Locknut | 3 | Inner cable | 5 | Operating rod |
| 2 | Adjuster nut | 4 | Return spring | 6 | Rod bearing |

each end are undone and the pipe drawn out of the connection. The clips which may hold it to the car body are bent back and it is then removed. Underneath the car, exposed unions can be particularly stubborn, defying the efforts of an open-ended spanner. As few people will have the special split ring spanner required, a self-grip wrench is the only answer. If the pipe is being renewed new unions will be provided. If not, one will have to put up with the possibility of burring over the flats on the union and use a self-grip wrench for refitting also.

6   Flexible hoses are always fitted to a rigid support bracket where they join a rigid pipe, the bracket being fixed to the bodyframe and/or suspension unit. The rigid pipe unions must first be removed from the flexible union. Then the locknut securing the flexible pipe to the bracket must be unscrewed, releasing the end of the pipe from the bracket. As these connections are usually exposed, they are more often

than not rusted up and a penetrating fluid is virtually essential to aid removal. When undoing them, both halves must be supported as the bracket is not strong enough to support the torque required to undo the nut and can easily be snapped off.

7   Once the flexible hose is removed examine the internal bore. If clear of fluid it should be possible to see through it. Any specks of rubber which come out, or signs of restriction in the bore, mean that the inner lining is breaking up and the pipe must be renewed.

8   Rigid pipes which need renewal can usually be purchased at any local garage where they have the pipe, unions and special tools to make them up. All that they need to know is the pipe length required and the type of flare used at the ends of the pipe. These may be different at each end of the same pipe.

9   Refitting the pipes is a straightforward reversal of the removal

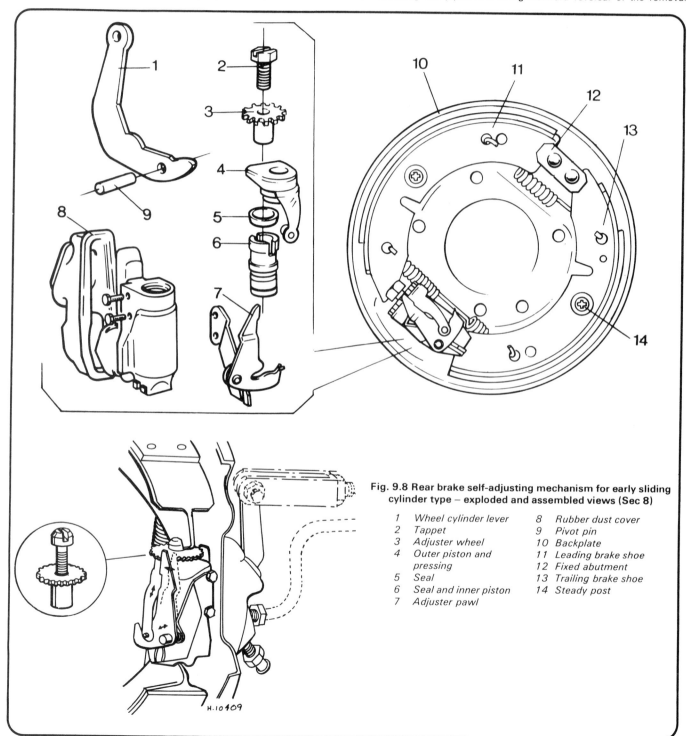

**Fig. 9.8 Rear brake self-adjusting mechanism for early sliding cylinder type – exploded and assembled views (Sec 8)**

1   Wheel cylinder lever
2   Tappet
3   Adjuster wheel
4   Outer piston and pressing
5   Seal
6   Seal and inner piston
7   Adjuster pawl
8   Rubber dust cover
9   Pivot pin
10  Backplate
11  Leading brake shoe
12  Fixed abutment
13  Trailing brake shoe
14  Steady post

H.10409

procedure. It is best to get all the sets (bends) in the pipe made preparatory to refitting. Also any acute bends should be put in by the garage on a bending machine otherwise there is the possibility of kinking them and restricting the bore area and fluid flow.

10 With the pipes refitted, remove the polythene from the reservoir cap and bleed the system as described in Section 13.

## 8 Hydraulic wheel cylinders (rear) — inspection and repair

1 If it is suspected that one or more of the wheel cylinders is malfunctioning, jack up the suspect wheel and remove the brake drum as described in Section 5.

2 Inspect for signs of fluid leakage around the wheel cylinder and if there are any, proceed as described in paragraph 5.

3 Next get someone to press the brake pedal very gently a small amount. Watch the wheel cylinder and see that the piston moves out a little. On no account let it come right out or it will need reassembly and bleeding. On releasing the pedal pressure make sure the retraction springs on the shoes move the piston back into position without delay. If the piston moves satisfactorily make sure also that the cylinder body is free to slide endways in the slot in the backplate. If it should be seized it will mean that only one brake shoe is being applied.

4 If there is a leak, or the piston does not move (or only moves very slowly under excessive pressure) then the rubber piston seals will need renewal at least.

5 Seal the reservoir cap and remove the brake shoes as described in Section 5.

6 Disconnect the brake fluid pipes where they enter the cylinder and plug the ends of the lines to minimise loss of fluid.

7 Remove the split pin and clevis pin from the handbrake operating link and the rubber dust cover.

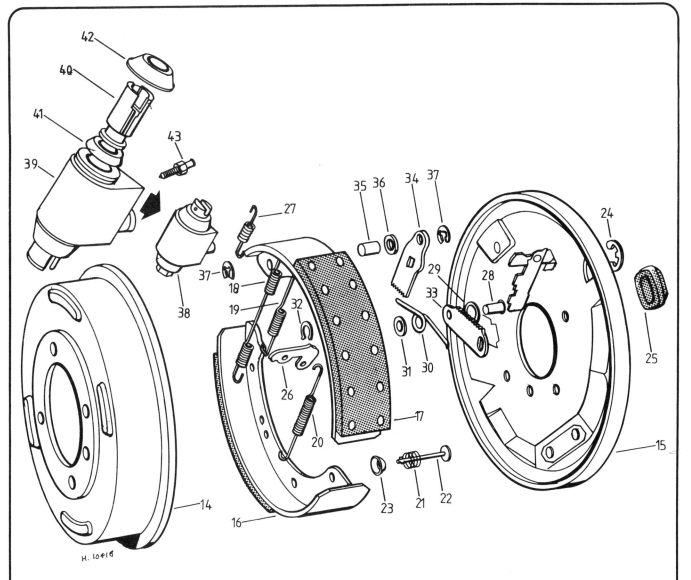

H. 10418

**Fig. 9.9 Rear brake self-adjusting mechanism for later type vehicles with double piston slave cylinders (Sec 8)**

| | | | |
|---|---|---|---|
| 14 *Drum* | 21 *Tensioning spring* | 29 *Washer* | 37 *Circlip* |
| 15 *Backplate* | 22 *Steady pin* | 30 *Ratchet lever spring* | 38 *Wheel cylinder assembly* |
| 16 *Shoe* | 23 *Retainer cup* | 31 *Washer* | 39 *Wheel cylinder* |
| 17 *Lining* | 24 *Cylinder retaining circlip* | 32 *Circlip* | 40 *Piston* |
| 18 *Retractor spring* | 25 *Rubber boot* | 33 *Lower ratchet lever* | 41 *Seal* |
| 19 *Retractor spring (handbrake lever)* | 26 *Handbrake lever* | 34 *Upper ratchet lever* | 42 *Boot* |
| 20 *Retractor spring* | 27 *Shoe to piston link spring* | 35 *Pivot pin (upper lever)* | 43 *Bleed nipple* |
| | 28 *Clevis pin (lever pivot)* | 36 *Washer* | |

8 Where the cylinder is of the type retained by U-shaped clips, these can be withdrawn by inserting a pointed tool into the base of the 'U'. Remove the cylinder.

9 Pull out the piston, complete with seal and the spring. Examine the piston and cylinder for signs of wear or scoring, and if there are any, the whole assembly must be renewed. If they are in good condition only the seal needs renewal. Pull the old one off the piston and thoroughly clean the whole assembly using clean hydraulic fluid or methylated spirit.

10 Fit the new seal to the piston, employing the fingers only, so the lip faces away from the slotted end of the piston. Lubricate with brake fluid, and feed into the cylinder body, seal end first.

11 Where applicable, fit the new seal to the outer piston, coat with brake fluid, and refit into the inner piston.

12 Refit the cylinder to the backplate, ensuring the dust cover and handbrake link are correctly positioned. Refit U-clips if applicable.

13 Reconnect the handbrake cable and hydraulic pipes and refit the brake shoes and drum as described in Section 5. Bleed the hydraulic system as described in Section 13.

## 9 Disc calliper – removal, inspection, repair and refitting

1 Any indications of fluid leaks or piston seizures in the front brake callipers will mean that they have to be removed for repair.

2 Jack up the car and remove the wheel and brake pads as described in Section 3.

3 To facilitate piston removal depress the brake pedal now to force them out as far as they can go up to the disc.

4 Seal the fluid reservoir cap with polythene sheet and disconnect the hydraulic pipe union from the body of the calliper.

5 The calliper is held to the stub axle by two bolts. Do not under any circumstances loosen the other bolts as these hold the two halves of the calliper together. The calliper can then be lifted away.

6 Provided the pistons are not seized they can be drawn out by hand, but in any case if some air pressure can be applied to the fluid inlet it will make things easier. If one piston is very tight try using methylated spirit to ease it. If drastic measures are necessary try and confine any damage to the piston rather than the calliper body.

7 Remove the dust seals and retaining rings from the annular grooves in the cylinder bores and then pull out the piston fluid seals from their grooves.

8 Examine the pistons and bores for signs of wear and scores. If

there are signs of wear the whole assembly will probably need renewal.

9 The cylinders and pistons should be thoroughly cleaned in hydraulic fluid or methylated spirit and care taken to avoid contamination by dirt or mineral oils.

10 Lubricate the piston seal with hydraulic fluid, and fit into the annular groove in the bore, using only the fingers.

11 Lubricate the piston with hydraulic fluid, open the bleed screw, and enter the piston squarely into the bore. Ensure the anti-squeak step is correctly positioned, and the piston is the correct way round.

12 Fit the dust seal on the piston followed by the seal retainer. Close the bleed screw.

13 Refit the calliper, and tighten the securing bolts to the correct torque figure.

14 Refit the pads and shims as described in Section 3, reconnect the hydraulic pipe and bleed the system as described in Section 13. Refit the wheel and road test the car.

## 10 Master cylinder (single circuit system) – removal and refitting

1 If the disc calliper pistons and rear wheel hydraulic cylinders are in order and there are no leaks elsewhere, yet the brake pedal still does not hold under sustained pressure, then the master cylinder seals may be assumed to be ineffective. To renew them the master cylinder must be removed.

2 Remove the parcel tray.

3 Disconnect the master cylinder pushrod from the brake pedal by removing the clevis pin.

4 Remove the return spring and retaining clip.

5 Unscrew the hydraulic pipe union and push the pipe to one side.

6 Remove the two nuts and washers holding the master cylinder to the bulkhead and lift the unit away. Empty the contents of the reservoir into a clean container.

7 Refitting is a reversal of the removal procedure, after which the braking system must be completely bled.

## 11 Master cylinder (single circuit system) – dismantling, overhaul and reassembly

1 Unless there are obvious signs of leakage, any defects in the master cylinder are usually the last to be detected in the hydraulic system.

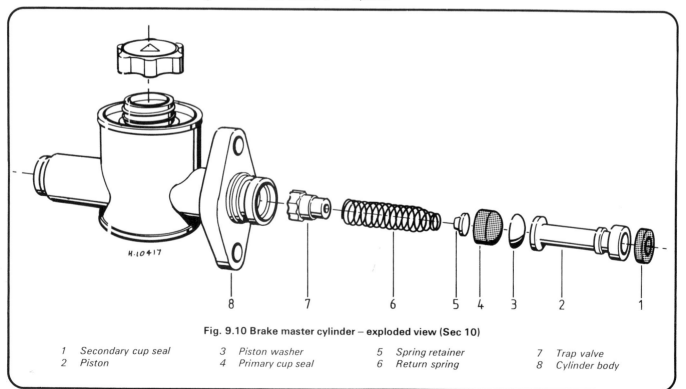

H.10417

**Fig. 9.10 Brake master cylinder – exploded view (Sec 10)**

| | | | |
|---|---|---|---|
| 1 Secondary cup seal | 3 Piston washer | 5 Spring retainer | 7 Trap valve |
| 2 Piston | 4 Primary cup seal | 6 Return spring | 8 Cylinder body |

2 Before assuming that a fault in the system is in the master cylinder the pipes and wheel cylinders should all be checked and examined as described in Sections 7 and 8.

3 Remove the master cylinder from the car as described in the previous Section.

4 Dismantle and reassemble the unit as described for the clutch master cylinder in Chapter 5.

## 12 Servo unit – removal, overhaul and reassembly

1 The servo unit, fitted to some cars, is an additional source of power boost to the hydraulic system for brake application. It uses the vacuum from the inlet manifold on a larger diameter diaphragm. This drives a piston in an intermediate hydraulic slave cylinder, thus supplementing the pressure applied on the foot pedal. If the servo unit should fail, the hydraulic system will still be open to permit pressure from the master cylinder to reach the wheel cylinders. The driver should be warned, however, that considerably more pedal pressure will be needed when the servo is inoperative. If the servo unit needs removal for any reason, it must be remembered that no braking will be

available, other than from the handbrake, unless a direct hydraulic line is made between the master cylinder and the four way connector.

2 The servo is mounted low down on the left-hand wing valance panel. To remove it, first disconnect the battery and remove the carburettor air cleaner. Loosen the clamping bolt on the bracket clip at the slave cylinder end and disconnect the vacuum pipe from either the inlet manifold or the servo. Seal the master cylinder reservoir cap with polythene sheet to minimise fluid loss and then disconnect both the hydraulic pipes at the servo slave cylinder. Try and cap the pipe ends with something to keep out dirt and keep in the fluid. Undo the nuts holding the shell and mounting bracket to the bodywork and lift the unit out.

3 Before dismantling the unit, make sure the exterior is perfectly clean and prepare an equally clean work bench on which to work. A complete repair kit which includes diaphragms and seals for the air valve, vacuum piston and hydraulic piston, should be obtained in advance.

4 Grip the servo unit in a well padded vice by the slave cylinder body with the air valve uppermost.

5 Remove the rubber pipe from the end cover connection.

6 Undo the screws securing the plastic air valve cover and lift off the cover assembly complete, which comprises the filter and valve. If the

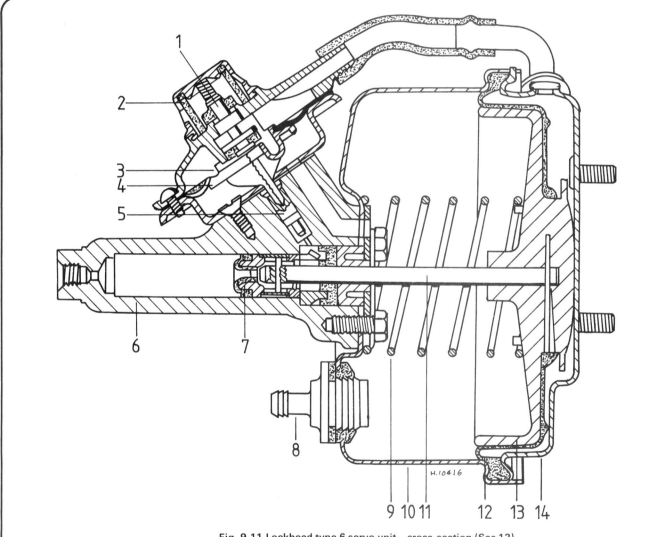

**Fig. 9.11 Lockheed type 6 servo unit – cross-section (Sec 12)**

| | | |
|---|---|---|
| 1 Air valve and air valve return spring | 4 Air valve diaphragm support | 7 Slave cylinder piston | 10 Servo shell |
| 2 Air filter | 5 Air valve piston | 8 Vacuum connection and non-return valve | 11 Pushrod |
| 3 Air valve diaphragm | 6 Slave cylinder | 9 Servo return spring | 12 Servo rubber |
| | | | 13 Piston |
| | | | 14 Servo end cover |

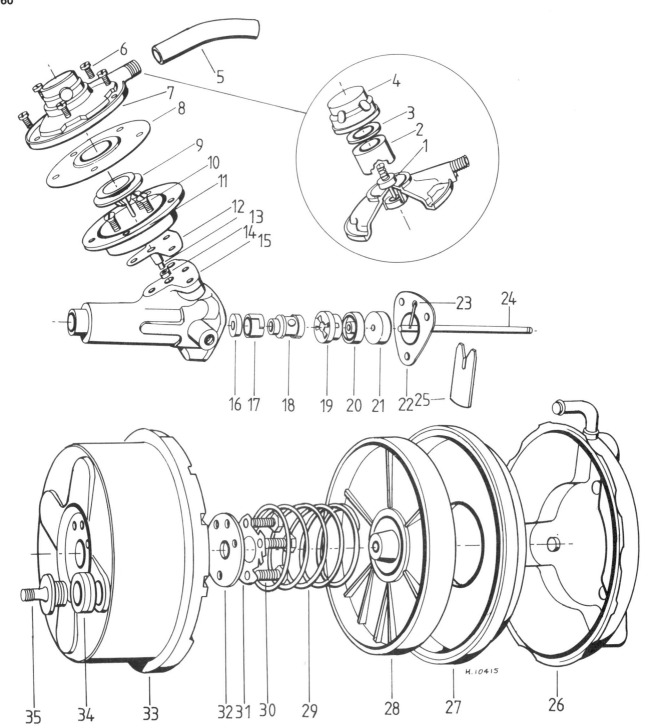

**Fig. 9.12 Lockheed type 6 servo unit – exploded view (Sec 12)**

1  Air valve and air valve return spring
2  Air valve
3  Sorbo washer
4  Air valve cover dome
5  Connection hose
6  Air valve cover fixing screws
7  Air valve unit cover
8  Air valve diaphragm
9  Air valve diaphragm support

10  Air valve fixing unit securing screws
11  Air valve unit lower housing
12  Joint – air valve unit to slave cylinder
13  Air valve piston
14  Air valve piston rubber cap
15  Slave cylinder
16  Slave piston rubber seal
17  Retainer for connecting pin (23)

18  Slave cylinder piston
19  Plastic spacer
20  Rubber cup
21  Plastic bearing
22  Joint – slave cylinder to servo shell
23  Retainer pin – piston (19) to pushrod (24)
24  Pushrod
25  Retaining key – pushrod (24) to diaphragm support (28)
26  End cover

27  Servo rubber diaphragm
28  Diaphragm support
29  Servo return spring
30  Bolts – slave cylinder to servo shell
31  Locking plate
32  Abutment plate
33  Servo shell
34  Rubber seal mounting – vacuum non-return valve
35  Vacuum connection and non-return valve – plastic

air valve is suspect a new assembly, which is part of the complete repair kit, will have to be obtained (ie these individual parts cannot be obtained separately).

7   The dome containing these items is a snap fit into the air valve cover.

8   Remove the rubber diaphragm and its plastic support, and the three valve housing securing screws will then be revealed. Undo these and take off the housing and joint washer.

9   To get the air control valve piston out of its cylinder will require a low pressure inside the slave cylinder. This can be done by blocking one of the two hydraulic fluid unions on the slave cylinder with a finger and applying air pressure from a foot pump to the other. When it is out remove the rubber cup from the piston (for renewal).

10   The non-return valve which is mounted in a rubber grommet can be pushed out by thumb pressure. Remove the grommet also.

11   It is now necessary to remove the end cover from the main servo shell. This is a twist fit bayonet type of connection and to remove it calls for an anti-clockwise twist as far as the stops in the cover will permit. It will then come off. Although there is a special tool for this (C2030) one can achieve the same result by drilling three holes in a plate to which the vacuum shell can be bolted, and then clamping the plate in the vice and twisting the cover off.

12   Put the unit back into the vice as before. To remove the diaphragm it is not necessary to free the retaining key from the pushrod. Turn the diaphragm support so the retaining key points downwards. Then supply light fluctuating pressure to the backplate against the main return spring and the retaining key will drop out.

13   Hold on to the diaphragm support and take it and the diaphragm and the return spring from the servo shell.

14   The bolts holding the servo shell to the slave cylinder are now exposed. Bend back the locking plate tabs from the bolt heads and remove the bolts, locking plate and abutment plate.

15   The shell can now be taken from the slave cylinder. Retrieve the washer between the two.

16   The pushrod can now be drawn from the slave cylinder together with the piston assembly.

17   Slide the bearing cup and spacer off the pushrod, noting the order and position in which they came off.

18   Prise the rubber seal off the slave piston.

19   If the rod is to be detached from the piston, the following action will be required but a new retaining clip will be needed. It should not normally be necessary to separate them. Open up the retaining clip by twisting a small screwdriver in the join and this will expose the connecting pin which can be pushed out. This disconnects the slave piston from the connecting rod. This unit is now completely dismantled.

20   Examine all rubber cups and seals for wear and renew as necessary. If the air valve unit is in good condition and it is only necessary to clean the filter, blow it through with a tyre foot pump. Do not use any cleaning fluids or lubricants on the filter.

21   Wash all slave cylinder components in clean hydraulic fluid, and remove any deposits from the slave cylinder walls in the same way. If the slave cylinder is scored then it must be renewed.

22   Reassembly must be done in very clean conditions as a single speck of grit in the wrong place can cause total malfunction. It is best to wash your hands, get new clean cloths and lay out all the components on a sheet of clean white paper. Five minutes' extra attention now could save you another complete dismantling operation later.

23   Use clean hydraulic fluid as a lubricant when reassembling the hydraulic components.

24   If the piston and pushrod were separated, push the rod into the rear of the piston against the spring until the connecting pin hole is open. Fit the pin followed by the retaining clip. It is important to ensure the clip fits snugly in its groove. Any protrusions will score the cylinder wall.

25   Refit the rubber seal to the slave piston using only the fingers, ensuring that the lips of the seal face away from the pushrod.

26   Lubricate (with hydraulic fluid only) the cylinder bore and insert the piston. Then refit in correct order, over the pushrod the spacer cup and bearing into the mouth of the slave cylinder. Ensure that each item placed into the cylinder has its sealing lips neither bent nor turned back and that each is bedded individually in turn.

27   The servo shell is now assembled in the reverse order given in previous paragraphs. If the locking plate has been used more than once before (ie the servo has already been twice dismantled) a new

one should be fitted. Tighten the bolts evenly to a torque figure of 17 lbf ft (23.05 Nm). Tap up the locking plate tabs.

28   To refit the diaphragm, support and spring, pull out the pushrod as far as possible. Fit the spring and diaphragm support ensuring the spring ends are correctly located over the abutment plate and the diaphragm support boss.

29   Press the diaphragm support over the pushrod with the key slot facing upwards, and when the groove in the pushrod and the slot in the diaphragm are lined up, insert the key.

30   Ensuring the support and diaphragm are quite clean and dry, fit the diaphragm to the support, gently stretching the inner edge to ensure it seats properly in the groove of the support.

31   Smear the outer edge of the diaphragm with disc brake lubricant (not grease or hydraulic oil). This prevents it from binding when the lid cover is refitted to the servo shell.

32   If no service tool is available, fix the end cover onto the vehicle mounting bracket (if you did not leave it there when taking it off) using the normal mounting units. Offer up the servo unit to the end cover so that when twisted clockwise, the pipe will line up with the elbow on the end cover when the turn is completely up to the stops.

33   With the unit back on the bench, refit the non-return valve and its mounting grommet.

34   To refit the air valve assembly, first fit the rubber piston cup to the spigot of the pipe ensuring that the lips face away from the spigot shoulder. Lubricate the cup with a little hydraulic fluid and insert it into the slave cylinder, taking care that the lips do not get bent back.

35   Fit the joint washer and valve housing to the slave cylinder using the three securing screws.

36   Fit the diaphragm support into the diaphragm and make sure that the inner ring fits snugly into the groove in the support. Then place the spigot of the support into the hole in the air valve piston. Use no lubricants.

37   Line up the screw holes in the diaphragm and the valve housing.

38   If the air filter and dome have been removed now is the time to snap the complete assembly back into the air valve cover.

39   Place the valve cover over the diaphragm so that projections in the cover engage the slots in the diaphragm. Refit all five securing screws finger tight. Tighten them down firmly, but not overtight, in a progressive pattern roughly North, South, East, West. This tightening sequence is important as the air valve must seat evenly and precisely. Any leak renders the whole servo inoperative.

40   Refit the rubber pipe from the valve cover port to the end cover elbow.

41   Refitting of the unit on the car is a reversal of the removal procedure. Keep all pipes well clear of the exhaust. Bleed the hydraulic system in the normal manner when reconnected and test without delay.

## 13   Hydraulic system – bleeding

**Note:** *Refer to Section 19 for special procedures applicable to dual circuit systems.*

1   The system should need bleeding only when some part of the system has been dismantled which would allow air into the fluid circuit; or if the reservoir level has been allowed to drop so far that air has entered the master cylinder.

2   Ensure a supply of clean non-aerated fluid of the correct specification is to hand in order to replenish the reservoir during the bleeding process. It is advisable, if not essential, to have someone available to help, as one person has to pump the brake pedal while the other attends to each wheel. The reservoir level has also to be continously watched and replenished. Fluid bled out should not be re-used. A clean glass jar and a 9 to 12 in length of $\frac{1}{8}$ in internal diameter rubber tube that will fit tightly over the bleed nipples is also required.

3   Bleed the front brakes first as these hold the largest quantity of fluid in the system. Deal with the left-hand brake first. Where a servo is fitted, depress the foot brake pedal several times to destroy the vacuum.

4   Make sure the bleed nipple is clean and put a small quantity of fluid in the bottom of the jar. Fit the tube onto the nipple and place the other end in the jar under the surface of the liquid. Keep it under the surface throughout the bleeding operation.

5   Unscrew the bleed screw a half turn and get the assistant to depress and release the brake pedal in short sharp bursts when you direct him. Short sharp jabs are better than long slow ones because

they will force any air bubbles along the line ahead of the fluid rather than pump the fluid past them. It is not essential to remove all the air the first time. If the whole system is being bled, attend to each wheel for three or four complete pedal strokes and then repeat the process. On the second time around operate the pedal sharply in the same way until no more bubbles are apparent. The bleed screw should be tightened and closed with the brake pedal fully depressed which ensures that no aerated fluid can get back into the system. Do not forget to keep the reservoir topped up throughout.

6    When all four wheels have been satisfactorily bled, depress the foot pedal which should offer a firmer resistance with no trace of 'sponginess'. The pedal should not continue to go down under sustained pressure. If it does there is a leak or the master cylinder seals are worn out.

### 14  Brake pedal – removal and refitting

Should the brake pedal pivot shaft become excessively sloppy due to wear in the pivot shaft, there could be a lot of lost motion between the initial movement of the pedal and application of the brakes. This is not a satisfactory state of affairs. To remove the pedal and shaft

assembly, follow the procedures as laid down for the clutch pedal in Chapter 5, Section 6.

### 15  Stop light switch

The stop light switch is a pressure operated contact mounted in the hydraulic system on the face of the fourway connector. If the brake lights do not work when the pedal is depressed, check first that the bulbs are all right. Then remove both leads from the terminals on the switch and touch them together. With the ignition switched on the brake lights should now work. If they do, the switch is faulty and should be unscrewed and a new one fitted. Bleed the hydraulic system afterwards.

### 16  Dual braking system – general description

Certain models are fitted with a dual braking system, consisting of two separate hydraulic circuits operated from a tandem master cylinder. One circuit serves the rear brakes, and the other the front. Should there be a break in one circuit with consequent loss of pressure

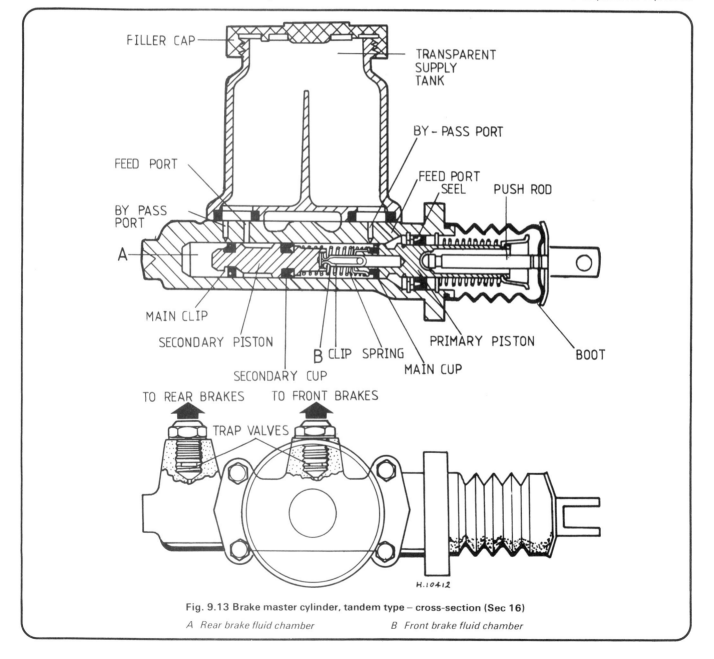

Fig. 9.13 Brake master cylinder, tandem type – cross-section (Sec 16)

*A  Rear brake fluid chamber*                 *B  Front brake fluid chamber*

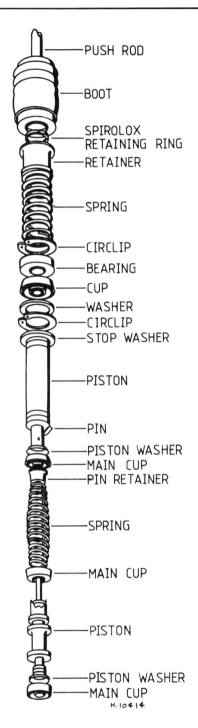

PUSH ROD

BOOT

SPIROLOX RETAINING RING

RETAINER

SPRING

CIRCLIP

BEARING

CUP

WASHER

CIRCLIP

STOP WASHER

PISTON

PIN

PISTON WASHER

MAIN CUP

PIN RETAINER

SPRING

MAIN CUP

PISTON

PISTON WASHER

MAIN CUP

H.10414

Fig. 9.14 Brake master cylinder, tandem type – exploded view of piston assembly (Sec 16)

it means that there is still the other remaining to halt the car. Dual brake system models are fitted with servo assistance to the front wheel circuit only. A pressure failure switch is incorporated into the hydraulic circuit so that immediate indication is given of the failure of one circuit. It consists of a double-ended piston held in central balance in a cylinder, between the opposing pressure of each hydraulic circuit. Should one pressure differ from the other the piston will move and operate a switch which lights an indicator on the instrument panel. The same light is operated by a switch on the handbrake also – which helps to indicate that the electrics are working properly.

## 17 Tandem master cylinder and pressure failure switch – removal, overhaul and refitting

1  The cylinder is disconnected by undoing the hydraulic pipe unions and unscrewing the two mounting bolts as for a conventional cylinder. Before attempting to dismantle the unit have a complete repair kit available. Special circlip pliers are also needed. The conventional variety will not reach the circlips in the bore of the cylinder.

2  Remove the rubber boot and pushrod and place the cylinder in a soft-jawed vice with the bore mouth upwards. Push down the spring retainer. This will reveal a 'Spirolox' locking ring in a groove in the cylinder wall. Carefully hook this out using a small screwdriver, pushing the end in an anti-clockwise direction. Remove the retainer and spring.

3  Remove the first circlip. Pull off the nylon bearing and cup seal from the primary piston. This will involve moving the piston up and down in the bore. Remove the plain washer.

4  The second circlip is now accessible and should be removed. The piston assembly and stop washer can now be drawn from the cylinder.

5  To fit new seals the pistons will have to be separated. Do this by compressing the spring between them and punching out the pin from the end of the primary piston which hooks into the loop from the secondary piston.

6  Apart from the cup already taken out, there are three main cups and two piston washers fitted to the pistons. Note carefully how these are fitted and where, before pulling them off. The odd one is in fact that on the rear end (the connecting link end) of the secondary piston. The internal bore is larger and there are no dimples in the lip.

7  Maintaining scrupulous cleanliness, and using fingers only, fit the new cup and washers, and reassemble the pistons. Examine the bore of the cylinder which should show no signs of scoring or damage. The cups on the secondary piston should have their lips pointing towards their respective ends of the piston. The washer behind the head cup should have the concave side against the seal cup. The same applies to the washer behind the cup of the primary piston.

8  When reassembling the pistons to the cylinder make sure the lips are not turned back. Lubricate the bore with brake fluid before inserting the assembly. The stop washer should be put over the end of the primary piston (when it is in the bore) and the piston assembly pressed down until the circlip groove is revealed. Make sure the circlip fits securely. Fit the plain washer, the cup and nylon guide bearing. Insert the circlip in the outer groove. Position the return spring, insert the spring retainer, compress to reveal the retaining ring groove, and fit the retaining ring. Release the spring.

9  Coat the inside of the boot with special rubber grease and insert the pushrod into the boot and the rear of the piston. Then fit the boot over the cylinder with the small hole facing away from the supply tank.

10  If the trap valves are to be taken out of the two outlet pipe unions in the cylinder, first carefully remove the adaptor fittings and discard the copper gaskets, which must be renewed each time they are taken out.

## 18 Pressure failure switch – overhaul

The seals of the pressure switch may need renewal and this is simply done by first unscrewing the switch and withdrawing it. Then undo the end cap and pull out the piston. The seals may then be removed.

## 19 Dual hydraulic system – bleeding

The dual system requires a slightly different approach from the single line system (see Section 13), as the pressure equalising switch has to be balanced in a central position. Ensure first there is no residual vacuum in the servo by operating the brake pedal several times. Do not restart the engine. Begin bleeding with the rear brakes, and if the rear brake system only has been opened then a bleed valve on the front system will have to be opened at the same time to permit fluid to be released. After finishing the rear brakes, bleed the front. If the pressure warning light should remain on (handbrake off!) after completing the bleeding, open a rear bleed nipple and apply light pressure to the brake pedal. Immediately the light goes out close the bleed valve and then

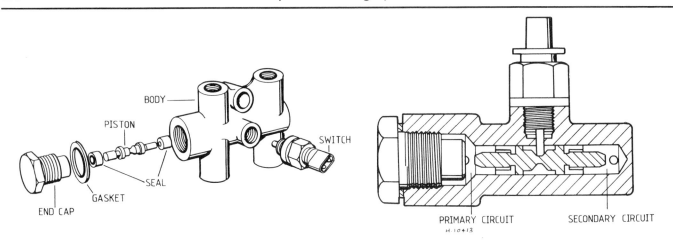

**Fig. 9.15 Pressure failure switch, dual circuit braking system – exploded and cross-sectional views (Sec 18)**

release the pedal. If the light should stay on, even after one complete down stroke of the pedal, close the bleed valve at the end of the pedal stroke and do the same thing at one of the front brakes. If the warning light flashes on and off intermittently when the brakes are applied, there must be a pressure variation between the two systems which should be investigated for fluid leaks.

### 20  Fault diagnosis – braking system

| Symptom | Reason(s) |
|---|---|
| Pedal travels almost to floorboards before brakes operate | Brake fluid level too low<br>Calliper leaking<br>Wheel cylinder leaking<br>Master cylinder leaking (bubbles in master cylinder fluid)<br>Brake flexible hose leaking<br>Brake line fractured<br>Brake system unions loose<br>Rear automatic adjusters seized |
| Brake pedal feels springy | New linings not yet bedded in<br>Brake discs or drums badly worn or cracked<br>Master cylinder securing nuts loose |
| Brake pedal feels spongy and soggy | Calliper or wheel cylinder leaking<br>Master cylinder leaking (bubbles in master cylinder reservoir)<br>Brake pipe line or flexible hose leaking<br>Unions in brake system loose<br>Air in hydraulic system |
| Excessive effort required to brake car | Pad or shoe linings badly worn<br>New pads or shoes recently fitted – not yet bedded-in<br>Harder linings fitted than standard causing increase in pedal pressure<br>Linings and brake drums contaminated with oil, grease or hydraulic fluid<br>Servo unit inoperative or faulty<br>One half of dual braking system inoperative<br>Discs or drums badly worn or scored<br>Seizure in one or more hydraulic cylinders |
| Brakes uneven and pulling to one side | Linings and discs or drums contaminated with oil grease or hydraulic fluid<br>Tyre pressures unequal<br>Radial ply tyres fitted at one end of the car only<br>Brake calliper loose<br>Brake pads or shoes fitted incorrectly<br>Different type of linings fitted at each wheel<br>Anchorages for front suspension or rear suspension loose<br>Brake discs or drums badly worn, cracked or distorted<br>Seizure in one or more hydraulic cylinders |
| Brakes tend to bind, drag or lock-on | Air in hydraulic system<br>Wheel cylinders seized<br>Handbrake cables too tight |

# Chapter 10 Electrical system

## Contents

Alternator: Delco Remy type DN460 – general description .......... 16
Alternator: Delco Remy type DN460 – testing in the car ............. 17
Alternator: Lucas type 10AC – description and maintenance ....... 8
Alternator: Lucas type 10AC – dismantling and reassembly ........ 11
Alternator: Lucas type 10AC – precautions and testing ................ 9
Alternator: Lucas type 10AC – removal and refitting .................... 10
Alternator: Lucas types 15ACR and 16ACR – testing
in the car ....................................................................................... 14
Alternator: Lucas type 16AC – testing in the car .......................... 13
Alternator: Lucas types 16AC, 15ACR and 16ACR – general
information ..................................................................................... 12
Alternator: Lucas types 16AC, 15ACR and 16ACR – servicing .... 15
Alternator control: Lucas type 4TR – general description ............. 36
Alternator control: Lucas type 8TR – general description ............. 37
Battery – charging and electrolyte replenishment ......................... 4
Battery – maintenance and inspection .......................................... 3
Battery – removal and refitting ...................................................... 2
Control box: Lucas type RB340 – current regulator adjustment .. 34
Control box: Lucas type RB340 – cut-out adjustment .................. 35
Control box: Lucas type RB340 – general description ................... 31
Control box: Lucas type RB340 – maintenance ............................ 32
Control box: Lucas type RB340 – voltage regulator adjustment .. 33
Dip, flasher, main beam and horn switches .................................. 59
Direction indicator system: type FL5 – fault finding ..................... 41
Dynamo – dismantling, repair and reassembly .............................. 7
Dynamo – maintenance and testing .............................................. 5
Dynamo – removal and refitting ..................................................... 6
Fault diagnosis – electrical system ............................................... 64
Fault diagnosis – windscreen wiper system (Lucas type DL3A) ... 44
Flasher unit: type 8FL – description and fault diagnosis .............. 42
Front sidelamp and flasher assembly ........................................... 56
Fuse unit: Lucas type 8FJ – general description ............................ 38
Fuse unit: 8-fuse type – Series 4 and 5 models ........................... 39
Fuse unit: 8-fuse type – Series 6 models onwards ....................... 40
General description ........................................................................ 1
Hazard warning flasher unit: type 9FL – fault tracing and
rectification ................................................................................... 60
Headlamps: Cibie type (rectangular) – description, adjustment,
removal and refitting ..................................................................... 55
Headlamps: F700 Mk 10 type – description, adjustment,
removal and refitting ..................................................................... 51
Headlamps: Lucas type F575 (dual system) – description,
adjustment, removal and refitting ................................................. 54
Headlamps: 2FR type (rectangular) – description, adjustment,

removal and refitting ..................................................................... 52
Headlamps: 4FR type (rectangular) – description, adjustment,
removal and refitting ..................................................................... 53
Horn: Lucas type 6H – maintenance and testing ........................... 50
Instrument panel and instruments (certain early types) –
checking, removal and refitting ..................................................... 61
Instrument panel and instruments (alternative early types) –
checking, removal and refitting ..................................................... 62
Instrument panel and instruments (later types) – checking,
removal and refitting ..................................................................... 63
Rear side, stop and flasher lamp assemblies – early types .......... 57
Rear side, stop and flasher lamp assemblies – later types .......... 58
Starter motor: Lucas type M35G (pre-engaged) – description,
maintenance and testing ............................................................... 26
Starter motor: Lucas type M35G (pre-engaged) – dismantling
and reassembly ............................................................................. 28
Starter motor: Lucas type M35G (pre-engaged) – removal
and refitting .................................................................................. 27
Starter motor: Lucas type M35G-1 – circuit testing ..................... 19
Starter motor: Lucas type M35G-1 – dismantling, repair
and reassembly ............................................................................. 21
Starter motor: Lucas type M35G-1 – drive pinion dismantling,
repair and reassembly ................................................................... 22
Starter motor: Lucas type M35G-1 – general description .............. 18
Starter motor: Lucas type M35G-1 – removal and refitting .......... 20
Starter motor: Lucas type M35J – dismantling, overhaul
and reassembly ............................................................................. 25
Starter motor: Lucas type M35J – general description .................. 23
Starter motor: Lucas type M35J (inertia drive) – removal
and refitting .................................................................................. 24
Starter motor: Lucas type M35J PE – dismantling, overhaul
and reassembly ............................................................................. 30
Starter motor: Lucas type M35J PE – general description ............ 29
Windscreen washer (electrical) – maintenance and testing ........... 49
Windscreen washer (manual) – maintenance and testing ............. 48
Windscreen wiper system: Lucas type DL3A – dismantling, and
reassembly .................................................................................... 46
Windscreen wiper system: Lucas type DL3A – general
description ...................................................................................... 43
Windscreen wiper system: Lucas type DL3A – removal and
refitting .......................................................................................... 45
Windscreen wiper system: Lucas type 15W – general
description ...................................................................................... 47

## Specifications

### Battery

| | |
|---|---|
| Number of plates ......................................................... | 9 or 11 |
| Capacity at 20 hr rating (amp hr) ............................... | 39 to 40 (9 plate) or 50 to 55 (11 plate) |
| Voltage and polarity .................................................... | 12 volt negative earth |

### DC generator

| | |
|---|---|
| Type ............................................................................. | Lucas C40-1 or C40L, shunt wound, two-pole, two brush |
| Field resistance ........................................................... | 5.9 ohms |
| Minimum length of brushes ........................................ | 0.25 in (6.4 mm) |
| Brush spring tension: | |
|     New brushes ......................................................... | 30 ozf (0.85 kgf) |
|     Brushes worn to 0.25 in (6.4 mm) ....................... | 15 ozf (0.42 kgf) |

Control box type ................................................................................ RB340, current/voltage regulator

## Alternator

| Type | 10AC | 16AC | 15ACR | 16ACR | DN460 |
|---|---|---|---|---|---|
| Rotor resistance (ohms) | 3.47 | 4.3 | 4.3 | 4.3 | 2.6 to 2.9 |
| Minimum brush length (in (mm)) | 5/32 (4) | 0.2 (5) | 0.2 (5) | 0.2 (5) | 0.2 (5) |
| Brush spring tension (ozf) | 7.5 to 8.5 at 13/32 in | 7 to 10 | 9 | 9 | 8 at $\frac{3}{4}$ in |
| Brush spring tension (gf) | 210 to 240 at 10 mm | 198 to 283 | 255 to 368 | 255 to 368 | 277 at 19 mm |
| | *Brush face flush with brush box* | | | | |
| Warning lamp control | 3AW | — | — | — | — |
| Field isolating relay | 6RA | — | — | — | — |
| Control box type | 4TR | 8TR | — | — | Motorola |
| Rectifier pack model | — | 4DS5 | 4DS5 | 4DS5 | — |
| Warning lamp bulb (watts) | 2.2 | 3 | 3 | 3 | 3 |

## Starter

| Type | M35G-1 | M35G | M35J, M35J PE |
|---|---|---|---|
| Minimum brush length | $\frac{5}{16}$ in (7.9 mm) | $\frac{5}{16}$ in (7.9 mm) | $\frac{3}{8}$ in (9.5 mm) |
| Brush spring tension: | | | |
|   New brushes | 30 to 34 ozf (850 to 910 gf) | 30 to 34 ozf (850 to 910 gf) | 28 ozf (800 gf) with new brush protruding $\frac{1}{16}$ in (1.5 mm) from brush box |
|   Minimum with worn brushes | 25 ozf (711 gf) | 25 ozf (711 gf) | — |

## Lamp bulbs

| | Lucas reference | Rating |
|---|---|---|
| Headlamp (single circular): | | |
|   Right-hand drive models | Lucas Mk 10 sealed beam | 60/45W |
|   Left-hand drive models | 410 | 45/40W |
|   France | 411 | 45/40W |
|   North America | Sealed beam | — |
| Headlamp (rectangular): | | |
|   Early models (with bulb) | 451 | 80/60W |
|   Later and left-hand drive models | 410 | 45/40W |
|   France | 411 | 45/40W |
| Headlamp (rectangular) | Sealed beam | 75/60W |
| Headlamp (twin): | | |
|   Right-hand drive models: | | |
|     Inner | No 1A | 50W |
|     Outer | No 2A | 50/37.5W |
|   Left-hand drive models: | | |
|     Inner | No 1A | 37.5W |
|     Outer | 410 | 45/40W |
|   France (inner and outer) | 411 | 45/40W |
| Sidelamp, glovebox lamp, wing flasher | 989 | 5W |
| Front and rear indicators, reversing lamp | 382 | 21W |
| Stop and tail | 380 | 21/5W |
| Rear number plate, boot lamp | 501 or 989 | 5W capless or 5W |
| Interior (roof) lamp | 254 | 6W |
| Panel (instrument) lamps | 987 | 2.4W |
| Warning lamps, clock | 501 or 989 | 5W capless or 5W |

## Wiper motor

| Type | Lucas DL3A | Lucas 15W |
|---|---|---|
| Normal light running current | 3.3 amps | 1.5 amps |
| Normal final gear speed | 44 to 48 rpm | 46 to 52 rpm |
| High speed running current (light) | 2.5 amps | 2 amps |
| High speed final gear speed (light) | 60 to 70 rpm | 60 to 70 rpm |

## Fuses

| Unit | 8FJ | 8-fuse unit (Series 4 and 5) | 8-fuse unit Series 6 onwards) |
|---|---|---|---|
| No of fuses | 3 | 8 | 8 |
| Fuse ratings | 35A | 16A (three) 8A (five) | 16A (one) 8A (seven) |
| In-line fuses | — | 15A (one) 8A (one) | 15A (two) |

## 1 General description

1 The electrical system is of the 12 volt earth return type. Earth polarity is negative.

2 The main items employed are either a DC generator or an alternator for charging, an electro-mechanical starter motor, and a 12 volt battery.

3 Great care should be taken when fitting service replacements, to ensure they are compatible with the electrical system polarity. If this is not done, irreversible damage can be sustained by certain units.

## 2  Battery – removal and refitting

1  The battery is situated at the front right-hand side of the engine compartment.

2  Disconnect the earth lead (negative) from the terminal by unscrewing the centre screw and twisting the terminal cover off. Do not use any striking force, or damage could be caused to the battery. Remove the positive lead in the same way.

3  Slacken the nuts holding the battery clamp stays until the assembly can be disengaged. Lift the battery out, keeping it the right way up to prevent spillage.

4  Refitting is a reversal of this procedure. Refit the positive lead first and smear the terminal posts and connections with petroleum jelly (not grease) to prevent corrosion.

5  The dangers of explosion with a battery, particularly where it is well-charged and gassing must be emphasised. It cannot be too strongly stressed that a battery should be kept away from all naked lights and sources of sparks. A single spark can be enough to cause the unit to explode and be thrown in many pieces over a considerable distance. The danger to the person is therefore obvious.

## 3  Battery – maintenance and inspection

1  Check the battery electrolyte level weekly by lifting off the cover or removing the individual cell plugs. The tops of the plates should be just covered with the liquid and if not, add distilled water so that they are just covered. Do not add extra water with the idea of reducing the intervals of topping up. This will merely dilute the electrolyte and reduce charging and current retention efficiency. On batteries fitted with patent covers, troughs, glass balls and so on, follow the instructions in the handbook or marked on the cover of the battery to ensure correct addition of water.

2  Keep the battery clean and dry all over by wiping it with a dry cloth. A damp top surface could cause tracking between the two terminal posts with consequent draining of power.

3  Every three months remove the battery and check the support tray clamp and battery terminal connections for signs of corrosion – usually indicated by a whitish-green crystalline deposit. Wash this off with clean water to which a little ammonia or washing soda has ben added. Smear the terminals with petroleum jelly and the battery mounting with protective paint to prevent the metal being eaten away. Clean the battery thoroughly and repair any cracks with a proprietary sealer. If there has been any excessive leakage the appropriate cell may need an addition of electrolyte rather than just distilled water.

4  If the electrolyte level needs an excessive amount of replenishment and no leaks are apparent it could be due to overcharging as a result of the battery having been run down and then left to recharge from the vehicle rather than an outside source. If the battery has been heavily discharged for one reason or another it is best to have it continuously charged at a low amperage for a period of many hours. If it is charged from the car's system under such conditions the charging will be intermittent and greatly varied in intensity. This does not do the battery any good at all. If the battery needs topping up frequently, even when it is known to be in good condition and not too old, then the voltage regulator should be checked to ensure the charging output is being correctly controlled. An elderly battery, however, may need topping up more than a new one because it needs to take in more charging current. Do not worry about this provided it gives satisfactory service.

5  When checking a battery's condition a hydrometer should be used. Readings for various states of charge are given in Section 4. If towards the end of a charging period one or more cells do not appear to be gassing in the same way as the remainder, it is probable that the cell or cells in question are breaking down and the life of the battery is limited.

## 4  Battery – charging and electrolyte replenishment

1  It is possible that in winter time when the load on the battery cannot be recuperated during normal driving time (from a dynamo), external charging will be required. This is best done overnight at a 'trickle' rate of 1 to 1.5 amps. Alternatively a 3 to 4 amp rate can be used over a period of four hours or so. Check the specific gravity in the latter case and stop the charge when the reading is correct. Most modern charging sets reduce the rate automically when the fully charged state is neared. Rapid boost charges of 30 to 60 amps, or more may get you out of trouble, or can be used on a battery that is nearing the end of its useful life, but are not advised for a good battery that may have run flat for some reason.

2  Electrolyte replenishment should not normally be necessary unless spillage has occurred. Top-up the cell with a solution of mixed electrolyte obtainable from a motor store or garage. If the cell is topped right up but the specific gravity is low, withdraw some of the electrolyte with a pipette and replace it with new solution. Recharge the battery and check the specific gravity using a hydrometer. When making up electrolyte at home, rather than purchasing it ready-mixed, very great care must be taken. A solution of one part sulphuric acid to two and a half parts water is required, but never add water to sulphuric acid or an explosion will occur. Always pour the acid slowly on to water, using a glass vessel for the solution.

3  When taking hydrometer readings, the specific gravity readings obtained should be compared with the following tables:

Type 'D' and 'A' batteries, at electrolyte temperature of 60°F (15.6°C):

|  | Climate below 80°F (26.7°C) | Climate above 80°F (26.7°C) |
|---|---|---|
| Fully charged | 1.270 to 1.290 | 1.210 to 1.230 |
| Half charged | 1.190 to 1.210 | 1.130 to 1.150 |
| Discharged | 1.110 to 1.130 | 1.050 to 1.070 |

Type 'F' batteries, at electrolyte temperature of 60°F (15.6°C):

|  | Climate below 90°F (32°C) | Climate above 90°F (32°C) |
|---|---|---|
| Fully charged | 1.277 to 1.297 | 1.227 to 1.247 |
| Half charged | 1.190 to 1.220 | 1.160 to 1.180 |
| Discharged | 1.100 to 1.130 | 1.080 to 1.100 |

## 5  Dynamo – maintenance and testing

1  The fanbelt tension should be checked at least every 5000 miles. In fact, do this when the bonnet is raised for any other purpose. The belt is correctly adjusted when a total of $\frac{5}{8}$ in deflection can be obtained in the centre of the longest free run. To adjust, slacken the three generator mounting bolts and swing it in the required direction. Tighten the bolt in the slotted bracket first. Check the tension again before finally tightening the other two. If in doubt as to the final adjustment, always err on the side of the belt being a little slack rather than too tight. If too tight, excessive strain will be imposed on the dynamo and water pump bearings. If too slack it will slip and squeal.

2  The dynamo shaft bush at the commutator end should receive two or three drops of engine oil through the hole in the end cover every 5000 miles.

3  If the dynamo is suspected of being faulty it may be checked without taking it from the car. Ensure the fanbelt is adjusted correctly, the two lead terminals are clean and secure, and the battery terminals clean and tight. Check that the terminal connections on the control box 'D' and 'F' are those that come from the 'D' and 'F' terminals on the dynamo and that the leads are intact. This can be done with a continuity test on each wire.

4  Pull off the leads from the terminal on the dynamo and then join the terminals with a short length of non-insulated wire. Using crocodile clips, attach a voltmeter with the positive lead to the centre of the bridge wire on the dynamo terminals and the negative to a good earth nearby. Switch off all ancillary equipment. Start the engine and increase the revolutions smoothly to a maximum of 1000 rpm. The voltmeter should rise immediately with no fluctuations, to give a reading of 15 volts. Do not increase engine speed in an attempt to increase the voltage if it is low. If the voltage is sub-normal the dynamo should be removed for further examination. If a radio suppressor is fitted between the 'D' terminal and earth check again with this removed. The suppressor itself may cause the fault.

## 6  Dynamo – removal and refitting

1  Slacken the two dynamo retaining bolts and the nut on the sliding link, and move the dynamo in towards the engine so the fanbelt can be removed.

2  Disconnect the two leads from the dynamo terminals (photo).

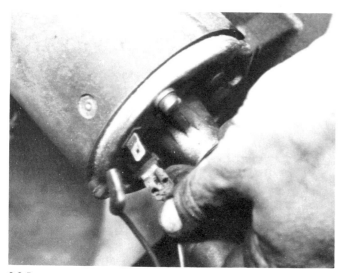

6.2 Dynamo terminal connections

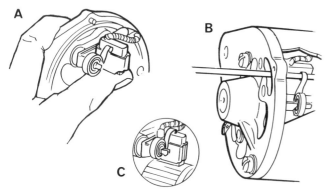

## Fig. 10.1 Dynamo type C40L – brush gear details (Sec 7)

A  *Fitting the spring to hold the brush up in the holder*
B  *Hooking up the spring through the endplate to refit*
   *it on the brush*
C  *Correctly fitted brush*

3    Remove the nut from the sliding link bolt, and remove the two upper bolts. The dynamo is then free to be lifted away.
4    Refitting is a reversal of the above procedure. Do not finally tighten the retaining bolts and the nut until the fanbelt has been tensioned correctly.

## 7   Dynamo – dismantling, repair and reassembly

1    Clamp the dynamo in a vice and remove the two through-bolts which hold the assembly together.
2    Remove the commutator end bracket by pulling it straight off the end of the armature shaft.
3    Remove the generator from the vice and draw the drive end bracket complete with armature from the yoke or casing.
4    Do not dismantle further at this stage. Examine the carbon brushes in the holders of the commutator end bracket. They may be lifted out of their holders after the pressure springs are hooked out. The length of the brushes should be no less than $\frac{1}{4}$ inch (6.35 mm). If necessary, fit new ones. Note that the C40 and C40L have a different type of brush fitted.
5    Examine the commutator. This should not be burnt or scored in any way. Clean it off with a little petrol on a rag. Traces of pitting, scoring or burring, if slight, can be cleaned off with fine glass paper. Do not use emery paper. Make sure there are no flat spots, by tearing the glass paper into strips and drawing it round the commutator evenly. Do not try to clean off too much by this method as the commutator must remain circular in section.
6    To test the armature is not difficult but a voltmeter or bulb and 12 volt battery are required. Figs. 10.3 and 10.4 show how the battery, voltmeter and probe connectors are used to test whether (a) any wire in the windings is broken or (b) whether there is an insulation breakdown. In the first test the probes are placed on adjacent segments of a clean commutator. All voltmeter readings should be similar. If a bulb is used, it will glow very dimly or not at all if there is a fault. For the second test any reading or bulb lighting indicates a fault. Test each segment in turn with one probe and keep the other on the shaft. Should either test indicate a faulty armature the wisest action is to obtain a replacement dynamo. The field coils may be tested if an ohmmeter or ammeter can be obtained. With an ohmmeter the resistance (measured between the terminal and the yoke) should be 6 ohms. With an ammeter, connect it in series with a 12 volt battery again from the field terminal to the yoke. A reading of 2 amps is normal. Zero amps or infinity ohms indicate an open circuit. More than 2 amps or less than 6 ohms indicates a breakdown of the insulation. Unless you can get the field coils readily repaired it is better to obtain a replacement unit.
7    The drive end bearing should have no play. If it needs renewal (rare except where the fanbelt has been persistently over-tightened), remove the pulley nut and washers and draw off the pulley. Tap the

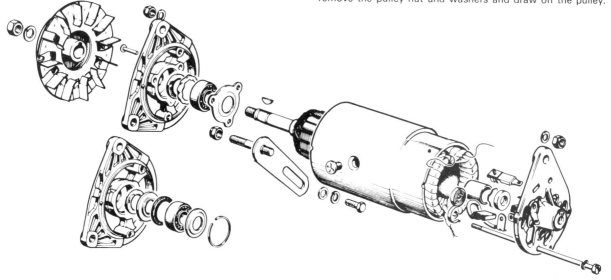

Fig. 10.2 Dynamo type C40L – exploded view (Sec 7)

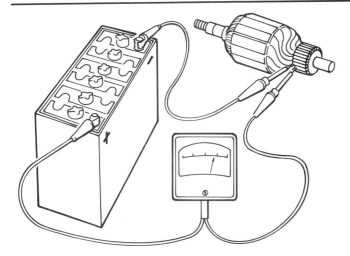

**Fig. 10.3 Dynamo armature – open circuit test (Sec 7)**

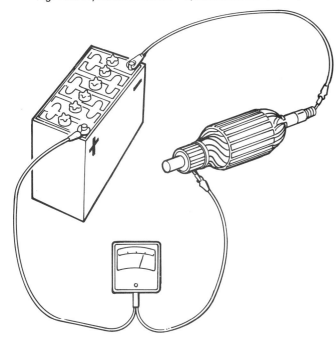

**Fig. 10.4 Dynamo armature – insulation winding test (Sec 7)**

key out of the shaft using a screwdriver under one end. Guard against it flying off and getting lost. Remove the circlip from the bearing housing. Support the end cover across the jaws of a vice, with the armature hanging down. Tap the end of the shaft with a soft-faced mallet to drive it out of the bearing housing with the bearing. The bearing itself can be taken off the shaft by the same method. When fitting a new bearing, pack it with grease and fit it into the end cover. Fit the pressure ring, retaining plate and circlip. Place the retaining cup over the armature shaft so that the open end faces the armature. Support the end cover on the vice jaws and carefully tap the armature through the bearing with a soft mallet. Refit the spacer, the key, the pulley, washer and nut.

8    To refit the bush in the commutator end bracket, a suitable extractor with which to withdraw the old bush must first be acquired. Soak the new bush in engine oil for twenty four hours. Clean the felt ring and the ring retainer, and refit. Using a properly-machined shouldered mandrel, with the pilot end of the same diameter as the armature shaft, press the bush home until flush with the inside face of the bracket. Do not attempt to ream the bush when fitted, or porosity will be adversely affected.

9    If new brushes have been fitted, make sure they are a free sliding fit in their holders. If there are signs of sticking they may be relieved by careful rubbing with a fine file.

10  Refit the armature/drive end cover assembly into the main yoke and fit the commutator end cover by hooking back the brush springs. Allow them to rest on the sides of the brushes which should be drawn back. The brushes will then be held and can be released and the springs brought to bear after the end cover has been assembled (see Fig. 10.1).

11  Note that both end covers have locating pips which register in corresponding cut-outs in the yoke. When fitting the commutator end cover, see that the blade terminal of the field coil connection fits in the proper slot and that the insulating sleeve round it is intact. Refit the through-bolts and before tightening them right up, check the end plates are fully and correctly in position. Spin the armature to ensure it is not binding or touching the field coils and then unhook the brush springs and lower the brushes onto the commutator with the springs on top. Finally, place a few drops of engine oil in the oil hole of the commutator bearing bush.

## 8    Alternator: Lucas type 10AC – description and maintenance

1    The alternator is a generator capable of producing alternating current, which is rectified into direct current so that it may be used in the car electrical system to charge the battery. Its main advantage is that it is lighter, more robust and has a much higher output at low engine revolutions. Incorporated in the charging circuit there is also the following:

(a) *A relay to switch the energising current to the field winding when the ignition switch is turned on*
(b) *A voltage control unit*
(c) *A warning lamp control unit*

Of these, only the voltage control unit is capable of being adjusted. However, the average owner is not advised to do this.

2    Maintenance is minimal. Both bearings, one ball and one needle roller, are sealed. The only items subject to any wear are the slip ring carbon brushes, this being minimal. The only other regular attention needed is to make sure that the ventilation holes in the slip ring end cover are kept clear and that the fan-belt tension is maintained correctly.

## 9    Alternator: Lucas type 10AC – precautions and testing

1    If the charging system of the car develops a fault, one cannot set about finding out where it may be in the same way as one could do for a dynamo. Trial and error procedures and connections are out. Due to the relatively sophisticated electronic circuitry, the polarity of the system (positive and negative) is very important. Wrong connections can cause damage, even if the motor is not running.

2    Before carrying out any tests to find out what trouble may exist in the circuit the following precautions *must* be observed:

(a) *Never disconnect the battery with the alternator running*
(b) *Observe the polarity of the system throughout*
(c) *Make sure the battery polarity is suitable. A mistaken reverse connection will damage the diode rectifiers*
(d) *Do not earth the brown/yellow cable if disconnected at 'AL' on the warning lamp control*
(e) *Do not earth the brown/green cable if disconnected from the alternator*
(f) *Always disconnect the battery earth before disconnecting the alternator output cable*
(g) *Disconnect battery terminals before connecting an external charging source*
(h) *A booster battery connection must always be made in parallel ie negative to negative – positive to positive*
(i) *Always disconnect the battery and alternator if electric welding is to be done in the bodywork*

3    With the foregoing precautions in mind, carry out the following tests to establish which component is faulty. Firstly, check the fanbelt for wear and tension. Disconnect the battery earth cable. If no ammeter is fitted, disconnect the main output lead from the alternator and wire in an ammeter (of 75 amps capacity) between the lead and the terminal (photo). Disconnect the 'F' and '–' leads from the voltage regulator and join them together. Reconnect the battery earth lead,

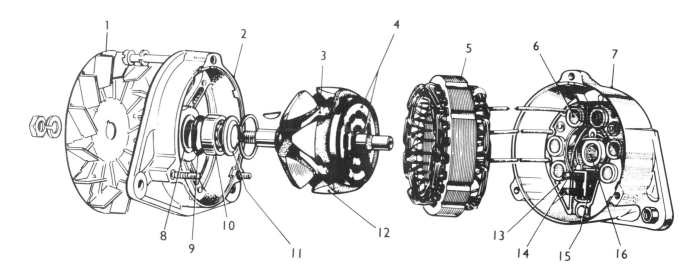

Fig. 10.5 Alternator type 10AC – exploded view (Sec 8)

| | | | |
|---|---|---|---|
| 1 Fan | 5 Stator | 9 O-ring oil seal | 13 Diode heat sink |
| 2 Drive end shield | 6 Diodes | 10 Bearing | 14 Brushes |
| 3 Rotor field windings | 7 Slip ring end shield | 11 Bearing retaining plate | 15 Brush holder |
| 4 Slip rings | 8 O-ring retaining washer | 12 Rotor | 16 Needle roller bearing |

9.3 Alternator terminal connections

10.1 Removing alternator

switch on and run the engine speed up to 2100 rpm. A 25 amp reading should be obtained. If a low reading is obtained, the circuit connections are badly made (especially earth) or the alternator is faulty. If there is no reading at all, check that there is voltage across the two field terminals by applying a voltmeter across the two cable ends normally attached to the alternator field terminals. If there is no voltage, then the 6RA isolating relay is faulty. (Conversely, there should be no voltage across these two terminals when the ignition switch is off.)

4    If the 6RA relay appears faulty, continue the test by disconnecting the lead from terminal C2 and connect it temporarily to C1. If the alternator output is now correct, a new relay unit is indicated.

5    If the alternator output is still incorrect then the control unit may be faulty. The way to test this is to fit another control unit which is known to be in order.

6    If the alternator output is wrong yet again, the alternator must be faulty.

## 10 Alternator: Lucas type 10AC – removal and refitting

Disconnect the battery leads. The alternator is then removed in the same manner as the dynamo. Note that the two main mounting bolts are underneath (photo).

## 11 Alternator: Lucas type 10AC – dismantling and reassembly

1    The owner should only dismantle the alternator if he has verified that it is faulty. Even then, he should only dismantle it with the

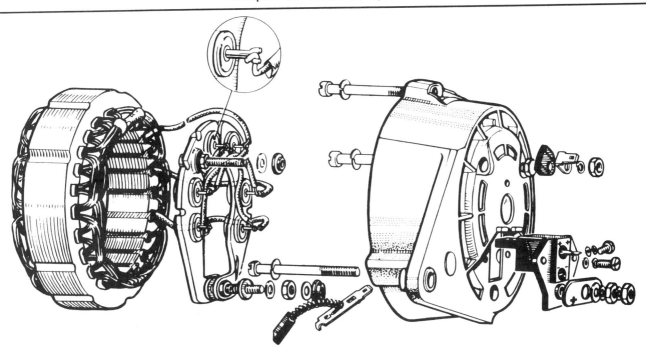

Fig. 10.6 Alternator type 10AC – brush gear and rectifier diodes – exploded view (Sec 11)

intention of examining the slip ring brushes which can be easily renewed.

2    Remove the shaft nut, spring washer, pulley and fan. Mark the drive end bracket, stator laminations and slip ring end cover so they can be reassembled the same way. Undo the three through-bolts. Take out the end bracket and rotor.

3    At the other end, remove the terminal nuts and washers, insulators, brush box screws and 2BA bolt.

4    The stator and heat sink assembly may then be taken out.

5    The brushes are held in by tongues at the root of each field terminal blade and can be removed by closing up the tongues. If the brushes are approaching the specified minimum acceptable length, they must be renewed. When fitting new brushes, check that they slide freely in their holders. Clean the faces of the slip rings with a petrol moistened cloth while the opportunity presents itself.

6    Reassemble the alternator in the reverse order and if the brushes

have been renewed, test the output. If the alternator is still not serviceable it should be exchanged for another unit.

### 12 Alternator: Lucas types 16AC, 15ACR and 16ACR – general information

1    These alternators are similar in design to the 10AC alternator described in Section 8, except that a field isolating relay is no longer required, due to a modified arrangement for the field supply diodes. The earlier 8-pole rotor and stator have been superseded by 12-pole equivalent, and on the 15ACR and 16ACR versions there is a built-in electronic voltage regulator unit. The 16ACR is similar to the 15ACR alternator except for a higher nominal dc output.

2    Maintenance, precautions, removal and refitting procedures are as described in Sections 9, 10 and 11.

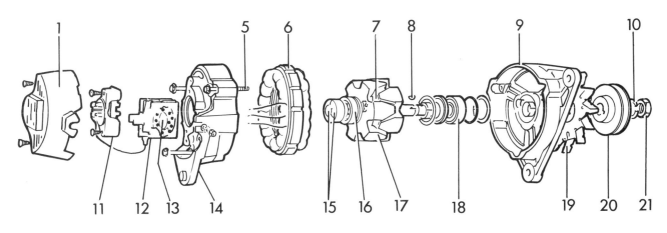

Fig. 10.7 Alternator type 16AC – exploded view (Sec 12)

| | | |
|---|---|---|
| 1 Cover | 9 Drive end bracket | 14 Slip ring end bracket | 18 Drive end bearing |
| 5 Through-bolts | 10 Spring washer | 15 Slip rings | 19 Fan |
| 6 Stator | 11 Brush box moulding | 16 Slip ring bearing | 20 Pulley |
| 7 Field winding | 12 Rectifier pack | 17 Rotor | 21 Nut |
| 8 Shaft key | 13 Rectifier assembly bolt | | |

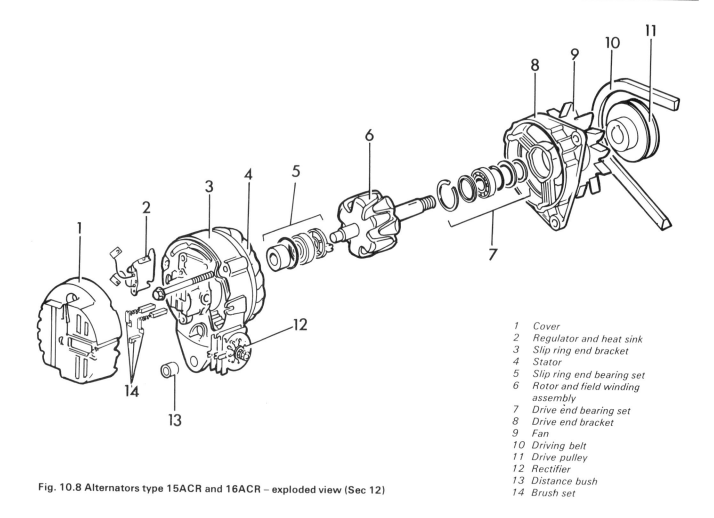

1   Cover
2   Regulator and heat sink
3   Slip ring end bracket
4   Stator
5   Slip ring end bearing set
6   Rotor and field winding
    assembly
7   Drive end bearing set
8   Drive end bracket
9   Fan
10  Driving belt
11  Drive pulley
12  Rectifier
13  Distance bush
14  Brush set

Fig. 10.8 Alternators type 15ACR and 16ACR – exploded view (Sec 12)

## 13  Alternator: Lucas type 16AC – testing in the car

1   Before testing the alternator in the event of malfunction, check the fanbelt tension and adjust if necessary (see Section 1 of Chapter 2).
2   Check that all connections in the charging circuit are tight, clean and undamaged.
3   Disconnect the battery earth lead temporarily.
4   If no ammeter is fitted to the car, disconnect the alternator main output lead from the positive (+) terminal. Connect a moving coil ammeter capable of reading up to 60 amps dc between the disconnected output lead and the alternator positive (+) terminal.
5   Disconnect the 'F' and negative (–) terminal leads from the 8TR regulator unit. Join the leads (not the terminals) together.
6   Reconnect the battery earth lead.
7   Switch the headlamps on with main beam selected, turn on the ignition and check that the warning lamp illuminates.
8   Start the engine and check that the warning lamp extinguishes at 800 rpm (approximately) as engine speed slowly increases.
9   Increase engine speed to approximately 3100 rpm and check that the current is not less than 25 amps.
10  If the requirements of paragraphs 8 and 9 are not satisfied a fault in the alternator is indicated.
11  If the requirements of paragraphs 8 and 9 are satisfied, but the charging system is faulty, first check through the wiring. If this is satisfactory, a faulty voltage regulator is indicated.
12  Rectification of alternator faults (with the exception of attention to the brushes and slip rings), or voltage regulator faults, are best entrusted to a car electrical specialist due to the possibility of further damage being caused during investigation or renewal of components.

## 14  Alternator: Lucas types 15ACR and 16ACR – testing in the car

### Alternator output

1   Assuming correct fanbelt tension and condition, and with the engine switched off, disconnect the battery earth lead.
2   Remove the two screws retaining the moulded end cover, then take off the cover.
3   Link the green inner brush lead (F) and black earth lead (–).
4   Connect a test circuit as shown inside the dotted lines of Fig. 10.9, taking great care that polarities are correct, then reconnect the battery earth lead. Proceed to the checks in paragraphs 5 and 6 without delay, since the variable resistor must not be connected for longer than absolutely necessary; also ensure the resistor is initially set to give maximum resistance or it may become permanently damaged.
5   Switch the ignition on, check that the warning lamp is illuminated, then start the engine and increase the speed to approximately 800 rpm. The lamp should now be extinguished.
6   Increase the engine speed to approximately 3200 rpm, adjust the variable resistor to give a voltmeter reading of 14 volts and check the ammeter reading is approximately equal to the rated alternator output given in the Specifications.
7   Switch off the engine and disconnect the variable resistance without delay.
8   If the requirements of paragraphs 5 and 6 are not satisfied, a fault in the alternator is indicated. Apart from attention to brushes and slip rings, alternator faults are best left to a car electrical specialist.

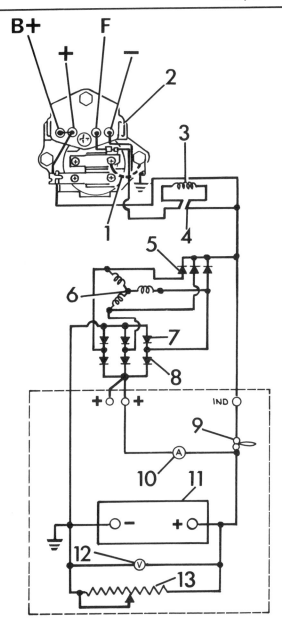

**Fig. 10.9 Alternator types 15ACR and 16ACR – test circuit (Sec 14)**

| | |
|---|---|
| 1 Link bridging 'F' and negative terminals | 8 Live side output diodes (3) |
| 2 Voltage regulator | 9 12 volt 2.2W bulb |
| 3 Exciter field diodes | 10 0-40 or 0-60 ammeter (d.c.) |
| 4 Slip rings | 11 Car battery |
| 5 Exciter field diodes | 12 0-20 voltmeter (a.c.) |
| 6 Stator winding | 13 0-15 ohm 35 amp rated |
| 7 Earth side output diodes (3) | variable resistor |

### Regulator test

9   If the requirements of paragraphs 5 and 6 of the alternator output test are satisfied but there is still a fault in the charging circuit, use the same test circuit but remove the variable resistor and the bridging link between (F) and (–).

10   Run the engine up to approximately 3200 rpm and check that when a current of 10 amps is recorded, the voltmeter reading is in the region of 13.6 to 14.4 volts. Any appreciable deviation from this value indicates that the regulator is at fault and requires specialist attention.

11   On completion, disconnect the battery earth lead, remove the test circuitry, then reconnect the battery earth lead.

## 15  Alternator: Lucas types 16AC, 15ACR and 16ACR – servicing

1   Servicing, other than renewal of the brushes, is not recommended. The major components should normally last the life of the unit; in the event of failure a factory exchange replacement should be obtained.
2   To renew the brushes, remove the two cover screws and withdraw the moulded cover.
3   Unsolder the three stator connections to the rectifier assembly noting carefully the order of connection. Take great care that the diodes are not overheated or permanent damage will result. See also paragraph 9 of this Section.
4   On 16AC alternators, withdraw the two brush moulding securing screws and slacken the nut on the rectifier screws and slacken the nut on the rectifier assembly bolt. The brush moulding and rectifier can now be withdrawn together, complete with the cable which links them.
5   On 15ACR and 16ACR alternators, pull off the brush wire, earth wire and suppressor wire (if fitted) from the Lucas terminals on the rectifier. Slacken the nut on the rectifier assembly bolt and withdraw the rectifier, then remove the brush moulding securing screws. Unscrew the bolt securing the regulator to the end bracket, then withdraw the brush box and regulator complete with the cable which links them.
6   If the brush protrusion has worn to 0.2 in (5 mm) or less, they should be renewed. Do not lose the leaf spring fitted at the side of the inner brush.
7   Should a brush stick, clean it with petrol or lightly rub with a smooth file.
8   The surfaces of the slip rings should be clean and smooth. If necessary, clean with a petrol moistened cloth. If there is evidence of burning, use only very fine glasspaper to clean (not emery).
9   Reassembly is the reverse of the removal procedure, but for the soldering operation it is important to use only M grade 45/55 tin-lead solder. To prevent overheating of the rectifier diodes, the pins should be lightly gripped with a pair of long-nosed pliers to act as a heat sink whilst soldering. This operation should be carried out as quickly as possible. Also take care that the pins are not bent since this will damage the hermetic seal.

## 16  Alternator: Delco Remy type DN460 – general description

1   The DN460 alternator is a 14-pole machine which, although considerably different with respect to design, functions in a similar manner to the Lucas 15ACR and 16ACR models.

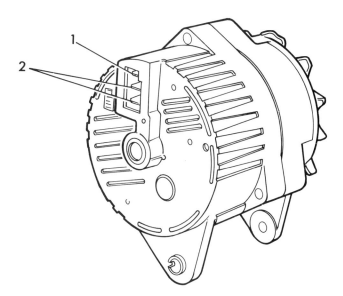

**Fig. 10.10 Delco Remy alternator type DN460 (Sec 16)**

1   Indicator lamp terminal
2   Positive terminals

2   Precautions, removal and refitting procedures are as described in Sections 9, 10 and 11.
3   The manufacturers do not recommend any periodic maintenance.
4   It is recommended that in the event of the alternator requiring repair, the job should be carried out by a car electrical specialist.

---

### 17 Alternator: Delco Remy DN460 – testing in the car

#### Faulty warning light operation

1   If the warning light is on when the ignition is switched off, a faulty rectifier bridge is indicated and the alternator should be passed to a car electrical specialist for repair. This condition will also give an undercharged battery.
2   If the warning light is off when the ignition is switched on (engine not running), this will lead to an undercharged battery. To trace the fault, disconnect the 'IND' terminal from the alternator and temporarily earth it. If the light fails to illuminate when the ignition is switched on, check the switch, light and associated leads for continuity.
3   If the light illuminates as paragraph 2, reconnect the 'IND' lead, then use a screwdriver, as shown in Fig. 10.11 to earth the field winding.
4   If the light is now extinguished, check the wiring connection between the 'IND' alternator terminal and the wiring harness. If these are satisfactory, a fault in the brushes, slip rings or field windings is indicated. If the light is still illuminated, a fault in the regulator unit is indicated.

#### Undercharged battery

5   This condition may be accompanied by erroneous warning light indications and, where evident, it is important to ascertain that all wiring connections are clean and tight, and that the fan belt is correctly adjusted (see Chapter 2, Section 11).
6   To check the alternator, switch on the ignition (engine not running) and connect a dc voltmeter, capable of registering 12 volts, between the alternator positive (+) and earth, then between the alternator 'IND' terminal and earth. A zero reading indicates a fault in the alternator.

#### Overcharged battery

7   In cases where an overcharged battery is evident, as indicated by excessive usage of distilled water, a faulty alternator is indicated.

---

### 18 Starter motor: Lucas type M35G-1 – general description

1   The starter motor is mounted on the clutch bellhousing on the left-hand side of the engine. It is secured by two bolts. It has four field coils and four commutator brushes, two of which are earthed. When the motor spins the drive pinion is thrown forward on a spiral spline to engage with the flywheel ring gear which is then turned. When the engine fires, the overrun of the flywheel throws the pinion back out of mesh.
2   A starter motor is not normally looked at until it goes wrong. However, it is worthwhile giving a periodic check – say, every 5000 miles. This can be done by sliding back the band in order to expose the commutator and brush gear. If an air jet can be used to blow out the dust so much the better. Any signs of dust should be cleaned off with petrol on a cloth and the commutator wiped dry with a non-fluffy cloth. Make sure that the connections are perfectly clean and tight. Look to see if any of the brushes are badly worn. Ensure that the fixing bolts are tight.

---

### 19 Starter motor: Lucas type M35G-1 – circuit testing

1   If the starter motor fails to turn the engine, there are two likely reasons to investigate:

   (a)   *Faulty battery: The electrical connections between switch, solenoid, battery and starter motor are somewhere failing to pass the necessary current from the battery through the starter to earth.*

   (b)   *Faulty solenoid switch: The starter motor is either jammed or electrically defective.*

2   To check the battery, switch on the headlights. If they go dim after a few seconds, the battery is faulty. If the lamps glow brightly, operate the starter switch and see what happens to the lights. If they dim, then you know that power is reaching the starter motor but failing to turn it. Check that it is not jammed by fitting a suitable spanner over the squared end of the shaft and making sure it turns easily. If it is not jammed, the starter will have to come out for examination. If the starter should turn very slowly, go on to the next check.
3   If, when the starter switch is operated, the lights stay bright, then power is not reaching the starter. Check all connections from battery to solenoid switch to starter for perfect cleanliness and tightness. With a good battery fitted this is the most usual cause of starter motor problems. Check that the earth link cable between the engine and frame is also intact and cleanly connected. This can be overlooked when the engine is taken out.
4   If no improvement has been achieved, turn off the headlights to avoid discharging the battery completely. It is likely that a clicking noise will have been heard when operating the starter switch. This is the solenoid switch operating, but it does not necessarily follow that the main contact is closing properly. (**Note**: *if no clicking has been heard from the solenoid it is certainly defective.* The solenoid contact can be checked by putting a voltmeter or bulb across the main cable connection on the starter side of the solenoid and earth. When the switch is operated, there should be a reading or lighted bulb. If not, the solenoid switch is faulty. (Do not put a bulb across the two solenoid terminals. If the motor is not faulty the bulb will blow). If, finally, it is established that the solenoid is not faulty and 12 volts are getting to the starter then the starter motor must be the culprit.

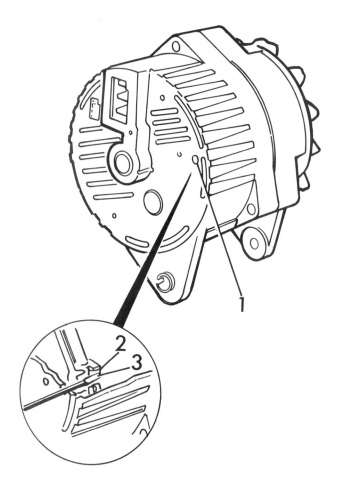

Fig. 10.11 Delco Remy alternator type DN 460 – testing (Sec 17)

   *1    Test hole*
   *2    Screwdriver (blade horizontal) to earth the field winding*
   *3    Screwdriver*

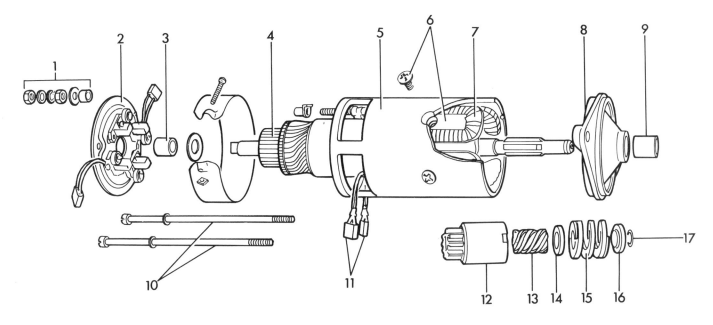

**Fig. 10.12 Starter motor, Lucas M35G -1 – exploded view (Sec 18)**

| | | | |
|---|---|---|---|
| 1 | Terminal nuts and washer | 6 | Pole shoes and screws |
| 2 | Commutator end bracket | 7 | Field coils |
| 3 | Bearing bush | 8 | Drive end bracket |
| 4 | Commutator | 9 | Bearing bush |
| 5 | Yoke | | |

| | | |
|---|---|---|
| 10 | Through-bolts | |
| 11 | Insulated brushes | |
| 12 | Pinion and barrel assembly | |
| 13 | Screwed sleeve | |

| | |
|---|---|
| 14 | Buffer washer |
| 15 | Main spring |
| 16 | Shaft collar |
| 17 | Jump ring |

## 20 Starter motor: Lucas type M35G1 – removal and refitting

1 Disconnect the battery to prevent accidental short circuits.
2 Remove the main cable from the terminal post on the starter motor (photo).
3 Undo the two bolts, one above and one below, holding the motor to the bellhousing. It may then be drawn out. In the photographs the exhaust pipe is shown disconnected from the manifold but this is not necessary to remove the starter (photo).
4 Refitting is a reversal of the removal procedure. Make sure the main terminal is away from the engine, ie do not fit the starter the wrong way up.
5 Note that on some models it is necessary to remove the air cleaner for access purposes. On Holbay engined vehicles, move the front end

of the starter motor towards the air cleaner and not directly backwards.

## 21 Starter motor: Lucas type M35G-1 – dismantling, repair and reassembly

1 Grip the motor in a vice if possible and remove the band cover over the brush gear.
2 Using a piece of stiff hooked wire pull back each of the four carbon brush springs and lift each brush from its holder.
3 Unscrew the two through-bolts and the commutator end bracket may then be taken off. The pinion end bracket complete with armature and drive assembly may then be removed from the yoke.

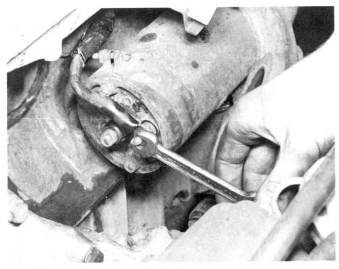

20.2 Disconnecting starter motor lead

20.3 Removing starter motor securing bolts

4   Before proceeding further, it is advisable to check that both the armature and field coils are in order. There is no point in renewing bearings and brushes if the remainder of the unit is unserviceable. To test the armature, proceed in exactly the same way as for the dynamo armature described in Section 7. To test the field coils for continuity is also straightforward. A 12 volt bulb and battery connected in series can be applied with prods to the connections of the field coil brushes. The bulb should light. This, however, only indicates continuity. To test the insulation requires a 110 volt supply (ac will do). Wire a 110 volt bulb (a 220 volt bulb will also do) into the circuit, and test prod between the field coil terminal and the yoke of the motor. If the lamp lights (or glows dimly with a 220 volt bulb), the insulation is broken down and the field coils need renewal.

5   If either the armature or field coils are in need of renewal it is recommended that a complete exchange unit be obtained.

6   The bearing bushes should be checked for wear and removed if necessary by pressing them out with a close fitting mandrel with a suitable size shoulder. Press the new bearing into position using the same tool. Porous bushes should be immersed in clean, thin engine oil before fitting. To renew the bush in the driving end plate will require the starter pinion assembly to be removed first, in order to withdraw the shaft. This is explained in Section 22.

7   If the carbon brushes are below minimum length of $\frac{5}{16}$ in (7.9 mm) they should also be renewed. The two brushes attached to the end cover (not insulated) can be unsoldered and new ones clipped in and re-soldered to the terminal eyelets. The other two brushes connected to the field coils need a little care and attention. Originally they have been resistance brazed to aluminium end tags of the coils. Aluminium cannot be soldered so the old leads must be cut, leaving sufficient copper – at least $\frac{1}{8}$ in (3 mm) – to solder the new leads onto. The insulation must also be in perfect condition because no part of the connecting wire must touch the yoke. When soldering the flexible lead make sure no solder runs along the braid. This would reduce its flexibility and possibly cause it to fracture.

8   Reassembly of the starter motor is a reversal of the dismantling process. Check the brushes in their holders for freedom of movement. If necessary, clean the brushes with petrol, or ease the sides with a fine file in difficult cases. Before putting the end cover in place make sure the brushes are so arranged that they can be easily hooked into position and that their leads are not trapped. Remember also that the springs should all be conveniently ready. The brushes should not be able to fit into the wrong brush boxes but it is worth noting that the two fixed to the end plate only go into holders to which they are attached at the base. (The other two holders are insulated from the end plate).

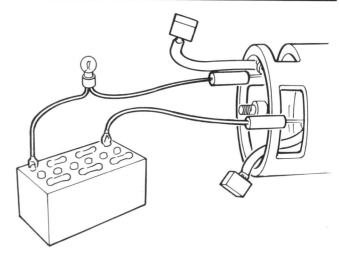

Fig. 10.13 Starter motor, Lucas M35G-1 – field coil continuity test (Sec 21)

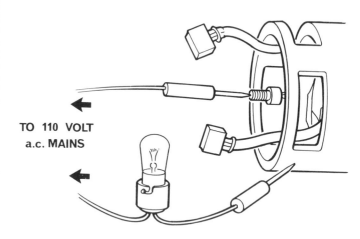

**TO 110 VOLT a.c. MAINS**

Fig. 10.14 Starter motor, Lucas M35G1 – field coil insulation test (Sec 21)

## 22  Starter motor: Lucas type M35G-1 – drive pinion dismantling, repair and reassembly

1   Persistent jamming or reluctance to disengage indicates that the starter pinion assembly needs attention. The starter motor should first be removed.

2   With the motor removed, clean the drive with petrol, taking care to keep any liquid from running into the motor. If there is a lot of dirt, this could be the sole trouble. The pinion should move freely in a spiral movement along the shaft against the light spring and return easily on being released. To do this the spiral splines must be completely clean and free of oil. Oil merely collects dust and gums up the splines. Both springs should be intact. The larger one acts as a shock absorber when the moving pinion engages the stationary flywheel ring gear.

3   Should either spring be broken, or the spiral splines be badly worn, preventing the pinion from moving smoothly, remove the starter drive from the shaft. This requires the heavy spring to be compressed so that the jump ring located in a groove round the shaft inside the shaft collar can be removed. This calls for either a special tool or a device to be made up which will enable the spring to be compressed between the jaws of a vice. Such a device has to be very robust to overcome the strength of the spring.

4   With the jump ring removed, the components of the drive assembly can be removed from the shaft. Renew any parts as necessary, noting that if the pinion is renewed the spiral splined sleeves should also be renewed. Reassembly is a reversal of the dismantling procedure, once again requiring the services of the device to compress the buffer spring.

## 23  Starter motor: Lucas type M35J – general description

1   The Lucas M35J starter motor is of the inertia type, and has a series-wound, four-pole, four-brush motor with an extended shaft which carries a conventional inertia drive.

2   The armature shaft rotates in two porous bronze bushes. A squared extension of the shaft protrudes to enable the shaft to be rotated to clear any jamming between the inertia drive and engine flywheel ring gear. The armature features a face-type moulded commutator.

3   A plastic brush box is riveted to the commutator end bracket. It holds four wedge-shaped brushes and captive coil springs. The brushes are keyed to ensure correct fitting.

4   The field winding is a continuously wound strip with no joints. One end is attached to two brush flexibles, while the other is attached to a single flexible which is earthed to the yoke.

5   The yoke is windowless and has no through-bolts. The commutator end bracket is secured by four screws which align with tappings in the yoke. The drive end bracket is attached by two slot-headed bolts which screw into tappings provided in the end faces of two of the pole-shoes.

6   The principle of operation of the inertia type starter motor is as follows: When the ignition switch is turned, current flows from the battery to the starter motor solenoid switch which causes it to become energised. Its internal plunger moves inwards and closes an internal switch so allowing full starting current to flow from the battery to the starter motor. This creates a powerful magnetic field to be induced into the field coils which causes the armature to rotate.

7    Mounted on helical splines is the drive pinion which, because of the sudden rotation of the armature, is thrown forwards along the armature shaft and so into engagement with the flywheel ring gear. The engine crankshaft will then be rotated until the engine starts to operate on its own and, at this point, the drive pinion is thrown out of mesh with the flywheel ring gear.

## 24 Starter motor: Lucas type M35J (inertia drive) – removal and refitting

1    To dismantle the starter motor drive, use a press or large valve spring compressor to push the retainer clear of the circlip which can then be removed. Lift away the retainer and main spring.
2    Slide off the remaining parts with a rotary action of the armature shaft.
3    It is important that the drivegear is free from oil, grease and dirt. With the drivegear removed, clean all parts in paraffin. Under no circumstances oil the drive components: this can cause the pinion to stick.
4    Reassembly of the starter motor drive is the reverse sequence to dismantling. Use a press or the large valve spring compressor to compress the spring and retainer sufficiently to allow a new circlip to be fitted to its groove on the shaft.

## 25 Starter motor: Lucas type M35J – dismantling, overhaul and reassembly

Should it be necessary to dismantle the starter motor completely, the following operations will facilitate overhaul. Bear in mind, though, that it may be more economical in terms of money plus time, to purchase an exchange unit. The other factor that may mitigate against overhaul is the need for special tools and test gear.
1    To strip the starter, remove the two bolts holding the drive end bracket to the yoke and take off the bracket, withdrawing the armature. Remove the thrust washer from the brush end of the armature.
2    Undo the four small bolts holding on the commutator end bracket. Pull the bracket aside. Note the way the flexible cable from the field windings to the brushes is fitted. Undo these brushes.
3    To separate the armature from the drive end bracket and inertia

drive, remove the inertia drive and slide the drive end bracket from the shaft.
4    Inspect the laminations for score marks. These may indicate a bent shaft, worn bearings or a loose pole shoe.
5    Clean the commutator with petrol. If the commutator is in good condition, it will be smooth and free from pits or burned spots.
6    If necessary, polish the commutator with fine glasspaper. If the commutator is badly scored, it will need skimming. Mount the armature in a lathe and rotate at high speed. Using a very sharp tool, take a light cut. Polish with fine glasspaper. Do not cut below the minimum skimming thickness of 0.080 in (2.05 mm). Do not undercut insulators between segments.
7    Inspect the porous bronze bearing bushes for wear and renew as necessary. To renew the commutator end bracket bush, drill out the two rivets and discard the plate and felt seal. Screw a 0.5 in (12.70 mm) tap squarely into the bush and withdraw. Prepare the porous bronze bush by immersing it in thin engine oil for twenty-four hours. Using a highly polished, shouldered mandrel, suitably dimensioned, and a suitable press, fit the bush. Do not ream the bush after fitting or its porosity may be impaired. Assemble the brush box, felt seal and plate. Secure with two rivets.
8    To renew the drive end bracket bush, remove the inertia drive, and slide the drive end bracket from the shaft. Support the bracket and press out the bush. Prepare the porous bronze bush by immersing it in thin engine oil for twenty-four hours. Using a highly polished, shouldered, mandrel suitably dimensioned, and a suitable press, fit the bush. Do not ream the bush after fitting or its porosity may be impaired.
9    The brushes should be renewed if worn down to a length of 0.375 in (9.5 mm).
10   The commutator end bracket brushes are supplied attached to a new terminal post. Withdraw the two brushes from the brush box. Withdraw the terminal post and remove the insulation piece. Reverse to assemble. Retain the longer flexible under the clip.
11   The field winding brushes are supplied attached to a common flexible. Cut old flexibles $\frac{1}{4}$ in (6 mm) from the joint. Solder the new flexible to the ends of the old flexible. Do not attempt to solder direct to the field winding strip as the strip may be produced from aluminium.
12   Check the field winding insulation from the yoke as follows: Drill out the rivet at the earth connection. Apply the normal 110 volt ac test-lamp circuit to the field winding and yoke. If the lamp lights, the insulation is faulty. If satisfactory, re-rivet the earth connection. Do not

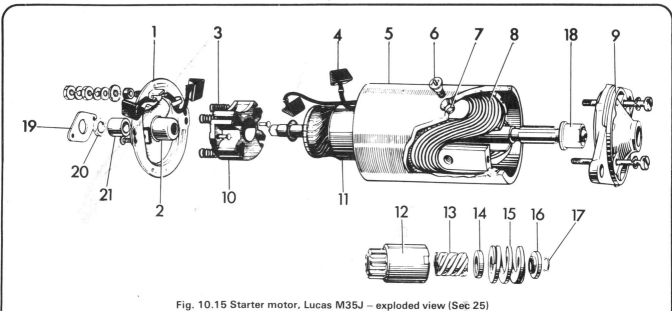

Fig. 10.15 Starter motor, Lucas M35J – exploded view (Sec 25)

| | | |
|---|---|---|
| 1  Commutator end bracket | 7  Pole shoe | 12  Pinion and barrel | 17  Jump ring |
| 2  Bush housing | 8  Field coils | 13  Screwed sleeve | 18  Bearing bush |
| 3  Brush spring | 9  Drive end brackets | 14  Washer | 19  Bush cover |
| 4  Brushes | 10  Brush box moulding | 15  Main spring | 20  Felt washer |
| 5  Yoke | 11  Armature | 16  Cup spring | 21  Bearing bush |
| 6  Pole retaining screw | | | |

attempt to disconnect the flexible from the field windings strip as the strip may be produced from aluminium.

13  To renew the field winding, drill out the rivet at the earth connection. Using a wheel-operated screwdriver, slacken the four pole-shoe screws. Remove two diametrically opposite screws and pole-shoes. Slacken the remaining two screws sufficiently to allow the field winding to be withdrawn from the yoke.

14  Assembly is the reverse of dismantling:

(a)  Insert the two field winding brushes into the brush box with the flexibles positioned as shown in Fig. 10.19
(b)  Position the commutator end bracket and secure it with four BA bolts
(c)  Fit the thrust washer
(d)  Insert the drive end bracket, armature and inertia drive assembly complete into the yoke
(e)  Fit the two drive end bracket nuts and spring washers

## 26  Starter motor: Lucas type M35G (pre-engaged) – description, maintenance and testing

1  The motor part of the pre-engaged starter is no different from the inertia type. The difference is in the method of engaging the driving pinion with the flywheel ring gear. The starter solenoid switch, in addition to making the electrical connection, now also operates a lever which moves the pinion into mesh with the ring gear just before the power is switched to the motor. This results in quieter operation and reduces much of the shock loading on the starter motor. To prevent the engine driving the starter, should the pinion stick, the drive is through a one-way roller type clutch. Also, the pinion is spring-loaded, so that in the event of an exact abutment of gear-teeth preventing engagement, the solenoid will still continue and make power contact and the pinion will move into engagement automatically as soon as the shaft moves. The operating lever, which connects the solenoid plunger to the pinion, pivots on an eccentric pin so that the pinion engagement may be set correctly in relation to the switch contacts.

2  Maintenance and testing procedures are the same as for the other type of starter but, of course, in this case the solenoid switch is mounted on the starter motor casing itself.

## 27  Starter motor: Lucas type M35G (pre-engaged) – removal and refitting

Removal and refitting procedures are the same as those for the inertia type, with the additional requirement that the two feed wires to the solenoid must be pulled off the Lucar connections.

## 28  Starter motor: Lucas type M35G (pre-engaged) – dismantling and reassembly

1  Having removed the starter motor from the car, the solenoid unit may be removed after disconnecting the link cable to the motor from the main terminal.

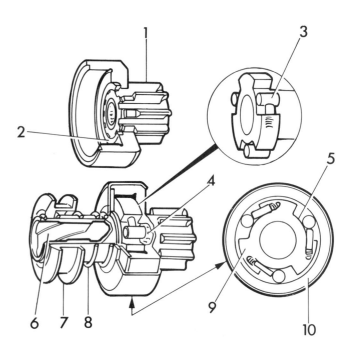

Fig. 10.16 Pre-engaged starter – pinion and roller clutch details (Sec 28)

| | | | |
|---|---|---|---|
| 1 | Alternative construction (pinion pressed and cleat-ringed into driven member) | 5 | Cam tracts |
| 2 | Soft metal cleating ring | 6 | Driving sleeve |
| 3 | Spring-loaded rollers | 7 | Operating bush |
| 4 | Bush | 8 | Engagement spring |
| | | 9 | Driving member |
| | | 10 | Driven member (with pinion) |

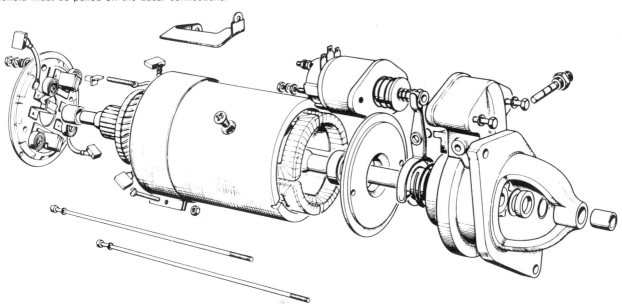

Fig. 10.17 Starter motor, Lucas M35G pre-engaged type (Sec 26)

2   The solenoid plunger can then be disengaged from the lever in the drive end bracket.
3   Take off the brushgear band cover and lift out the two insulated brushes from their holders. Then remove the two through-bolts which hold both end covers to the yoke.
4   Take the end bracket off the commutator and then slacken the locknut on the eccentric pivot bolt and unscrew the pivot bolt from the drive end bracket.
5   The armature should now be removed from the drive end bracket, followed by the engaging lever: Note which way round the lever goes.
6   If the thrust collar on the armature shaft is depressed a small jump ring is revealed. Remove this and the collar, and the drive unit can be drawn off. The driving pinion and clutch are a single assembly, but can be separated from the grooved operating bush by pushing back the bush to reveal another jump ring. This can be removed, thus releasing the bush from the spindle.
7   Checking of the armature field coils, and subsequently bearing bushes and brushgear, should be carried out as described in Section 21.
8   Reassembly is a reversal of the removal procedure. All the components of the drive pin and bearings should be liberally greased on assembly. Adjustment of the eccentric pin may be necessary. The best way is to connect a 6 volt supply between the small terminal of the solenoid and the solenoid casing. This will draw in the plunger as far as the springs which the low power will not permit it to overcome. If the pinion is held back lightly (towards the armature) to take up any lost motion, the gap between the end of the pinion and the thrust collar should be 0.010 in (0.28 mm). The eccentric pin should be moved to achieve this. The arrow head on the pivot bolt should point only towards the arrowed arc marked in the bracket, as the adjustment range is through 180° only.

## 29 Starter motor: Lucas type M39J PE – general description

The M35J PE starter motor comprises the motor part of the M35J starter previously described and a pre-engagement drive pinion mechanism. When the device is energised, a solenoid mounted on the motor body energises and actuates the drive pinion into engagement in the flywheel ring gear. To allow for the possibility of overrun, the pinion drive is transmitted through a one-way roller clutch.

## 30 Starter motor: Lucas type M35J PE – dismantling, overhaul and reassembly

1   It will be necessary to dismantle the starter motor if checks indicate that failure to turn the engine is due to faults with it. After some time the brushes will also wear sufficiently to warrant renewal.
2   The solenoid may be removed after detaching the short connecting cable from the other main terminal and removing the two securing nuts. If this is all that needs renewal, a new one can be fitted over the existing plunger now.
3   To dismantle the motor further, remove the short bolts, or through-bolts, which hold the commutator end bracket with the brush gear to the main yoke. Remove the split pin, washers and shims from the end of the shaft. The end bracket may then be carefully removed. Do not lose the thrust washer, which is located over the end of the shaft, inside.

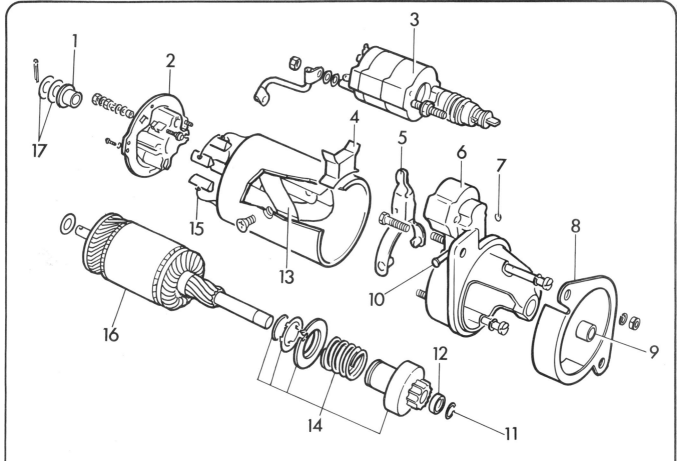

Fig. 10.18 Starter motor, Lucas M35J PE pre-engaged type – exploded view (Sec 30)

| 1 | Bush commutator end | 6 | Drive end bracket | 11 | Jump ring | 15 | Brush set |
|---|---|---|---|---|---|---|---|
| 2 | Commutator end bracket | 7 | Pivot pin retainer | 12 | Thrust collar | 16 | Armature |
| 3 | Solenoid | 8 | Dust cover | 13 | Field coil set | 17 | Thrust washer – shim set |
| 4 | Grommet | 9 | Bush – drive end | 14 | Drive – roller clutch | | |
| 5 | Engagement lever | 10 | Pivot pin | | assembly | | |

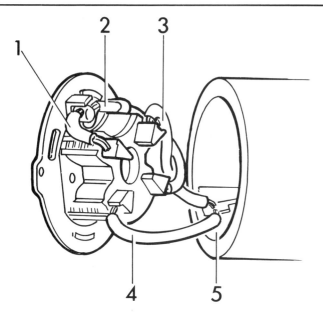

**Fig. 10.19 Starter motor, Lucas M35J PE pre-engaged type –
brush lead terminations (Sec 30)**

*1   Short brush – flexible, commutator end bracket*
*2   Long brush – flexible, commutator end bracket*
*3   Long brush – flexible , field winding*
*4   Short brush – flexible, field winding*
*5   Yoke insulator – field connection joint*

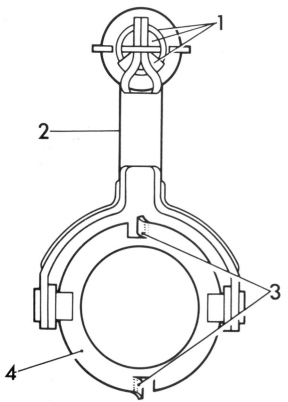

**Fig. 10.20 Engagement lever and solenoid plunger – correct
assembly (Sec 30)**

*1   Plunger, 'lost motion' spring
     and retaining plate*
*2   Drive engagement lever*
*3   Locking shoulders*
*4   Drive operating plate*

4   Remove the bolts holding the drive end cover in position (if necessary) and the end cover complete with armature and shaft may be drawn out of the yoke.

5   Take off the pivot pin retaining ring. Push out the pin.

6   To take the drive pinion and clutch assembly off the armature shaft, drive the thrust collar down the shaft with a piece of suitable tube and then remove the circlip which is exposed. If the driving gear assembly is worn, the whole unit should be renewed. Check the roller clutch is in good condition: it should lock and take up the drive in one direction immediately it is turned. When turned in the opposite direction it should rotate smoothly and evenly. The whole clutch unit should also slide easily without excessive play along the splines of the armature shaft.

7   Examination of the motor is similar to the procedure given in Section 25.

8   Assembly must be carried out in sequence, paying careful attention to several points:

9   Assemble the engagement lever to the solenoid plunger so the chamfered corner faces the solenoid. Then, make sure the retaining plate is correct, relative to the lever (see Fig. 10.20).

10   Fit the drive pinion and clutch assembly on the armature shaft, fit the engagement lever fork to the clutch, and assemble the whole to the drive end cover. Fit a new lever pivot and a new retaining ring.

11   Refit the yoke, and then lightly screw up the end cover bolts (if fitted).

12   Place the thrust washer over the commutator end of the shaft, fit all the brushes in their appropriate holders in the end cover and refit the end cover on the shaft. Both end covers have locating pips to ensure they are fitted correctly to the yoke.

13   Refit the through-bolts or end cover bolts as appropriate and tighten them up at both ends.

14   Refit the thrust washer and shims on the end of the shaft. Fit a split pin and, measure the endfloat gap between the thrust washer and the end cover with a feeler gauge. It should be no more than 0.010 in (0.25 mm). Additional shims should be added to reduce the endfloat as required.

15   Refit the rubber pad between the drive end bracket (under the solenoid plunger housing) and the yoke, and refit the solenoid. Reconnect the short cable to the solenoid terminal.

## 31  Control box: Lucas type RB340 – general description

1   The control box comprises two separate vibrating armature-type single contact regulators and a cut-out relay. One of the regulators is sensitive to changes in current and the other to changes in voltage.

2   Adjustment can only be made with a special tool which resembles a screwdriver with a multi-toothed blade. This can be obtained through Lucas agents.

3   The regulators control the output from the dynamo depending on the state of the battery and the demands of the electrical equipment, and ensure the battery is not overcharged. The cut-out is really an automatic switch and connects the dynamo to the battery when the dynamo is turning fast enough to produce a charge. Similarly it disconnects the battery from the dynamo when the engine is idling or stationary so that the battery does not discharge through the dynamo.

## 32  Control box: Lucas type RB340 – maintenance

1   Every 10 000 miles check the cut-out and regulator contacts. If they are dirty, rough or burnt, place a piece of fine glasspaper (*do not use emery paper or carborundum paper*) between the cut-out contacts, close them manually and draw the glass paper through several times. Disconnect the battery before cleaning the contacts.

2   Clean the regulator contacts in exactly the same way, but use emery or carborundum paper and not glasspaper. Carefully clean both sets of contacts with a rag moistened in methylated spirits.

## 33  Control box: Lucas type RB340 – voltage regulator adjustment

1   The regulator requires little attention during its service life, and should there be any reason to suspect its correct functioning, tests of all circuits should be made.

2 These checks include the tension of the fanbelt, to make sure it is not slipping and so providing only a very low charge rate. The battery should be carefully checked for possible low charge rate due to a faulty cell, or corroded battery connections.

3 The leads from the generator may have been crossed during refitting, and if this is the case then the regulator points will have stuck together as soon as the generator starts to charge. Check for loose or broken leads from the generator to the regulator.

4 If after a thorough check it is considered advisable to test the regulator, this should only be carried out by an electrician who is well acquainted with the correct method, using test bench equipment.

5 Pull off the Lucar connections from the two adjacent control box terminals 'B'. Join these cables together and insulate the join, to ensure damage is not sustained by their short-circuiting to adjacent terminals.

6 Connect a 0 to 20 volt moving coil voltmeter between control box terminal 'WL' (the connection wire may be removed if convenient, for this test), and a good earth (voltmeter negative to earth).

7 Start the engine and run it at about 2000 rpm. The voltmeter reading should lie between the following limits:

| Ambient temperature | Voltage setting |
| --- | --- |
| 10°C (50°F) | 14.9 to 15.5 |
| 20°C (68°F) | 14.7 to 15.3 |
| 30°C (86°F) | 14.5 to 15.1 |
| 40°C (104°F) | 14.3 to 14.9 |

If the reading is unsteady, this may be due to dirty contacts. If the reading is outside the specified limits stop the engine and adjust the voltage regulator in the following manner.

8 Take off the control box cover and start and run the engine at 2000 rpm. Using the correct tool, turn the voltage adjustment cam to raise or lower the setting. To check that the setting is correct, stop the engine, and then start it and run it at 2000 rpm noting the reading. Refit the cover and restore all connections to normal.

## 34 Control box: Lucas type RB340 – current regulator adjustment

1 The output from the current regulator should equal the maximum output from the dynamo which is 22 amps.

2 Remove the cover from the control box, and short circuit the voltage regulator contacts together by closing them with a clip.

3 Pull off the wires from the adjacent terminals 'B' and connect them together. Do not permit them to short on other items. Connect a 0 to 40 amp moving coil ammeter between the join in these cables and terminal 'B'.

4 Start the engine, switch on all lights, and run at about 2000 rpm, when an ammeter reading of 22 amps should be obtained. Adjust the current regulator cam if necessary with the proper tool, clockwise to raise the setting or anti-clockwise to lower it. An unsteady reading may be caused by dirty contacts. Clean as described in Section 32, and retest.

5 Restore connections to normal.

## 35 Control box: Lucas type RB340 – cut-out adjustment

1 The cut-out contacts should close at between 12.7 and 13.3 volts. If the setting is incorrect, withdraw the lead from terminal 'WL' on the control box, and connect the positive lead of a 0 to 20 volt moving coil voltmeter to the exposed terminal. Connect the other side of the voltmeter to a good earth. Start the engine.

2 Slowly increase engine speed, and observe the voltmeter pointer. This should rise steadily, and drop slightly at the point of contact closure. If outside the limits given in paragraph 1, adjust the setting as follows.

3 Using the Lucas tool, and with the engine speed reduced, turn the cut-out relay adjustment cam clockwise to raise the setting or anti-clockwise to lower it. Recheck, and adjust again if necessary until the correct setting is obtained.

4 Stop the engine and restore the original connections.

5 The contacts should open between 9.5 and 11 volts. To check, withdraw the cables from terminals 'B' and connect a 0 to 20 volt moving-coil voltmeter between terminal 'B' and a good earth. Join the detached cables, and insulate them to prevent short circuiting.

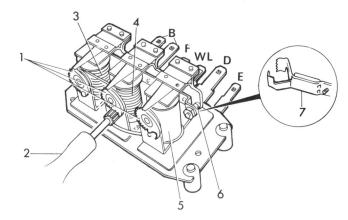

**Fig. 10.21 Dynamo control box, Lucas type RB340 (Sec 33)**

| | |
| --- | --- |
| 1 Adjusting cams | 5 Voltage regulator |
| 2 Lucas setting tool | 6 Voltage regulator contacts |
| 3 Cut-out relay | 7 Clip |
| 4 Current regulator | |

6 Start the engine, increase speed to about 3000 rpm, decelerate and observe the voltmeter. The reading should suddenly drop to zero between the limits of 9.5 and 11.0 volts.

7 If necessary, adjust by carefully bending the fixed contact bracket. Reduce the contact gap to raise the reading, increase the gap to lower the reading. Repeat and re-adjust as necessary.

8 Restore the original connections.

## 36 Alternator control: Lucas type 4TR – general description

1 This control is the only one required in an alternator charging circuit, the function of the unit being to maintain the alternator terminal voltage at a predetermined value. The use of silicon semiconductor devices results in a control which employs no moving parts.

2 The only adjustment which can be carried out is to the voltage setting. However, it is necessary to have an accurate, good quality voltmeter for this purpose, and additionally to follow a very careful procedure. In the circumstances, it is therefore advised that the average owner should consult an auto electrician if a fault is suspected in the unit.

## 37 Alternator control: Lucas type 8TR – general description

The comments in Section 36 apply equally to this unit. It may be employed as either a separate unit, or as a built-in unit, depending upon which alternator is being used.

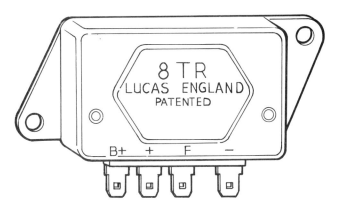

**Fig. 10.22 The 8TR regulator with 16AC alternators (Sec 37)**

## 38 Fuse unit: Lucas type 8FJ – general description

The unit holds three fuses which are in circuit, and has provision for storing two spares. The unit pushes into the bulkhead and is held in place by wedge-shaped clips moulded as part of the base. Connections to the fuse unit will be made clear by reference to the appropriate circuit diagram.

## 39 Fuse unit: 8-fuse type – Series 4 and 5 models

1  With the introduction of the Series 4 and 5 models, the three fuse unit made way for one with eight fuses. These are housed in a plastic holder mounted on the bulkhead. In-line fuses, provided for the heated rear window and hazard warning lights, are located close to the steering column. The eight fuses comprise:

| Fuse No | Colour/ Rating | Circuits protected |
|---|---|---|
| 1 | Red 16A | Ignition controlled: Horn, stop lamp, petrol gauge, water temperature gauge, screen wiper, blower |
| 2 | White 8A | Cigar lighter, interior lamps, clock |
| 3 | White 8A | Right-hand sidelamp, tail lamp, boot lamp and fascia illumination |
| 4 | White 8A | Left-hand sidelamp, tail lamp and number plate |
| 5 | Red 16A | Right-hand headlamp main beam |
| 6 | Red 16A | Left-hand headlamp main beam |
| 7 | White 8A | Right-hand dipped beam |
| 8 | White 8A | Left-hand dipped beam |

The two in-line fuses comprise:

| | | |
|---|---|---|
| In-line Fuse 15A | | Heated rear window (12 amp continuous) |
| In-line Fuse 8A | | Hazard warning system |

2  Always fit replacement fuses of the correct type and rating. If a replacement fuse blows almost immediately, the cause of this must be established. Do not renew again, or fit a fuse with a higher rating.

## 40 Fuse unit: 8-fuse type – Series 6 models onwards

Series 6 fuses have been altered slightly from those of the Series 4 and 5 as follows:

| Fuse No | Colour/ Rating | Circuits protected |
|---|---|---|
| 1 | White 8A | Ignition controlled: Horn, stop lamp, fuel gauge, water temperature gauge, screen wash, reverse lights, screen wiper, turn indicators, voltmeter (Sceptre only) |
| 2 | White 8A | Cigar lighter, interior light, clock, boot lamp |
| 3 | White 8A | Right-hand sidelamp, tail lamp, fascia lamps, rear fog lamps |
| 4 | White 8A | Left-hand sidelamp, tail lamp, number plate |
| 5 | Red 16A | Heated backlight |
| 6 | White 8A | Heater fan motor, voltmeter (Voltmeter to Fuse 1 on Sceptre) |
| 7 | White 8A | Right-hand dipped beam |
| 8 | White 8A | Left-hand dipped beam |

The in-line fuses comprise:

| | | |
|---|---|---|
| In-line Fuse 15A | | Hazard warning |

## 41 Direction indicator system: type FL5 – fault finding

1  The unit which causes the lights to flash intermittently is contained in a three inch long cylinder clipped under the dashboard. It has three terminals at one end.

2  If the flashers fail to work properly, check all the bulbs are

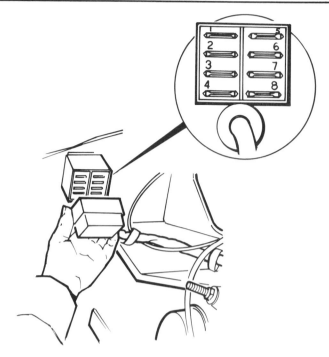

Fig. 10.23 Fuse box – 8-fuse unit (Sec 39)

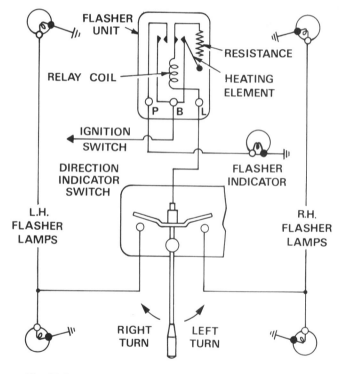

Fig. 10.24 Flasher unit type FL5 – circuit diagram (Sec 41)

serviceable and of the correct wattage. Check the nuts which hold the lamp bodies to the car are tight and free from corrosion. These are the means by which the circuit is completed and resistance here can affect the working of the coils in the flasher unit.

3  If still inoperative bridge the 'B' and 'L' terminals on the flasher unit, when the switch is operated the lights should go on (on the appropriate side) and stay on. If they do the flasher unit is faulty. If they do not, first make sure that with the ignition switched on, current is reaching the 'B' terminal at the flasher circuit. If it is then the indicator switch is faulty. If not, the connection from the ignition switch to the flasher unit is faulty (via the fuse).

## 42 Flasher unit: type 8FL – description and fault diagnosis

1 This unit is not interchangeable with the FL5 unit, and is produced in a number of different current ratings to suit the circuit into which it is fitted. The ratings are specified on the unit. Correct replacement bulbs must always be used to maintain proper operation.

2 The unit is held in a clip beneath the steering column. Removal is an obvious procedure.

3 Before deciding whether a replacement flasher unit is required, a proper wiring check should be carried out; intermittent or continuous short circuits can cause failure. Testing by substituting a new unit is strongly advised against.

4 Remove the flasher unit. Switch off the ignition, disconnect the two wires and connect them to an ammeter 0 to 10 amperes. Switch on the ignition. Move the direction indicator switch to each 'on' position, when the respective indicator lamps should light and the ammeter indicate the current rating marked on the flasher unit. A high reading in both switch positions indicates a switch fault. A high reading on one side indicates a wiring, connection and/or lamp fault on that side. Test each section of the circuit. A low current reading implies excessive circuit resistance. If on both sides, the fault is either in the supply to the flasher, or in the switch contacts. If on one side only, check the bulbs are of the correct wattage and the bulb connections to the lamp holder (both supply and earth) are good. Check the snap connectors and wiring. If there is no ammeter reading check the No 1 fuse. Check the supply line connections between the fuse block and terminal 'B'.

5 If a hazard warning switch is fitted, check continuity between terminals 7 and 8 with the switch 'off'. If there is no continuity the switch is faulty. Faulty contacts in this switch can make the flasher unit inoperative.

## 43 Windscreen wiper system: Lucas type DL3A – general description

A two-speed system is employed, the layout of which can be clearly seen from Fig. 10.26. A three-position switch gives 'off', 'normal' and 'high' speed positions.

## 44 Fault diagnosis – windscreen wiper system (Lucas type DL3A)

1 If the wipers fail to operate, first check that current is reaching the motor, by switching on and using a voltmeter or 12 volt bulb and two wires between the '+' terminal on the motor and earth. On two-speed motors there are three leads from the motor. There should be a reading from two of them.

2 If no current is reaching the motor, check if there is any at the switch. If there is, a break has occurred in the wiring between switch and motor.

3 If there is no current at the switch, go back to the ignition switch and so isolate the area of the fault.

4 If current is reaching the motor but the wipers do not operate, switch on and give the wiper arms a push – they or the motor could be jammed. Switch off immediately if nothing happens, or further damage to the motor may occur. If the wipers run the reason for the jamming must be found. It will almost certainly be due to wear in either the linkage of the wiper mechanism or the mechanism in the motor gearbox.

5 If the wipers run too slowly, it will be due to something restricting the free operation of the linkage or a fault in the motor. Check the current being used by connecting an ammeter in the circuit. If it exceeds three amps something is restricting free movement. If less, then the commutator and brush gear in the motor are suspect.

6 If wear is obviously causing malfunction or there is a fault in the motor, remove the motor or wiper mechanism for further examination and repairs.

## 45 Windscreen wiper system: Lucas type DL3A – removal and refitting

1 Disconnect the battery and remove the air intake grille in front of the windscreen. It is held in position by three screws. Detach the water pipe.

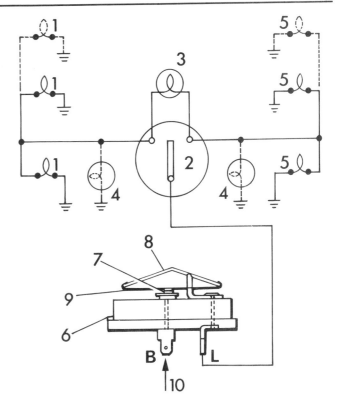

Fig. 10.25 Flasher unit type 8FL – circuit diagram (Sec 42)

1 Direction indicator lamps (left-hand)
2 Direction indicators switch
3 Pilot warning lamp
4 Alternative connection for two pilot warning lamps
5 Direction indicator lamps
  (right-hand)
6 Base moulding
7 Contacts
8 Vane
9 Metal ribbon
10 Supply terminal

2 Remove the wiper blades and arm assemblies by pulling them off the splined spindles. Be careful not to bend the arms – the boss should be levered a little if it is tight.

3 Remove the nut, washers and rubber bushes holding the spindles to the bulkhead.

4 From inside the car, remove the screws and studs securing the parcel shelf and also the right-hand demister air tube which is held onto the heater box by two nuts.

5 Remove the glove box lid by undoing the five screws and unhooking the check strap. Remove the two screws holding the box itself in position and lift that out.

6 The cables leading to the motor are next disconnected and the large self-tapping screw which holds the motor and mechanism to the bulkhead bracket is then removed. The whole assembly can then be lifted out.

7 When refitting the assembly make sure that the earthing cable is refitted to the securing screw and that the rubber bushes are fitted exactly as they came off.

## 46 Windscreen wiper system: Lucas type DL3A – dismantling and reassembly

1 The exploded drawings indicate the layout of the motor, and by removing the through-bolts, the commutator and brushgear can be examined. Normally, if the wiper motor fails, it is due to excessive loading, caused either by wear or by jamming of the wiper arm link mechanism. Consequently, renewal of the complete motor is the best answer. Brushgear can be obtained separately if it is conclusive that this is the only fault. Similarly, the large gearwheel and spindle can be

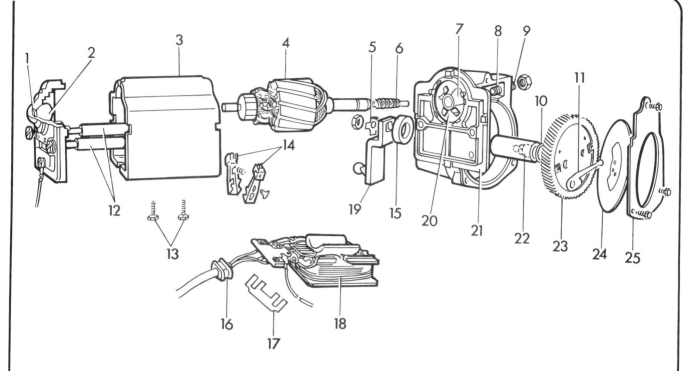

Fig. 10.26 Windscreen wiper motor type DL3A, two speed – exploded view (Sec 46)

| | | |
|---|---|---|
| 1 | Thrust pad | 8 | Thrust pad | 15 | Bush | 21 | Drive end bracket |
| 2 | Self-aligning bearing | 9 | Endplay adjuster | 16 | Grommet | 22 | Porous bronze bush |
| 3 | Yoke | 10 | Washer | 17 | Brush lever retainer | 23 | Final gear |
| 4 | Armature | 11 | Moving contact | 18 | Field coil | 24 | Limit switch fixed contact |
| 5 | Tab washer | 12 | Through-bolt | 19 | Rotating output crank | | plate |
| 6 | Worm gear | 13 | Pole-piece screws | 20 | Bearing retaining ring | 25 | Gearbox cover |
| 7 | Self-aligning bearing | 14 | Brushgear | | | | |

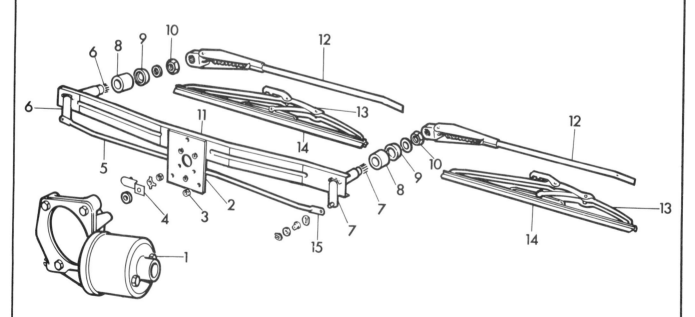

Fig. 10.27 Windscreen wiper mechanism – exploded view (Sec 46)

| | | |
|---|---|---|
| 1 | Motor unit | 5 | Primary link (left-hand) | 9 | Bush – front | 13 | Blade assembly |
| 2 | Mounting bracket | 6 | Spindle (left-hand) | 10 | Locknut | 14 | Squeegee |
| 3 | Nut | 7 | Spindle (right-hand) | 11 | Link set | 15 | Primary link (right-hand) |
| 4 | Rotary link | 8 | Bush – rear | 12 | Wiper arm | | |

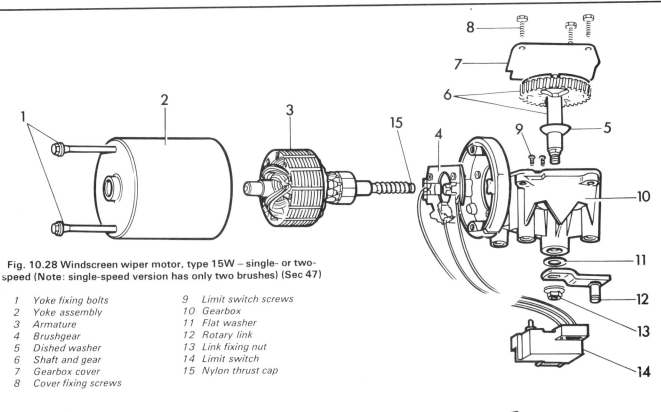

Fig. 10.28 Windscreen wiper motor, type 15W – single- or two-speed (Note: single-speed version has only two brushes) (Sec 47)

1   Yoke fixing bolts
2   Yoke assembly
3   Armature
4   Brushgear
5   Dished washer
6   Shaft and gear
7   Gearbox cover
8   Cover fixing screws
9   Limit switch screws
10  Gearbox
11  Flat washer
12  Rotary link
13  Link fixing nut
14  Limit switch
15  Nylon thrust cap

obtained. Any serious wear in the armature spindle bushes however, is not a matter of simply renewing the bushes as these are part of the end covers.

2   If a new motor is fitted (or the old one repaired) it is important to make sure the wiper arm mechanism operates smoothly and freely, or the motor could be ruined again. The nylon crankpin bushes should be renewed if worn, and the wiper spindles must be a good fit in their sleeves. If in doubt, renew the whole assembly.

## 47 Windscreen wiper system: Lucas type 15W – general description

1   This wiper supersedes the DL3A. Models with dynamos have a single-speed unit, those with alternators, a two-speed unit.
2   No general lubrication is required.
3   Fault diagnosis, removal and refitting procedures are generally as described in Sections 44, 45 and 46.

## 48 Windscreen washer (manual) – maintenance and testing

1   The washer is a simple pump which draws water from a reservoir and pumps it along a pipe to the jets. It is operated by the combined wiper/washer switch.
2   If nothing comes out of the jets when the pump is operated, disconnect the pipe from the jets. Operate the pump again, and if water comes from the pipes it is obviously the jets which are blocked. If no water comes down the pipe, trace all the pipes and connections to be sure that there are no breaks, hardened kinks or flattened sections. Blow through the pipes to make sure they are clear.
3   As a last resort, remove the pump from the back of the instrument panel (see Section 61) and check its operation with a piece of pipe in a bowl of water. If it does not pump, a replacement will be required.

## 49 Windscreen washer (electrical) – maintenance and testing

1   On some later models, a sealed motor and pump assembly is located in an external pocket of the plastic fluid container.
2   Maintenance of the assembly is limited to occasional removal of

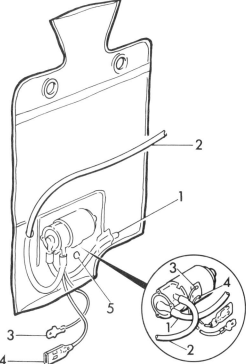

Fig. 10.29 Electric windscreen washer – pump and container (Sec 49)

1   Plastic pipe, pump inlet
2   Plastic pipe, pump outlet
3   Motor supply wire and terminal, coloured
4   Motor earth wire and terminal, black
5   Flap retaining stud, pump pocket

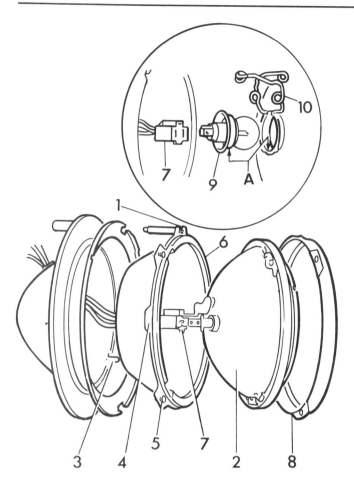

**Fig. 10.30 Headlamp, circular type F700 Mk 10 – exploded view
(Inset A shows bulb loctions) (Sec 51)**

| | |
|---|---|
| 1   Vertical adjustment screw | 7   Adaptor |
| 2   Sealed beam light unit | 8   Unit rim |
| 3   Tensioning spring | 9   Bulb (European type) |
| 4   Horizontal adjustment screw | 10   Bulb retainer (European |
| 5   Rim retaining screw |       type) |
| 6   Seating rim | |

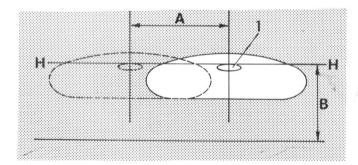

**Fig. 10.31 Main beam pattern for seven inch circular headlamps,
for early type 2FR headlamps with No 451 bulbs and No 1 (inner)
lamps of the four headlamp system (Sec 51)**

A      Distance between headlamp centres
B      Height of headlamp centres minus 2 in (5 mm)
H      Horizontal line 2 in (50 mm) below headlamp centres
1      Concentrated area of light 5 in (130 mm) wide at 25 ft (7.5 m)
Tolerance: 6 in (150 mm) left to 6 in (150 mm) right at 25 ft (7.5 m)

the container from the car, removal of the pump from the external pocket, disconnecting the plastic inlet pipe from the pump body and swilling the container in warm water. At the same time, check the pipes are not blocked.

3   If the unit fails to operate, check the wiring and fuse. If this is satisfactory, rig up a temporary lead between the right-hand (negative) motor terminal and earth. If the pump fails to operate when the ignition is switched on, the unit is faulty and must be renewed.

## 50   Horn: Lucas type 6H – maintenance and testing

1   Should either or both horns fail, the first thing to do is make sure that current is reaching the horn terminals. Do this by connecting a 12 volt test lamp to the feed wire and pressing the horn button with the ignition switch on. If the bulb lights, the fault must lie in the horn or the horn mounting. The tightness and cleanliness of the horn mounting is important as the circuit is made to earth through the fixing bolt. The connections should, of course, be a clean tight fit on the horn terminals.

2   If no current is reaching the horn, check the fuse and wiring connections as indicated in the wiring diagram.

3   Having established that the fault is in the horn, the adjusting screw can be used. Do not touch the centre screw which is preset and is not to be adjusted. The adjusting screw is near the terminals and can be turned in either direction. Rotate the screw anti-clockwise until all sound ceases. Rotate it clockwise for a quarter turn. As the fuse can be blown during adjustment, this should be temporarily shorted out.

4   If a satisfactory note cannot be obtained, the horn must be renewed.

## 51   Headlamps: F700 Mk10 type – description, adjustment, removal and refitting

1   These are normally sealed beam units, although certain European versions have renewable bulbs.

2   To remove the lamp unit either for renewal or bulb renewal, first remove the grille by taking out the crosshead screws.

3   Remove the screws holding the lamp rim, lift the unit forward, and detach the cable plug. In the case of renewable bulbs, unclip the holder and take out the bulb. Do not handle the glass parts of replacement bulbs.

4   When refitting the unit, make sure the three projections on the rear are correctly positioned. The top one is so marked.

5   Beam setting should normally be done with the proper optical equipment, but a good guide can be obtained by using the alignment diagram as given. This shows how the lights should aim in the main beam condition with a full complement of oil, fuel and water, facing squarely a vertical surface at a distance of 25 feet (7.6 metres). Each lamp should be masked whilst the other is adjusted by means of the vertical and horizontal adjustment screws provided. Ensure the tyres are correctly inflated and the vehicle is on level ground, whilst this is done. See the diagram for adjusting screws.

## 52   Headlamps: 2FR type (rectangular) – description, adjustment, removal and refitting

1   These are a renewable bulb type unit, the early and late bulbs being of differing types.

2   To renew the bulb, remove the grille, disengage the spring clip, draw the unit forward to clear the horizontal adjusting supports and turn slightly clockwise to disengage it from the vertical adjuster.

3   To renew a bulb on the early unit, press the contact plate towards the unit, rotate it anti-clockwise and withdraw it complete with bulb. Do not handle the glass envelope of replacement bulbs. On the later version, remove the cable connector, release the spring clips and withdraw the bulb.

4   Refitting the unit is the reverse of the removal procedure.

5   The general instructions concerning beam setting in Section 51 paragraph 5 are applicable. Employ the relevant diagram. Note that later types are adjusted on the dipped beam.

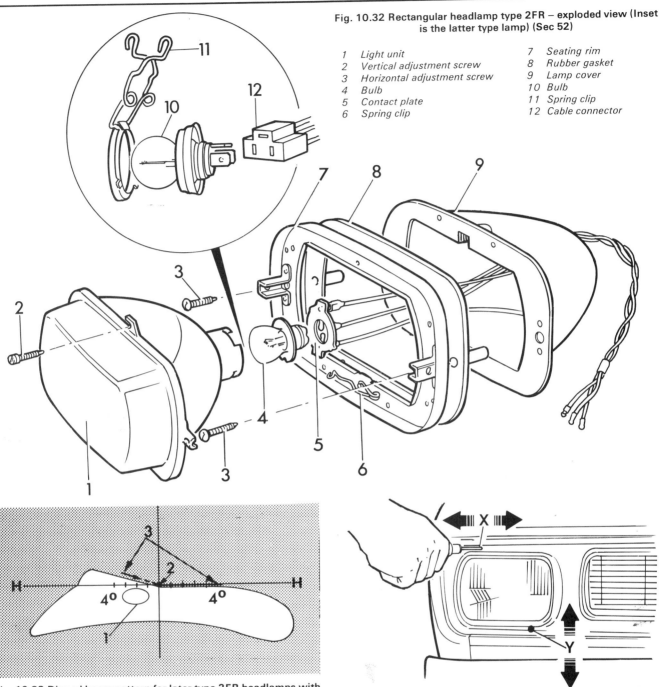

**Fig. 10.32 Rectangular headlamp type 2FR – exploded view (Inset is the latter type lamp) (Sec 52)**

1  Light unit
2  Vertical adjustment screw
3  Horizontal adjustment screw
4  Bulb
5  Contact plate
6  Spring clip
7  Seating rim
8  Rubber gasket
9  Lamp cover
10  Bulb
11  Spring clip
12  Cable connector

**Fig. 10.33 Dipped beam pattern for later type 2FR headlamps with bulb No 410 or 411 – also for 4FR headlamps (Sec 52)**

1  Concentrated area of light
2  Beam 'kink' aiming point
3  Beam 'cut-off' (light/dark boundary)
H  Horizontal line 4 in (100 mm) below headlamp centres
Tolerance of point 2: 6 in (150 mm) to left only at 25 ft (7.5 mm) – no tolerance to right permitted 1° = 5 in (130 mm) at 25 ft (7.5 m)

**Fig. 10.34 Headlamp type 4FR – adjusting screws (Sec 53)**

X – Horizontal adjustment
Y – Vertical adjustment

## 53 Headlamp: 4FR type (rectangular) – description, adjustment, removal and refitting

1   These units are similar to the 2FR rectangular units referred to in Section 52, except that they are retained by four screws which are accessible once the grille has been removed. When the headlights are withdrawn, care should be taken not to lose the four rubber anti-rattle pads.

2   Adjustment is provided by the two screws accessible through the front grille. The beam pattern is as for the later 2FR unit.

## 54 Headlamps: Lucas type F575 (dual system) – description, adjustment, removal and refitting

1   Dual circular $5\frac{3}{4}$ in (128 mm) Lucas sealed beam units are fitted to certain models. Others have similar assemblies with renewable pre-focus bulbs.

### Lucas unit – removal and refitting

2   Remove the securing screws and headlamp finisher.

3   Loosen the three screws securing the unit and rim. Turn the unit anti-clockwise to align the large keyhole slots with the screw heads.

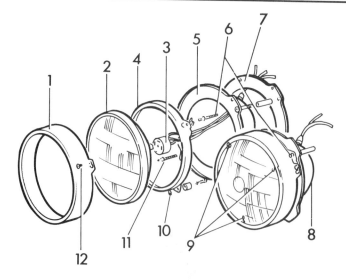

Fig. 10.35 Headlamp, dual type F575 (Sec 54)

1   Front rim
2   Light unit (2A)
3   Cable adaptor
4   Seating rim
5   Lamp body
6   Beam adjustment screw
    (vertical)
7   Sealing gasket
8   Lamp body
9   Aiming pads
10  Retaining ring
11  Beam adjustment screw
    (horizontal)
12  Rim retaining screw

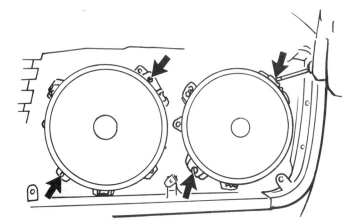

Fig. 10.36 Dual circular headlamps – beam adjusting screws
(Sec 54)

4   Lift the unit clear and detach the wiring connector. Where the bulb is of the renewable type, the holder may be unclipped and the bulb removed.
5   Do not attempt to clean the reflective surface on units fitted with a bulb.
6   Refitting is a reverse of the removal sequence.

## Marchal unit – removal and refitting

7   Remove the securing screws and headlamp finisher.
8   The unit is retained by three ball ends that 'snap' into recesses in the shell. Withdraw the light unit by forcing it out of the shell with finger and thumb pressure applied at the two adjusting screws.
9   Disconnect the wiring plug and remove the rubber plug from the bulb. Remove the bulb retaining springs, and lift out the bulb.
10  Refitting is a reverse of the removal procedure. Care must be taken not to touch the glass envelope of the bulb when fitting into the unit.
11  Beam adjustment should normally be performed with the proper optical equipment, but a good guide can be obtained by using the alignment diagram, Fig. 10.37. Each of the lamps should be masked while checking the alignment of the other lamp opposite. The lamps should be switched to main beam.

## 55 Headlamps: Cibie type (rectangular) – description, adjustment, removal and refitting

1   This headlight is fixed to the shell in exactly the same way as the Marchal unit fitted to the four headlamp model. Refer to Section 54, paragraph 8 after removing the screws and radiator grille.
2   Adjustment is as for the later type Lucas 2FR unit, described in Section 52.

## 56 Front sidelamp and flasher assembly

1   The units are not interchangeable from one side of the car to the other.
2   To renew bulbs, remove the two screws which hold the two-colour lens in position. Do not disturb the rubber lens seal unless it has deteriorated and needs renewal.
3   The bulbs may then be removed by pressing and twisting anti-clockwise.
4   Both bulbs are single filament type, and the bayonet caps will fit either way round.
5   When refitting the lens, do not overtighten the screws or the rubber seal will be over-compressed and made less effective.
6   It is important for correct completion of the circuit that the bulb holder sleeves and the unit fixing screws are all quite free of any signs of corrosion or rust. Also they must be tight. Intermittent operation or lamp dimness is usually caused by these faults.
7   Removal of the complete lamp assembly is effected by disconnecting the battery, and disconnecting the lamp cables at the snap connectors adjacent to the radiator. Remove the two bolts securing the lamp mounting plate, and remove the lamp complete with cables.

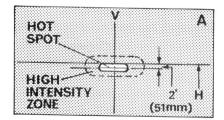
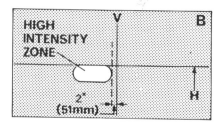
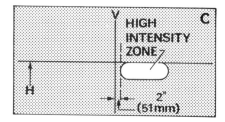

Fig. 10.37 Dual circular headlamps – beam alignment (Sec 54)

A   Inner lamps
B   Outer lamps, right-hand drive
C   Outer lamps, left-hand drive
H   Height of headlamp centre above ground
V   Vertical line through headlamp centre

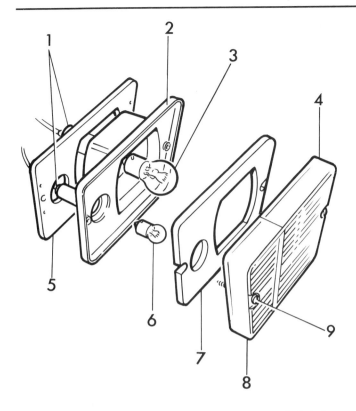

**Fig. 10.38** Front sidelamp and flasher assembly – exploded view
(Sec 56)

| | | | |
|---|---|---|---|
| 1 | Bulb holders | 6 | Sidelight bulb |
| 2 | Lamp body | 7 | Rubber lens gasket |
| 3 | Flasher bulb | 8 | Sidelight lens |
| 4 | Flasher lens | 9 | Fixing screw |
| 5 | Rubber mounting gasket | | |

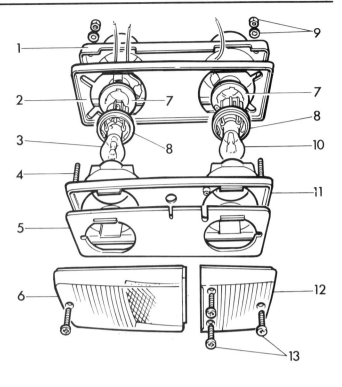

**Fig. 10.39** Rear side, stop and flasher assembly, earlier type –
exploded view (Sec 57)

| | | | |
|---|---|---|---|
| 1 | Rear plastic cover | 7 | Rubber sealing caps |
| 2 | Rubber mounting gasket | 8 | Bulb holders |
| 3 | Stop-tail light bulb | 9 | Lamp fixing nuts |
| 4 | Lamp body fixing stud | 10 | Flasher-light bulb |
| 5 | Lens sealing rubber | 11 | Lamp body |
| 6 | Stop-tail light lens and reflector | 12 | Flasher-light lens |
| | | 13 | Fixing screw |

## 57 Rear side, stop and flasher lamp assembly – early types

1   The units are not interchangeable from one side of the car to the other.
2   Each lens is separate, so depending on which bulb needs renewal, remove the appropriate lens. The stop/tail light lens is held by one screw and clips under the other lens so care should be exercised when removing it.
3   Bulbs are removed by pressing and turning anti-clockwise. If they are very tight, it may be necessary to remove the bulb holders from the rear of the clamp.
4   The stop/tail lamp bulb is a double filament type with an offset bayonet pin so it will only fit the holder one way round.
5   When refitting the lenses, do not overtighten the screws.
6   In cases of malfunction, make sure the lamp fixing nuts and the earth wire connection to one of the fixing studs are all corrosion-free and tight before checking the wiring circuit.

## 58 Rear side, stop and flasher lamp assembly – later types

1   Bulb renewal on later models has to be performed from inside the luggage compartment. Remove the four plastic thimbles.
2   Take off the plastic cover (if fitted) on Deluxe, Super, GL and GLS models or release the press studs securing the covering on the inside of the panel on Sceptre models. This will expose the rear lamp assembly bulb holders.
3   The two lamp holders are clipped in position and can be removed by a straight pull. The cables need not be disconnected when changing bulbs.

4   Refitting is a reverse of the removal procedure, but ensure that the wiring is located through the cut-outs in the cover and the four thimbles are pushed fully home.

## 59 Dip, flasher, main beam and horn switches

1   The switch is mounted on the steering column and if any or all of its parts go wrong, it has to be renewed as a complete unit.
2   To test the switch, the cowl round the steering column should be removed and the wires disconnected at the nearby snap connectors. By bridging the appropriate wires according to the colour coding in the wiring diagram, each part of the switch's function can be verified.
3   The switch is held to the steering column by two screws securing a clip and can be removed by simply unscrewing them.
4   When refitting a switch it should be positioned so that the flasher self-cancelling cam is set centrally when the wheels are in a straight ahead position.
5   It may be found on certain early cars that the dipping function is covered by using a floor switch. The circuitry remains unaltered on this version.

## 60 Hazard warning flasher unit: 9FL type – fault tracing and rectification

1   The 9FL hazard warning flasher unit is a heavy duty version of the 8FL direction indicator flasher unit.
2   In the event of malfunction of the system, it can be checked as described for the 8FL flasher unit in Section 42. The fuse, however, may be an in-line fuse in the lead to the flasher unit.

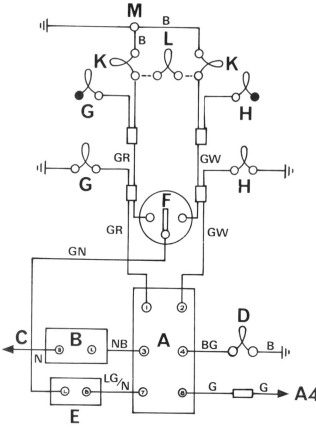

**Fig. 10.40 Hazard warning flasher unit type 9FL – circuit diagram (Sec 60)**

- A   Hazard warning switch
- B   Hazard warning flasher unit
- C   Supply wire from ignition or lighting switch
- D   Hazard warning light
- E   Flasher unit, direction indicator
- F   Switch, direction indicator
- G   Direction indicator lamps, left-hand
- H   Direction indicator lamps, right-hand
- K   Warning lamps, direction indicator
- L   Warning lamp, direction indicator, alternative
- M   Earth connection, plug and socket

*Wiring colour code:*

| | | | |
|---|---|---|---|
| N | Brown | R | Red |
| G | Green | W | White |
| LG | Light green | B | Black |

### 61 Instrument panel and instruments (certain early types) – checking, removal and refitting

**Note**: *This section covers Minx, Hunter I and II, Hillman GT models only*

1   The temperature gauge, fuel gauge, instrument voltage regulator and speedometer are housed in a rectangular shaped unit fitted to the back of the main panel. To remove any of these items is easiest in the long run to remove the whole unit first.
2   Disconnect the battery. Remove the cables from the gauges and voltage stabiliser on the back of the unit. The speedometer cable should be disconnected from the instrument together with the trip setting cable.
3   Pull the six panel and warning lights out of their sockets. Disconnect the choke cable at the carburettor. Remove the steering column cowl by taking out the four screws on the underside. Pull off the screenwasher pipes.
4   Remove the four screws securing the housing to the back of the panel and lift it out.

5   The gauges and voltage stabiliser may be detached by undoing their fixing screws. Do not renew either the temperature gauge or fuel gauge until it is quite certain that their respective sender units are working (see Chapters 2 and 3 for details). Should both gauges have failed at the same time it is likely that the voltage stabiliser is faulty. Check this before fitting new gauges. A continuity test across the two terminals 'B' and 'I' will indicate whether total failure has occurred or not.
6   The individual switches on the lower half of the main panel may be detached by unscrewing the slotted chrome ring, pulling off the finger bar and then withdrawing the switch from the back. Leave the wires connected until the switch is out and make a note of the connections.
7   The combined windscreen wiper/washer pump switch can be removed in the same manner. The knob is held on by a spring-loaded plunger which must first be released to pull it off. The pump and switch can be renewed separately.
8   Reassembly is a reversal of the removal procedure. Ensure the earth lead is fitted to the speedometer binnacle. Restart the clock, if one is fitted.

### 62 Instrument panel and instruments (alternative early types) – checking, removal and refitting

**Note**: *This section covers Vogue, Gazelle, Sceptre, Hunter De Luxe, Super GL and GT models only*

1   The instruments on Sceptre and Hunter GT models are removed from the rear of the panel, and from the front on other models.
2   To remove the panel, first disconnect the battery.
3   Disconnect the choke cable/s at the carburettor/s.
4   On Vogue and Gazelle models, disconnect the screen washer pipes and the brown/white glove box cable from its snap connector, then remove the bezel from the lighting switch.
5   Disconnect the speedometer cable at the instrument. Disconnect the speedometer trip cable.
6   Remove the oil pipe from the gauge.
7   Remove the two screws and then the heater control escutcheon. Remove the bezel from the lighting switch.
8   Remove the four screws (Vogue and Gazelle models) or six screws (Sceptre models) and take away the steering column cowl.
9   Disconnect the clock earth and withdraw the light bulb. Remove the radio speaker (if fitted).
10  Disconnect the wiring harness plugs and snap connectors. Remove the radio (if fitted).
11  Remove the two screws and detach the overdrive switch (if fitted), then detach the indicator/horn control.
12  On Sceptre models, raise the steering wheel to its highest point.
13  Disconnect the cables from the voltage stabiliser on the steering column bracket.
14  Remove the instrument panel by taking out the four screws.
15  Remove the screws securing the lower facia fixing rail finisher pad (Sceptre models).
16  Carefully withdraw the instrument panel partially.
17  Remove the securing screw and detach the lower finisher pad from the instrument panel.
18  Protect the steering column and wheel hub with a cover, and remove the instrument panel.
19  Refitting is the reverse of the removal procedure. Check that the oil gauge connection does not leak. Restart the clock immediately. Ensure the steering column cowl is correctly fitted.
20  Certain individual instruments are removable without first removing the complete panel. Where access can be gained, the fasteners should be undone, and the instrument taken away.
21  The instrument voltage stabiliser is mounted on the steering column support bracket behind the panel.

### 63 Instrument panel and instruments (later types) – checking, removal and refitting

**Note**: *This section covers Hunter De Luxe, Super GL, GLS and GT models only*

1   Disconnect the battery.
2   Disconnect the choke cable at the carburettor(s).
3   Remove the screws which secure the steering column control, and

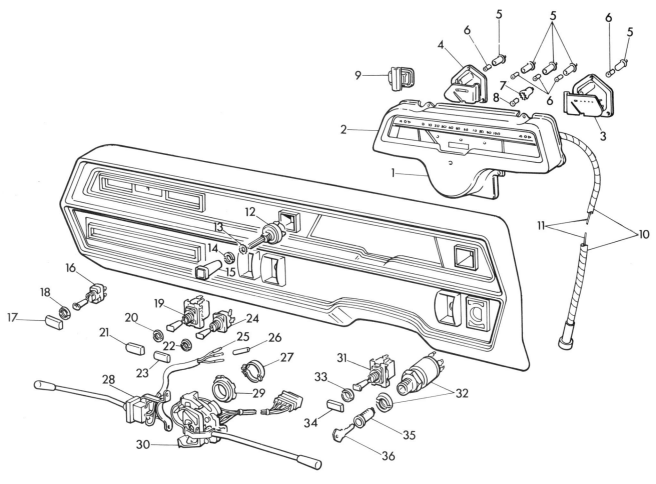

**Fig. 10.41 Instrument panel and instruments – early type (Sec 61)**

| | | | |
|---|---|---|---|
| 1 | Instrument housing | 11 | Speedo cable inner |
| 2 | Speedo head unit | 12 | Wiper/washer switch |
| 3 | Fuel gauge | 13 | Lockwasher |
| 4 | Temperature gauge | 14 | Locking ring |
| 5 | Lamp holders | 15 | Knob |
| 6 | Lamp bulbs | 16 | Glove box switch |
| 7 | Lamp holder | 17 | Switch knob |
| 8 | Bulb | 18 | Locking ring |
| 9 | Voltage regulator | 19 | Blower switch |
| | instrument(s) | 20 | Locking ring |
| 10 | Speedo cable outer | | |

| | | | |
|---|---|---|---|
| 21 | Knob | 29 | Cancelling striker |
| 22 | Locking ring | | bush |
| 23 | Knob | 30 | Horn, dip, flasher |
| 24 | Panel light switch | | switch |
| 25 | Direction indicator | 31 | Lighting switch |
| | connections | 32 | Ignition switch |
| 26 | Insulating sleeve | 33 | Locking ring |
| 27 | Cancelling striker | 34 | Knob |
| 28 | Direction indicator | 35 | Lock barrel |
| | switch | 36 | Key |

the U-clip inside.

4   Remove the steering column clamp bolts and allow the column to drop down a little.

5   Slacken the clamp screws for the steering column switch(es) and point the switch levers downwards.

6   Depress the heater control knob spring clips; remove the knobs.

7   *GT and GLS models:* Remove the two screws which retain the auxiliary instrument panel, draw the panel forwards, disconnect the brown/white lead to the lighting switch and the oil pressure gauge pipe. Draw the panel further forward, mark the relative lead positions for when refitting is required, disconnect the leads and remove the panel completely.

8   *De Luxe, Super and GL models:* Remove the two screws which retain the centre panel. Pull the panel forward, then push the switches out from the rear. Turn them through 90° and back through the aperture in the panel. Remove the radio (if fitted) and withdraw the panel.

9   *All models:* Remove the two screws which retain the heater control bracket to the top and bottom rails.

10  Detach the heater control, then pass it through the facia complete with the wires.

11  Depress the speedometer outer cable retaining button and withdraw the inner and outer cables.

12  Remove the speedometer trip cable after unscrewing the knurled nut.

13  Noting the pipe locations, disconnect the screenwasher pipes from the pump (if fitted).

14  Disconnect the four harness connections at the rear of the facia and the harness connection(s) from the column switch(es).

15  Where hazard and heated rear window switches are fitted, disconnect the harness leads.

16  Mark the leads to the windscreen wiper motor, then disconnect them.

17  Disconnect the snap connector in the glovebox light lead.

18  Disconnect the face level vent heater hoses.

19  Ease off the draught seals from the door aperture adjacent to the sides of the instrument panel.

20  Remove the nuts and washers from below the panel, located at either side of the radio speaker grille.

21  Remove one screw at each end of the panel and the four screws attaching the panel to the bottom facia rail.

22  Carefully lift the panel to permit the long screws at the sides of the

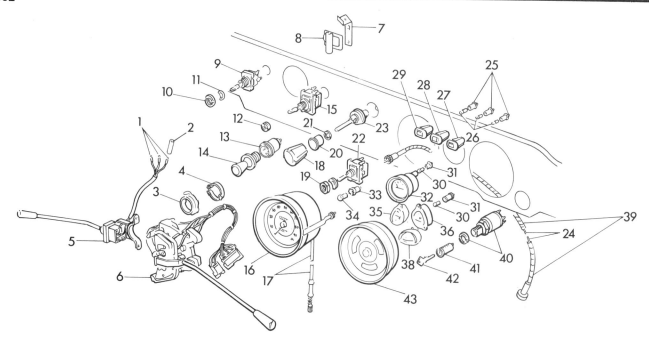

**Fig. 10.42 Instrument panel layout – Vogue and Gazelle models (Sec 62)**

1   Direction indicator
    connections
2   Insulating sleeve
3   Cancelling striker bush
4   Striker
5   Indicator switch
6   Horn, dip and flasher
    switch
7   Mounting bracket
8   Instrument voltage
    regulator
9   Panel light switch

10   Locking ring
11   Wave washer
12   Locking ring
13   Cigarette lighter socket
14   Cigarette lighter element
15   Blower switch
16   Speedometer head
17   Trip setting cable
18   Light switch knob
19   Locking ring
20   Bezel
21   Locking ring

22   Wiper switch
23   Light switch
24   Speedometer inner cable
25   Warning lamp holders
26   Wiper switch
27   Warning lamp lens
28   Warning lamp lens
29   Warning lamp lens
30   Instrument bulb
31   Bulb holder
32   Fuel gauge

33   Bulb holder
34   Instrument bulb
35   Ammeter
36   Oil pressure gauge
38   Temperature gauge
39   Speedometer cable
40   Ignition switch
41   Lock barrel
42   Key
43   Instrument bezel

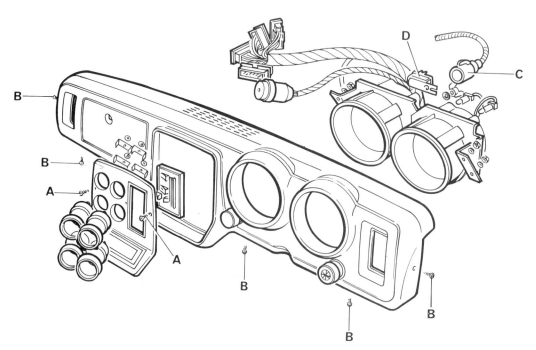

**Fig. 10.43 Instrument panel and instruments – later type (Sec 63)**

A   Fixing screws

B   Fixing screws

C   Outer speedometer cable
    button

D   Voltage stabilizer

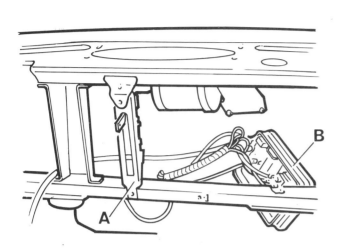

Fig. 10.44 Heater control and switch panel (Sec 63)

A   Heater control          B   Switch panel

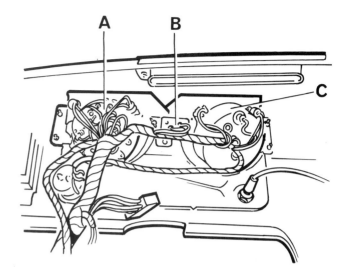

Fig. 10.45 Instrument panel – rear view (Sec 63)

A   Instrument cluster       C   Speedometer
B   Voltage stabilizer

speaker grille to clear the top rail, then pull the panel backwards and clear the facia.
23 Refitting the panel is essentially a reversal of the removal procedure, but ensure the contact surfaces at the rear of the panel, at the front of the facia rails, and the securing screws, are clean, since

they provide the earth return for the voltage stabilizer and instrument lighting. Do not overtighten the nuts on the top rail for fear of distorting the instrument panel. Check that when the steering column cowl is being fitted it does not impede the operation of the column switches.

## 64 Fault diagnosis – electrical system

| Symptom | Reason(s) |
|---|---|
| Starter fails to turn engine | Battery discharged<br>Battery defective internally<br>Battery terminal leads loose or earth lead not securely attached to body<br>Loose or broken connections in starter motor circuit<br>Starter motor switch or solenoid faulty<br>Starter motor pinion jammed in mesh with flywheel gear ring<br>Starter brushes badly worn, sticking, or brush wires loose<br>Starter motor armature faulty<br>Field coils earthed<br>Engine stiff after overhaul<br>Engine stiff due to mechanical fault |
| Starter turns engine very slowly | Battery in discharged condition<br>Starter brushes badly worn, sticking or brush wires loose<br>Loose wires in starter motor circuit |
| Starter spins but does not turn engine | Pinion or flywheel gear teeth broken or worn<br>Battery discharged<br>Dirty starter sleeve |
| Starter motor noisy or excessively rough engagement | Pinion or flywheel gear teeth broken or worn<br>Starter motor retaining bolts loose |
| Battery will not hold charge for more than a few days | Battery defective internally<br>Electrolyte level too low or electrolyte too weak due to leakage<br>Plate separators no longer fully effective<br>Battery plates severely sulphated<br>Fanbelt slipping<br>Battery terminal connections loose or corroded<br>Alternator/generator fault<br>Short in lighting circuit causing continual battery drain<br>Regulator unit not working correctly<br>Faulty connections in charging circuit |

| Symptom | Reason(s) |
| --- | --- |
| Ignition light fails to go out, battery runs flat in a few days | Fanbelt loose and slipping or broken<br>Alternator/generator brushes faulty<br>Alternator/generator brush springs faulty<br>Internal fault in alternator |
| Horn operates all the time | Horn push stuck down |
| Horn fails to operate | Blown fuse<br>Cable or cable connection loose, broken or disconnected<br>Horn has an internal fault |
| Horn emits intermittent or unsatisfactory noise | Cable connections loose<br>Horn incorrectly adjusted |
| Lights do not come on | If engine not running, battery discharged<br>Wire connections loose, disconnected or broken<br>Light switch shorting or otherwise faulty |
| Lights come on but fade out | If engine not running, battery discharged<br>Light bulb filament burnt out or sealed beam units broken<br>Wire connections loose, disconnected or broken<br>Light switch shorting or otherwise faulty |
| Lights give very poor illumination | Lamp glasses dirty<br>Lamps badly out of alignment |
| Lights work erratically – flashing on and off, especially over bumps | Battery terminals or earth connection loose<br>Lights not earthing properly<br>Contacts in light switch faulty |
| Wiper motor fails to work | Blown fuse<br>Wire connections loose, disconnected or broken<br>Brushes badly worn<br>Armature worn or faulty<br>Field coils faulty<br>Mechanism jammed due to wear, or other cause |
| Wiper motor works very slowly and takes excessive current | Commutator dirty, greasy or burnt<br>Armature bearings dirty or unaligned<br>Armature badly worn or faulty<br>Mechanism jamming due to wear or other cause |
| Wiper motor works but wiper blades remain static | Wiper motor gearbox parts badly worn<br>Interruption in the mechanism between motor and blades |

# Wiring diagrams

**Note**: *Space limitations have prevented inclusion of all wiring diagrams for models in the Hunter range. However, those given on pages 196 to 205 are representative of the full range, and should prove invaluable for fault tracing and the connection of electrical accessories*

## Wiring diagram key

| | | | | | |
|---|---|---|---|---|---|
| 1 | Battery | 42 | Hazard flasher switch | 83 | Clock battery |
| 2 | Starter solenoid | 43 | Hazard flasher warning lamp | 84 | Clock illumination |
| 3 | Starter motor | 44 | Hazard repeater (RH) | 85 | Interior light |
| 4 | Ignition switch | 45 | Hazard repeater (LH) | 86 | Interior light switch |
| 5 | Ignition warning light | 46 | Stop-light switch | 87 | Door pillar switch (RH) |
| 6 | Warning light simulator | 47 | Stop-light switch (RH) | 88 | Door pillar switch (LH) |
| 7 | Relay unit | 48 | Stop-light switch (LH) | 89 | Cigar lighter |
| 8 | Control box | 49 | Reverse light switch | 90 | Cigar lighter (rear) |
| 9 | Dynamo | 50 | Reverse light (RH) | 91 | Boot light |
| 10 | Alternator | 51 | Reverse light (LH) | 92 | Boot light switch |
| 11 | Fuses | 52 | Ignition coil | 93 | Glovebox light |
| 12 | Oil pressure warning light | 53 | Distributor | 94 | Glovebox light switch |
| 13 | Oil pressure warning light switch | 54 | Wiper motor | 95 | Cable connector |
| 14 | Lighting switch | 55 | Wiper switch | 96 | Ammeter |
| 15 | Headlight and sidelight switch | 56 | Tailgate wiper motor | 97 | Ammeter illumination |
| 16 | Horn push, headlight and indicator switch | 57 | Washer switch | 98 | Water temperature gauge illumination |
| 17 | Horn push, headlight flash and indicator switch | 58 | Washer bottle | 99 | Oil pressure gauge illumination |
| 18 | Horn (RH) | 59 | Voltage stabilizer | 100 | Instrument unit |
| 19 | Horn (LH) | 60 | Heater blower | 101 | Horn |
| 20 | Headlight main beam (RH) | 61 | Heater blower switch | 102 | Instrument lamps |
| 21 | Headlight main beam (LH) | 62 | Fuel gauge | 103 | Washer pump |
| 22 | Main beam warning light | 63 | Fuel tank unit | 104 | Tailgate washer pump |
| 23 | Dipswitch | 64 | Low fuel warning lamp | 105 | Tailgate wiper motor |
| 24 | Headlight dipped beam (RH) | 65 | Water temperature gauge | 106 | Tailgate wiper motor switch |
| 25 | Headlight dipped beam (LH) | 66 | Water temperature sender unit | | |
| 26 | Sidelight (RH) | 67 | Rear window demister element | | |
| 27 | Sidelight (LH) | 68 | Rear window demister switch | | |
| 28 | Rear light (RH) | 69 | Rear window demister warning light | | |
| 29 | Rear light (LH) | 70 | Panel light(s) | | |
| 30 | Number plate light | 71 | Panel light switch | | |
| 31 | Indicator flasher unit | 72 | Auxiliary panel light(s) | | |
| 32 | Indicator flasher unit (RH) | 73 | Switch illumination | | |
| 33 | Indicator flasher unit (LH) | 74 | Speedometer illumination | *Cable colour code* | |
| 34 | Indicator warning light | 75 | 3-in-1 instrument illumination | | |
| 35 | Indicator warning light (RH) | 76 | Fuel gauge illumination | R | Red |
| 36 | Indicator warning light (LH) | 77 | Overdrive connection | Y | Yellow |
| 37 | Indicator (front RH) | 78 | Tachometer | G | Green |
| 38 | Indicator (front LH) | 79 | Tachometer illumination | U | Blue |
| 39 | Indicator (rear RH) | 80 | Voltmeter | N | Brown |
| 40 | Indicator (rear LH) | 81 | Voltmeter illumination | P | Purple |
| 41 | Hazard flasher unit | 82 | Clock | W | White |
| | | | | B | Black |
| | | | | L | Light |
| | | | | K | Pink |
| | | | | O | Orange |
| | | | | S | Slate |

## Key to symbols

Alternative wiring for export models
Snap connector
Plug and socket connector
Earth through cable
Earth through unit

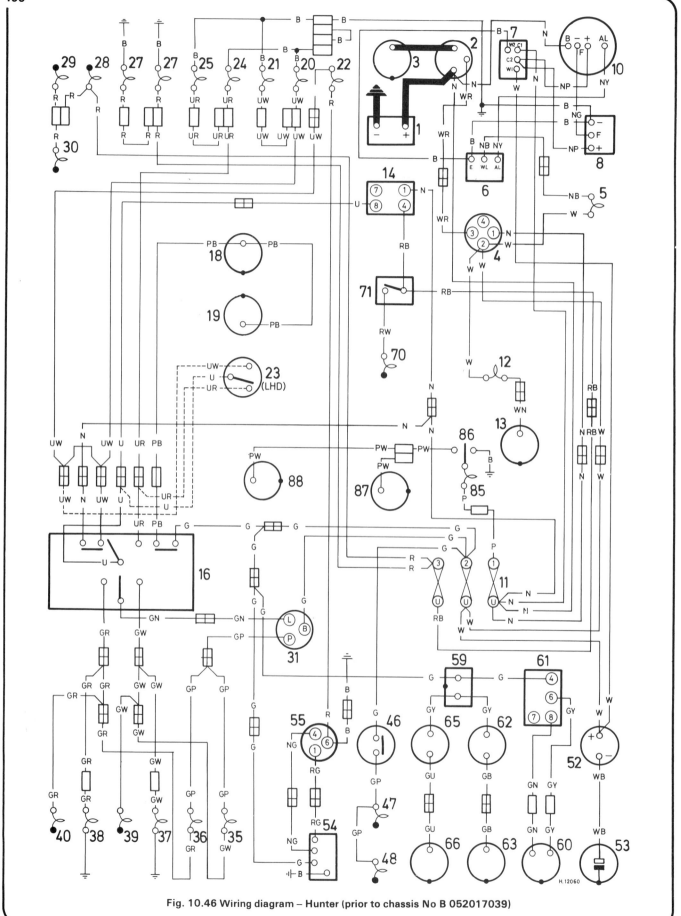

Fig. 10.46 Wiring diagram – Hunter (prior to chassis No B 052017039)

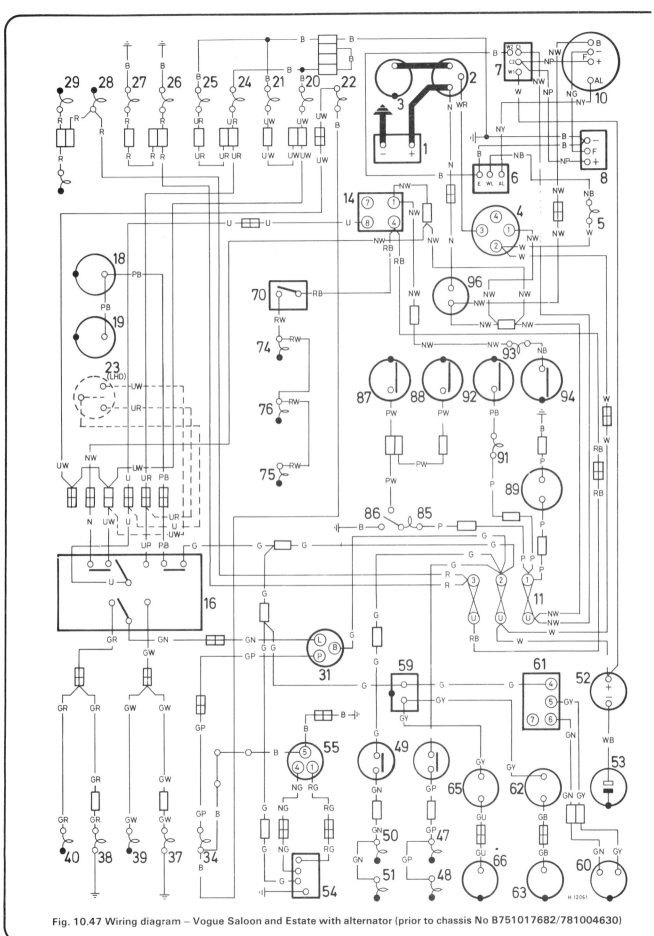

Fig. 10.47 Wiring diagram – Vogue Saloon and Estate with alternator (prior to chassis No B751017682/781004630)

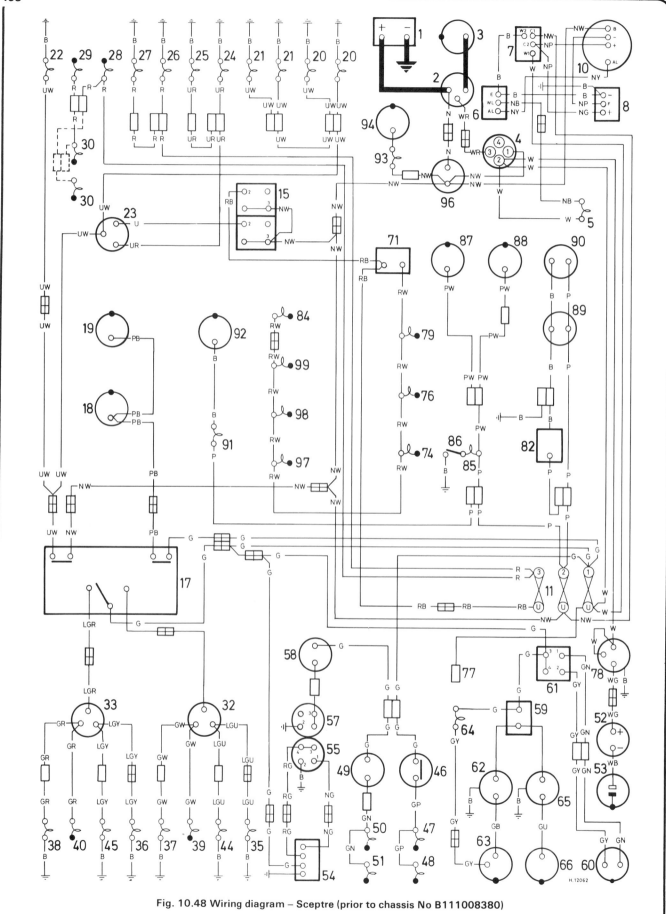

Fig. 10.48 Wiring diagram – Sceptre (prior to chassis No B111008380)

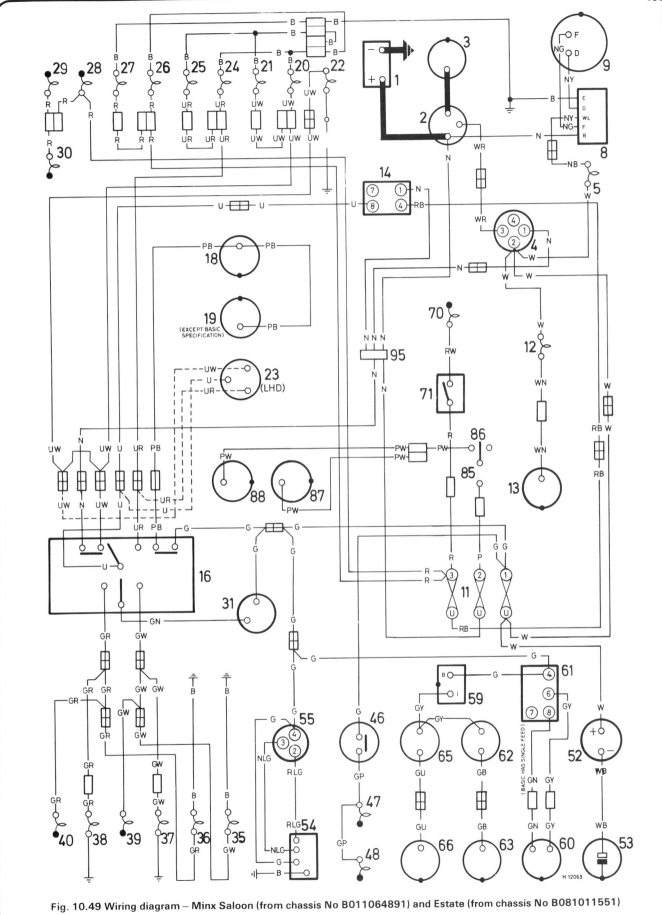

Fig. 10.49 Wiring diagram – Minx Saloon (from chassis No B011064891) and Estate (from chassis No B081011551)

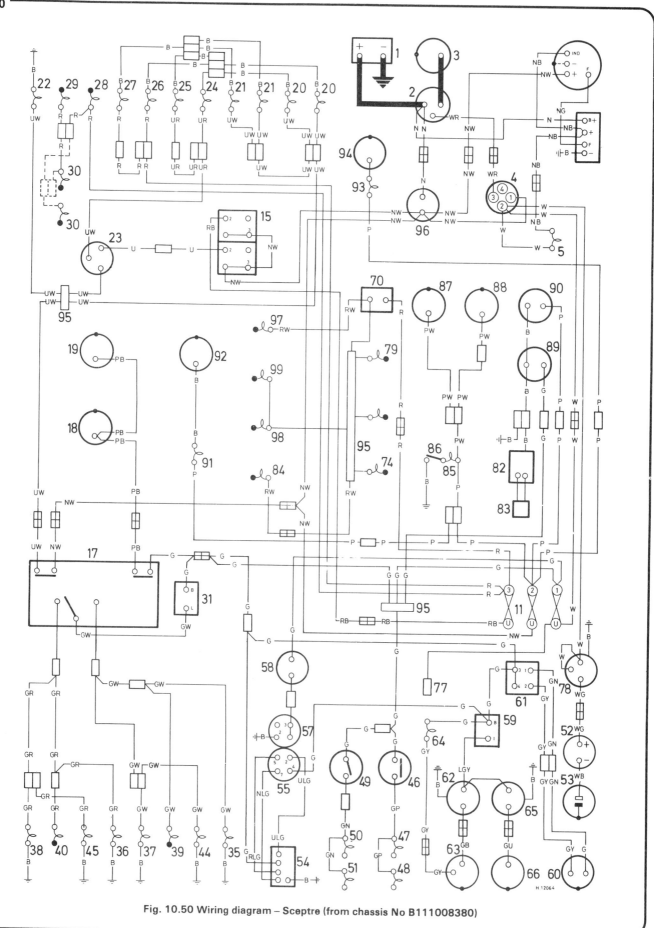

Fig. 10.50 Wiring diagram – Sceptre (from chassis No B111008380)

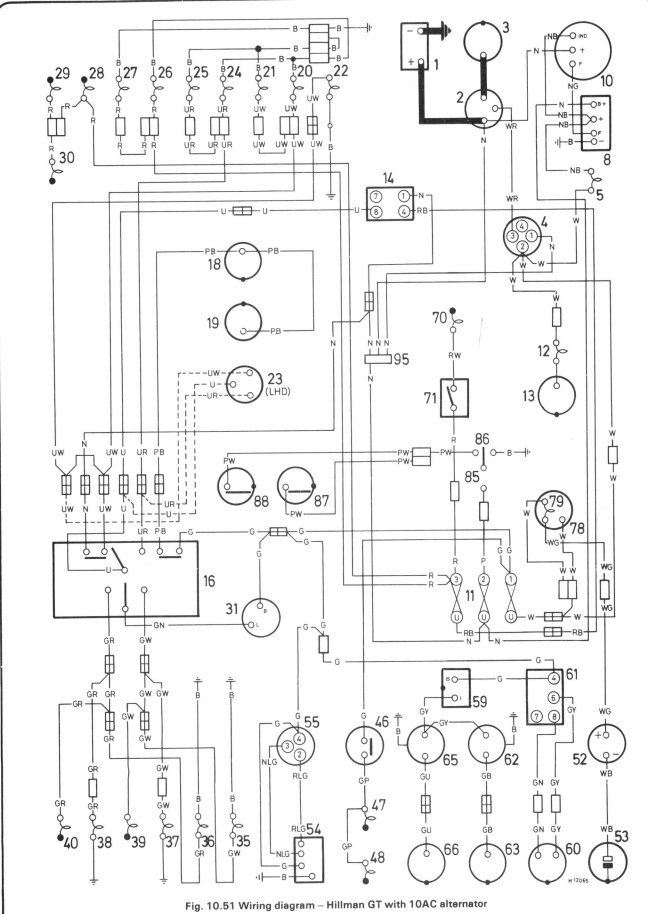

Fig. 10.51 Wiring diagram – Hillman GT with 10AC alternator

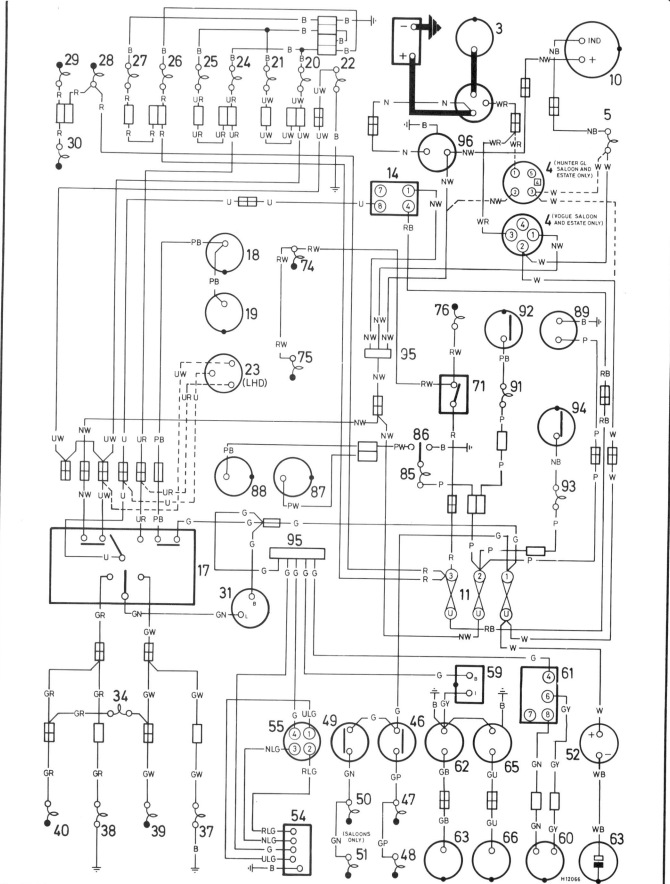

Fig. 10.52 Wiring diagram – Vogue Saloon and Estate with 16ACR alternator. Hunter GL Saloon (from chassis No LG 058600001) and Estate (from chassis No LG 087600001)

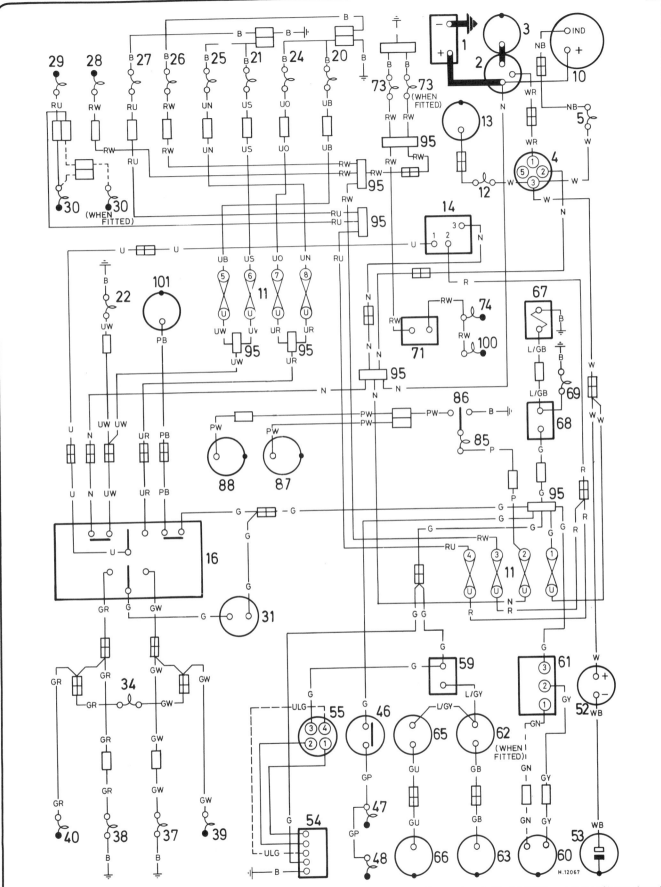

Fig. 10.53 Wiring diagram – Hunter De Luxe Saloon (from chassis No L4 064), Estate (from chassis No L4 160) and Super (from chassis No L4 075)

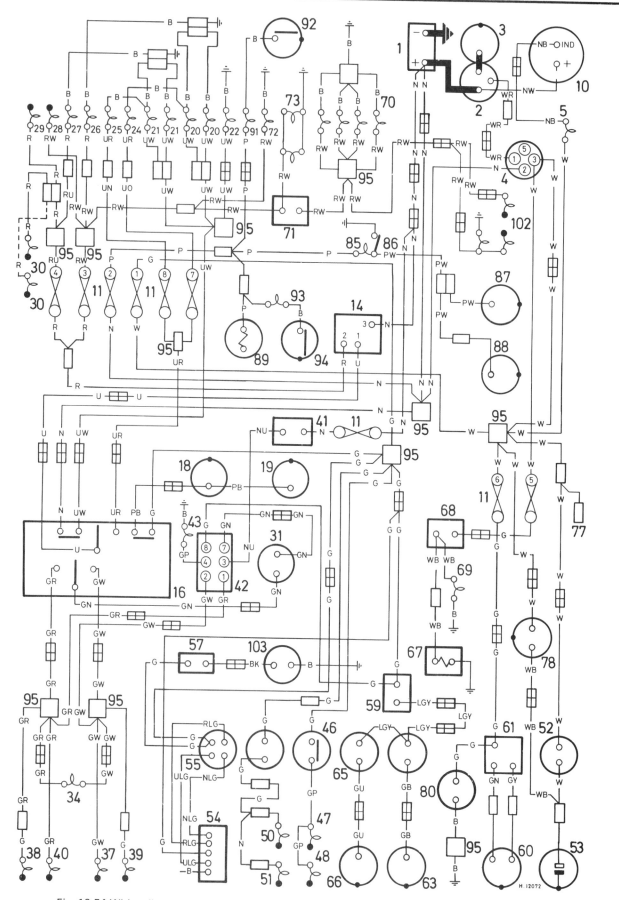

Fig. 10.54 Wiring diagram – Sceptre Saloon and Estate (from vehicles with Service No prefixed L5)

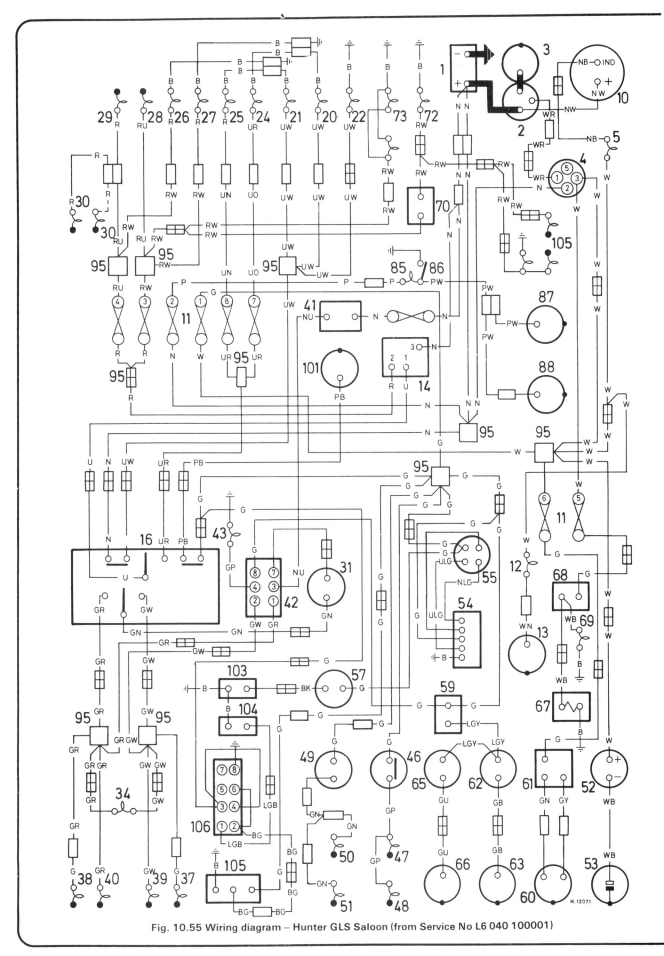

Fig. 10.55 Wiring diagram – Hunter GLS Saloon (from Service No L6 040 100001)

# Chapter 11 Suspension and steering

## Contents

Burman adjustable steering gear – removal and refitting ............. 16
Direction indicator switch – removal and refitting ........................... 14
Fault diagnosis – suspension and steering ........................................ 25
Front hubs and bearings – removal and refitting ............................ 22
Front strut replacement damper cartridge – fitting ........................ 9
Front suspension strut assembly – overhaul ................................... 8
Front suspension strut assembly – removal and refitting .............. 7
Front wheel bearings – adjustment .................................................. 21
General description ............................................................................ 1
Rear springs and dampers – removal and refitting ........................ 10
Routine maintenance ......................................................................... 2
Springs and dampers – inspection ................................................... 3
Stabiliser bar – removal and refitting .............................................. 4

Steering alignment ............................................................................ 24
Steering column cowling – removal and refitting ........................... 13
Steering column upper felt bush – removal and refitting .............. 20
Steering gear and linkage – inspection ........................................... 11
Steering gear – removal and refitting .............................................. 15
Steering gear with column lock – removal and refitting ................ 17
Steering linkage – removal and refitting ......................................... 12
Steering lock and ignition switch – removal and refitting ............. 19
Steering wheel with adjustable steering unit – removal and
refitting ............................................................................................. 18
Track control arm and bushes – removal and refitting .................. 6
Track control arm balljoint – removal and refitting ....................... 5
Wheel studs – removal and refitting ................................................ 23

## Specifications

### Front suspension

**Type** ............................................................ Independent MacPherson type strut with anti-roll bar

**Damper** ....................................................... Armstrong telescopic, integral with strut

**Spring free length**
Standard ......................................................... 14.15 in (35.9 cm)
Heavy duty ..................................................... 12.9 in (32.8 cm)

**Front hub endfloat** ..................................... 0.0015 to 0.004 in (0.040 to 0.10 mm)

**Toe-in (track)** ............................................. 0.12 in ± 0.062 in (3 mm ± 1.5 mm) (30' ± 15')

**Camber** ....................................................... Zero ± 0.75°

**Castor** ......................................................... 0.25° negative ± 0.5°

### Rear suspension

**Type** ............................................................ Asymmetric semi-elliptic springs

**Dampers** ..................................................... Telescopic direct acting

### Steering

**Type** ............................................................ Burman F-type recirculating ball

**Ratio** ........................................................... 16.4:1

**Turns, lock to lock** ..................................... $3\frac{1}{3}$

**Turning circle**
Early models .................................................. 33 ft 6 in (10.2 m)
Later and Holbay-engined models ................ 34 ft 2 in (10.4 m)

**Rocker shaft endfloat** ................................. Zero to 0.004 in (Zero to 0.10 mm)

**Inner shaft bearing pre-load** ..................... 0.002 to 0.004 in (0.05 to 0.1 mm)

**Worm helix lead** ......................................... 0.62 in (15.8 mm)

**Capacity (steering unit)** ......................................................... 0.56 pint (0.67 US pint, 0.32 litre)

*Wheels and tyres*
## Wheel type
Holbay engined models ........................................................... Deep pressed steel (No nave plates)
All other models ................................................................... Ventilated pressed steel disc

## Rim size
Holbay engined models ........................................................... 5J x 13 hump rim (safety ledge – later models)
All other models ................................................................... 4½J x 13 safety ledge; 5J x 13 hump (safety ledge – later models)

## Tyre sizes and pressures lbf/in$^2$ (kgf/cm$^2$)

| Early models | 5.60 x 13 Saloons | 6.00 x 13 Saloons | Estate Cars |
|---|---|---|---|
| Front* | 24 (1.7) | 25 (1.8) | 24 (1.7) |
| Rear* | 24 (1.7) | 25 (1.8) | 24 (1.7) |
| Front** | 28 (2) | 30 (2.1) | 26 (1.8) |
| Rear** | 28 (2) | 30 (2.1) | 36 (2.5) |
| Front† | 28 (2) | 30 (2.1) | 26 (1.8) |
| Rear† | 28 (2) | 30 (2.1) | 36 (2.5) |

| Later models | 155SR x 13 Super DL and GL | GT | Sceptre | GT | 165SR x 13 DL Estate GL Estate Sceptre Estate | Hunter GLS |
|---|---|---|---|---|---|---|
| Front* | 24 (1.7) | 26 (1.8) | 26 (1.8) | 24 (1.7) | 24 (1.7) | 26 (1.8) |
| Rear* | 24 (1.7) | 26 (1.8) | 26 (1.8) | 24 (1.7) | 24 (1.7) | 24 (1.7) |
| Front** | 24 (1.7) | 26 (1.8) | 26 (1.8) | 24 (1.7) | 24 (1.7) | 26 (1.8) |
| Rear** | 24 (1.7) | 26 (1.8) | 26 (1.8) | 24 (1.7) | 24 (1.7) | 24 (1.8) |
| Front† | 26 (1.8) | 26 (1.8) | 26 (1.8) | 24 (1.7) | 24 (1.7) | 26 (1.8) |
| Rear† | 30 (2.1) | 30 (2.1) | 30 (2.1) | 26 (1.8) | 32 (2.2) | 26 (1.8) |

  * Up to four occupants
 ** Continuous high speed
  † Four occupants plus luggage

| *Torque wrench settings* | lbf ft | Nm |
|---|---|---|
| **Front suspension** | | |
| Crossmember to body | 52 | 71 |
| Lower link to crossmember | 28 | 38 |
| Brake reaction rods – front nuts: | | |
|    Early models | 26 | 35 |
|    Late models | 40 | 54 |
| Brake reaction rods – rear bolts | 67 | 91 |
| Anti-roll bar – mounting bolts | 28 | 38 |
| Anti-roll bar – link nuts | 15 | 20 |
| Lower swivel bearing – main ball pin nut | 43 | 58 |
| Lower swivel bearing to strut | 17 | 23 |
| Lower swivel bearing to lower link | 34 | 45 |
| Top strut bearing – centre nut (maximum) | 35 | 47 |
|    using adaptor P 5026, set wrench to | 29 | 39 |
| Top strut bearing housing body | 15 | 20 |
| Steering arm to stub carrier | 38 | 51 |
| Strut gland nut | 27 | 37 |
| **Rear suspension** | | |
| Rear spring U-bolts | 34 | 46 |
| Rear spring shackle nuts | 25 | 34 |
| Rear spring front eye bolt | 28 | 38 |
| Dampers (upper fixing) | 6 | 8 |
| Dampers (lower fixing) | 28 | 38 |
| Dampers (Estate car) upper and lower fixing | 14 | 19 |
| **Steering** | | |
| Steering box to underframe | 31 | 42 |
| Relay lever to underframe | 31 | 42 |
| Steering linkage ball pin nuts | 40 | 54 |
| Drop arm (swing lever) to rocker shaft | 75 | 101 |
| Relay lever to relay shaft | 30 | 41 |
| Rocker shaft cover to steering box | 20 | 27 |

| | lbf ft | Nm |
|---|---|---|
| Outer column to steering box ............................................................................ | 20 | 27 |

**Roadwheels**

| | | |
|---|---|---|
| Roadwheel nuts ................................................................................... | 47 | 64 |

## 1  General description

The independent front suspension consists of a well tried MacPherson strut system. Each strut comprises a single telescopic damper unit, the foot designed to carry the wheel hub and brake assembly. A coil spring surrounds the damper. The top of the unit fits in a rubber mounted thrust bush in a reinforced section of the wing.

The lower end of the unit is linked to the front crossmember at each side by a radius arm. Fore and aft stabilisation is by a rod mounted forward to the side frame members. An anti-roll bar is fitted across the car between the suspension units. Rear suspension is by conventional semi-elliptic leaf springs mounted on rubber bushed shackle pins. Telescopic hydraulic dampers are used. The steering gear is a recirculating ball worm and nut unit which connects to the wheels via a drop arm, a centre track rod, a relay lever and two outer track rods, to the steering arms on each wheel.

## 2  Routine maintenance

1 Most of the suspension and steering is linked by either bonded rubber bushes or pre-packed and sealed balljoints. Routine maintenance therefore largely consists of routine inspection.
2 The only two items requiring addition or renewal of lubricant are the steering box and the front wheel bearings. Every 5000 miles the filler plug of the steering box and the surrounding area should be cleaned, removed and the oil level checked. The level should be up to the bottom of the filler hole. Every 30 000 miles the front hubs should be removed and the bearings repacked with grease. Inspection of the steering linkage balljoints, suspension bushes and damper mountings should be undertaken at every 5000 miles service and components renewed as necessary. For the owner who does his own maintenance this inspection is the area most often neglected. The fact that no grease can be pumped in or no adjustment made tends to deter the owner from going to the trouble of jacking the suspension off the ground and examining the whole system properly. Certain components cannot be repaired – only renewed. Defects in steering and suspension items can be extremely dangerous and the importance of this aspect of owner car care cannot be too highly stressed.

## 3  Springs and dampers – inspection

1 For safety reasons, the compulsory test for older vehicles pays particular attention to the condition of all the steering and suspension components.
2 The rear suspension should be examined for broken spring leaves. This will usually be obvious as the car will be down on the side affected, and broken leaves must be renewed.
3 The spring hanger and shackle pin bushes may be checked by jacking up the body and at the same time watching to see if there is any movement between the shackle pins and the frame when the weight is transferred. Mud normally collects round these mounting points, and a badly worn bush is usually immediately apparent because the movement prevents the mud from building up.
4 Check for any signs of movement also in the U-bolts clamping the springs to the axle tube. If any one is loose, check first that the axle is correctly located in the spring seat before tightening the U-bolt.
5 The top and bottom anchorage points of the rear hydraulic dampers should be firm. If there are signs of oil on the outside of the lower cylinder section it indicates that the seals have gone and the damper must be renewed. The damper may also have failed internally and this is more dificult to detect. It is usually indicated by excessive bounce at the rear end and axle patter or 'tramp' on uneven surfaces. When this occurs, remove the shock absorber in order to check its damping power in both directions. This does not apply to Girling Monitube gas-pressurised units, which have a self-extending action and act as a low-rate spring. Hand-testing is therefore not possible with this type. The best test of any suspension system is on the road. Static tests of dampers are not entirely conclusive. Further indications of failure, either front or rear, are noticeable pitching (bonnet goes up and down) when the car is braked and stopped sharply, excessive rolling on fast bends, and a definite feeling of insecurity on corners, particularly if the road surface is uneven. Drive over a roughish road and have somecne follow to watch how the wheels behave. Excessive

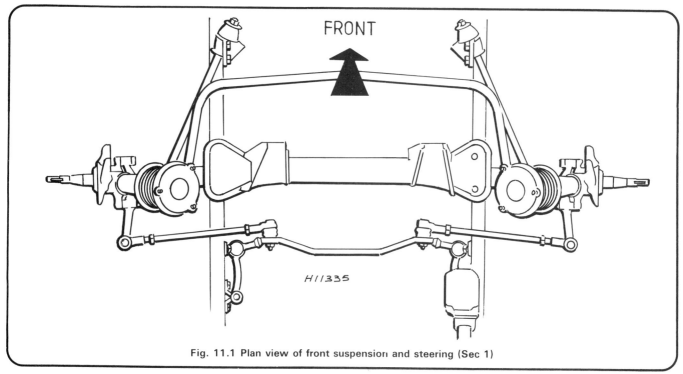

FRONT

H11335

Fig. 11.1 Plan view of front suspension and steering (Sec 1)

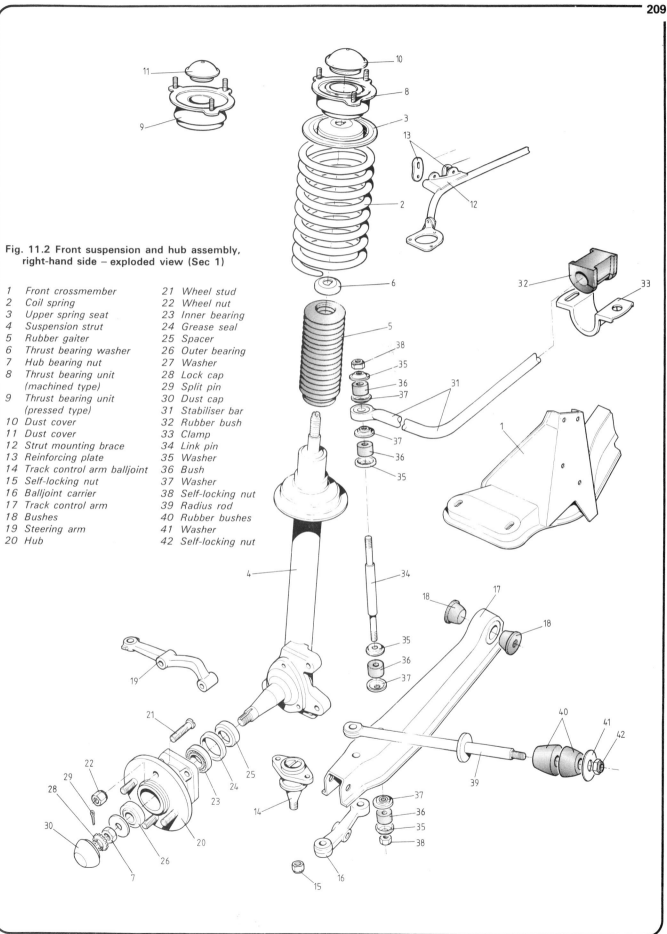

**Fig. 11.2 Front suspension and hub assembly, right-hand side – exploded view (Sec 1)**

| | | | |
|---|---|---|---|
| 1 | Front crossmember | 21 | Wheel stud |
| 2 | Coil spring | 22 | Wheel nut |
| 3 | Upper spring seat | 23 | Inner bearing |
| 4 | Suspension strut | 24 | Grease seal |
| 5 | Rubber gaiter | 25 | Spacer |
| 6 | Thrust bearing washer | 26 | Outer bearing |
| 7 | Hub bearing nut | 27 | Washer |
| 8 | Thrust bearing unit (machined type) | 28 | Lock cap |
| 9 | Thrust bearing unit (pressed type) | 29 | Split pin |
| | | 30 | Dust cap |
| 10 | Dust cover | 31 | Stabiliser bar |
| 11 | Dust cover | 32 | Rubber bush |
| 12 | Strut mounting brace | 33 | Clamp |
| 13 | Reinforcing plate | 34 | Link pin |
| 14 | Track control arm balljoint | 35 | Washer |
| 15 | Self-locking nut | 36 | Bush |
| 16 | Balljoint carrier | 37 | Washer |
| 17 | Track control arm | 38 | Self-locking nut |
| 18 | Bushes | 39 | Radius rod |
| 19 | Steering arm | 40 | Rubber bushes |
| 20 | Hub | 41 | Washer |
| | | 42 | Self-locking nut |

up and down 'patter' of any wheel is quite obvious and denotes a defective damper.

6    The front suspension should be checked by jacking the car up so the wheel is clear of the ground. Place another jack under the track control arm near the outer end. When the arm is raised by the jack any movement in the suspension strut ball stud will be apparent; so will any wear in the inner track control arm bush. There should be no vertical or horizontal play in either the balljoints or bushes at each end of the track control arms.

## 4    Stabiliser bar – removal and refitting

1    The stabiliser bar can become ineffective if bent, or if the mounting bushes deteriorate.

2    Leave the weight of the car on the front wheels. Remove the nuts and washers securing the ends of the bar to the top ends of the link pins from the track control arms.

3    Remove the two bolts securing the U-clamps and bushes to the side frame members.

4    Remove the stabiliser bar.

5    Renew any rubber bushes showing signs of deterioration. When refitting, particularly if new bushes have been used on the side frame clamps, it will help if the brackets are compressed by a G-clamp to ease refitting of the securing bolts. Tighten the nuts to the specified torque.

## 5    Track control arm balljoint – removal and refitting

1    Inspection will indicate if there is any free play in the outer balljoint. If there is, the joint will need renewal.

2    The joint is flanged and bolted to the base of the suspension strut, and secured in the carrier on the lower arm by a tapering pin and nut.

3    Jack up the car, support it with a stand under the side member and remove the roadwheel.

4    It improves accessibility if the disc calliper hub and dust plate are taken off, but this is not essential – especially if you have a pit or elevator. Undo the two bolts holding the balljoint to the foot of the strut. It should then be possible to move the lower arm away from the bottom of the strut. If difficulty is encountered, another jack can be placed under the hub or hub spindle to raise the strut a little.

5    Remove the balljoint nut from the bottom of the balljoint pin. The tapered pin is often a stubborn item to get out of the carrier. If a proper claw clamp, or slotted and tapered steel wedges are not available to apply the necessary pressure, success can often be achieved by placing one hammer head on one side of the carrier and hitting the opposite side with another. This, in effect, squeezes the taper out of its seating.

6    When fitting a new balljoint, make sure the mating flange faces are clean and free from scores or burrs so they fit perfectly flush. Fit it to the strut first and tighten the bolts to the specified torque. Then clean the taper pin and the bore in the carrier and fit them together. Tighten the nut to the specified torque.

## 6    Track control arm and bushes – removal and refitting

1    If the inner pivot bushes on the track control arm are worn out the arm will have to be removed to renew them.

2    With the weight of the car still on the front suspension, remove the bottom nut of the link pin which connects the stabiliser bar to the arm.

3    Jack up the front of the car and support it on stands placed under the side members. Remove the roadwheel from the side being dealt with.

4    Remove the large vertical bolt which holds the eye of the radius rod to the suspension arm (this also goes through the inner end of the carrier arm). Remove the horizontal bolt that holds the carrier to the end of the suspension arm.

5    If the pivot bolt at the inner end of the arm is now removed the arm may be taken out.

6    New bushes should be fitted to the inner end and in addition all the self-locking nuts used should be renewed. Otherwise reassembly is a simple reversal of the removal procedure. Tighten all nuts and bolts to the specified torque. It is advisable to get the steering alignment checked after assembly.

## 7    Front suspension strut assembly – removal and refitting

1    If the damping part of the suspension unit is not working properly, or the spring is broken and needs renewing, it will be necessary to remove the whole unit from the car first. Carefully prise out the dust cap from the thrust bearing in the wing valance and unscrew the nut by *one turn only* using tool number P5025 or a similar device (see Section 8, paragraph 5).

2    Jack up the front of the car and support it on stands underneath the side members. Remove the roadwheel. Detach the brake calliper from the hub, as described in Chapter 9.

3    Undo the two bolts which hold the steering arm to the foot of the strut but leave the arm connected to the track rod.

4    Remove the two bolts securing the steering arm to the foot of the strut, allowing the steering arm to remain connected to the outer track rod. Undo and remove the two bolts that secure the lower balljoint to the strut. Release the joint and leave the balljoint attached to the carrier.

5    Support the lower end of the strut on a block or jack before the next step of detaching it at the upper end.

6    The upper end is held to the wing valance by three studs from which the nuts should now be removed. The centre nut should not be touched. The whole unit may now be lifted away from the car.

7    When refitting the assembly renew all self-locking nuts and tighten them to the correct torque settings. It is important that rubber mountings should not be over-tightened. It is advisable to have the steering alignment checked after fitting.

## 8    Front suspension strut assembly – overhaul

1    Unless one is able to borrow the correct special tools needed to dismantle the strut assembly, damage can be caused to both damper and strut. Specialist services may therefore be required.

2    To dismantle the unit, it is convenient to refit it to a roadwheel, place the roadwheel on a bench and steady the strut by putting a wooden wedge between it and the tyre wall.

3    To remove the thrust bearing unit the pressure of the spring has to be relieved with compressor tool P5045. If a tool other than this is used, it must be remembered that although the amount of compressing required is minimal it must be able to relieve the spring to its free length; so must have sufficient travel.

4    Fit the tool securely and squarely on the spring, bolt heads upwards. Compress it evenly until the pressure is taken off the thrust bearing unit.

5    Remove the dust cap. Using tool P5025 the thrust bearing nut can be undone. The tool is in two parts. One part is a screwdriver engaging in the slot in the top of the damper piston rod to prevent it turning and the other is a socket wrench to undo the nut. A suitable tool can be improvised with a long tubular spanner and T-handled screwdriver, but two pairs of hands will be required.

6    The washer and bearing unit may then be taken off. The spring compressor should be released evenly until the tension is completely relieved. Remove the spring with its upper seat.

7    If it is desired to remove the damper unit from the strut, remove the rubber gaiter and push the piston rod right into the strut. Knock back the staking which locks the sealing nut into the strut tube.

8    The gland nut is one with four dog slots in it to accept special tool CS0015. Do not attempt to undo this nut with a hammer and pin punch. One slip, which may ruin the very fine threads, will be the virtual end of the whole unit

9    With the gland nut removed take out the rubber O-ring and from inside the top edge of the strut the damper rod should be pulled out, dislodging the guide bush and seal assembly from the top of the strut.

10   Drain out the oil, which is not re-usable.

11   Reassembly is simply a repeat of the dismantling process in reverse. Before commencing operations the following paragraphs should be read. Remember that the safety of the car depends much on this unit. The whole unit must be scrupulously clean, inside and out, before reassembly begins. Use petrol to clean out and let it dry off.

12   350 cc of fresh oil (Armstrong Fluid 788) is required for each damper unit and should be divided between the damper unit and the strut. It will be necessary to lift the damper guide bush out of the tube to get this oil in. The damper should then be primed with one or two

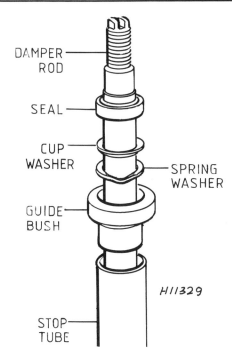

**Fig. 11.3 Front damper rod guide bush and seal (Sec 8)**

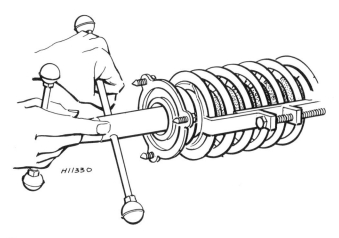

**Fig. 11.4 Front strut – dismantling, using spring compressors and tool No P5025 to remove the thrust bearing nut (Sec 8)**

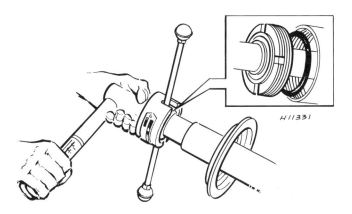

**Fig. 11.5 Front strut – fitting the gland nut, using special tool No CS 0015 with torque wrench (Inset: gland nut and O-ring) (Sec 8)**

long steady strokes of the piston until resistance is equal in both directions.

13 Fit a new seal and O-ring and also a new gland nut.

14 Make sure that everything is properly lined up when fitting the gland nut. Keep the damper piston rod pulled out at all stages of reassembly.

15 The threads of the gland nut are very easily crossed unless extreme care is taken. Make sure the threads on the end of the piston rod are not damaged during reassembly. Stake the gland nut.

16 Fit a new gaiter to protect the damper piston.

17 Do not refit a spring that does not correspond closely to the free length dimensions given the specifications. When compressing the spring to refit the upper bearing bush, care is needed to engage the piston rod in the thrust bearing plate and to prevent the piston being pushed back too far into the strut.

18 Observe the torque wrench loadings on the various nuts with accuracy. If the thrust bearing nut is overtight the steering will be stiff and the thrust bearing overloaded, causing early failure.

19 The special tools required for dismantling will be required for reassembly.

## 9 Front strut replacement damper cartridge – fitting

1 Replacement strut damper cartridges are available through normal motor vehicle factors. The cartridges are oil filled, sealed and self-priming but their operation should be checked before fitting. When the cartridge is being used to replace an early type damper, they must be fitted to both sides of the car.

2 To fit a replacement damper cartridge, follow the instructions given in Section 8, paragraphs 1 to 10.

3 Clean the strut internally and externally.

4 Insert the replacement cartridge into the strut.

5 Fit a new securing nut to the top of the strut, ensuring that it engages correctly with the threads in the strut.

6 Tighten the nut as far as possible using the wrench CS 0015.

7 Stake over the top edge of the strut into the slot in the nut.

8 Continue with the assembly operations as described in Section 8, paragraphs 16 to 19.

## 10 Rear springs and dampers – removal and refitting

1 To renew the rear dampers, jack up the car under the axle and remove the wheel for ease of access. Remove the lower anchor bolt, nut and lockwasher and pull the bottom of the damper from its location.

2 From inside the boot, remove the locknut from the top mounting spindle and then grip the flats on the spindle with a suitable spanner so the second nut can be removed.

3 The damper may then be taken out from underneath. When refitting, make sure first that all the rubber mountings and steel bushes are in good condition. Renew them if necessary. New bushes may come with the damper.

4 To renew a broken leaf, or to renew the front or rear mounting bushes, the rear springs must be detached: Jack up the car and support it on stands at the rear. Support the axle on a jack at a point away from the spring mountings. Remove the roadwheel.

5 Detach the lower end of the damper from the mounting.

6 Clean off all the dirt from the U-bolts and shackle pins. Soak the nuts and threads with a suitable easing fluid (penetrating oil).

7 Remove the U-bolt nuts and jack up the axle a little way to separate it from the springs.

8 Remove the nut and washer from the front hanger bolt. The bolt may prove very stubborn and if it needs driving out refit the nut to protect the threads. In any case one should be prepared to renew the bolt.

9 When removing the shackle plates at the rear end of the spring both nuts must first be removed. The pins may be very difficult to shift and it is not unknown to have to cut them off.

10 A broken spring can be renewed as a complete unit or the individual leaf can be renewed. If the leaf only is being renewed new spring clips, rivets and inserts will be required to reassemble the leaves. A replacement unit can usually be found at a breaker's and this is the simplest and cheapest way to go about it.

11 When reassembling the rubber bushes for the shackles, use some

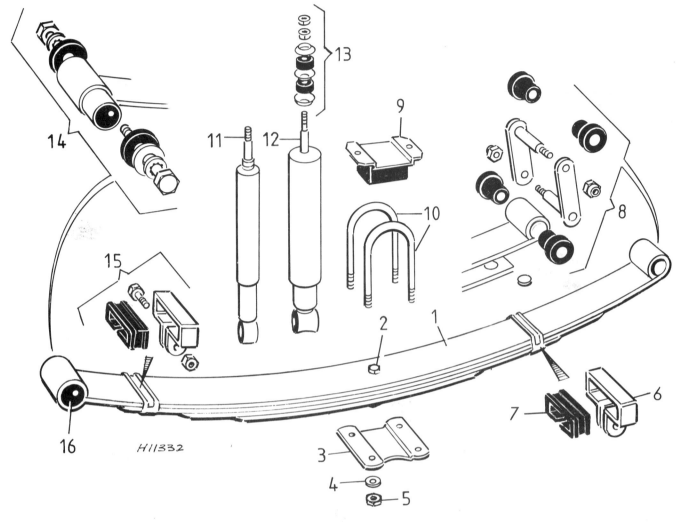

**Fig. 11.6 Rear suspension and damper (Sec 10)**

| | | | |
|---|---|---|---|
| *1* | *Main leaf* | *6* | *Spring clip* |
| *2* | *Dowel bolt* | *7* | *Spring clip rubber* |
| *3* | *Spring retainer* | *8* | *Rear shackle assembly* |
| *4* | *U-bolt washer* | *9* | *Bump/torque reaction rubber* |
| *5* | *U-bolt nut* | *10* | *U-bolts* |

| | | | |
|---|---|---|---|
| *11* | *Damper – Girling monitube* | *14* | *Front eye assembly* |
| *12* | *Damper – Woodhead-Monroe* | *15* | *Clip and rubber assembly* |
| *13* | *Damper – top mounting assembly* | *16* | *Eccentric bush – front eye* |

soapy water to lubricate them. The front spring hanger bush is a press fit unit into the spring. It will have to be driven out and a new one pressed in if it needs renewal. Note that there were different types of bush fitted to the front hanger over a period of time. The very early versions were fitted with an eccentric bolt hole which was positioned at 12 o'clock. These bushes are no longer used and the new replacements, still having an eccentric bolt hole, require that the hole be positioned at 45° up from the horizontal at the front. Other bushes have central bolt holes and others again have a triangular section. The latter require that one lobe of the triangle is positioned at 40° as indicated in Fig. 11.7. To summarise, bushes should always be replaced by new parts of the same type, except where the early version is originally found to be fitted, when the replacements should be as mentioned earlier in this paragraph. The bushes on both sides of the vehicle must be of the same type, or irregular behaviour of the suspension will occur. It should be noted that, on many early cars, a steel wedge is fitted between the axle pad and the spring. Ensure the thick end of the wedge faces forwards. However, where these are not fitted, they should only be included in cases of serious vibration. For cars with single propeller shafts, the use of wedges was discontinued from the following serial numbers onwards.

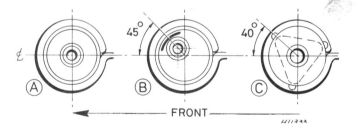

**Fig. 11.7 Rear spring front eye bushes – various types (Sec 10)**

*A   Steel jacketed centre pin*
*B   Steel jacketed eccentric pin*
*C   Flanged triangular section*

| | |
|---|---|
| *Minx* | B011001229 |
| *Hunter* | B051008444 |
| *Gazelle* | B711000270 |
| *Vogue* | B751002748 |

For cars with two-piece propeller shafts, the same part number spring wedge was re-introduced but fitted with the thin end to the front.

12 When refitting the spring to the hanger it is usually easier to fit the front end first. Refit the shackle pins and bushes. Refit the nuts but do not tighten them yet. Lower the axle and position it so that it locates correctly onto the spring (and wedge if fitted) and put the U-bolts and clamp plate in position. Tighten up the U-bolt nuts only moderately.

13 The damper should next be fitted to the lower mounting.

14 The car should be lowered to the ground, bounced a few times to settle the bushes and all the nuts tightened to the specified torque.

## 11 Steering gear and linkage – inspection

1 Wear in the steering gear and linkage is indicated when there is considerable movement in the steering wheel without corresponding movement at the road wheels. Wear is also indicated when the car tends to 'wander' off the line one is trying to steer. There are three main steering 'groups' to examine in such circumstances. These are the wheel bearings, the linkage joints and bushes, and the steering box.

2 Jack up the front of the car and support it on stands under the side frame members so that both front wheels are clear of the ground.

3 Grip the top and bottom of the wheel and try to rock it. It will not take any great effort to be able to feel play in the wheel bearing. If this play is very noticeable, adjust it straight away as it could confuse further examinations. It is possible that during this check play may be discovered in the lower suspension track control arm balljoint (at the foot of the suspension strut). If so, the balljoint will need renewal as described in Section 5.

4 Grip each side of the wheel and try rocking it laterally. Steady pressure will, of course, turn the steering but an alternated back and forth pressure will reveal any loose joint. If some play is felt, obtain assistance so that while one person rocks the wheel from side to side, the other can look at the joints and bushes on the track rods and connections. Excluding the steering box itself there are seven places where play may occur. The two outer balljoints on the two outer track rods are the most likely, followed by the two inner joints on the same rods where they join the centre track rod. Play in these means renewal of the balljoint. Next are the two swivel bushes, one at each end of the centre track rod. Play in these means the whole track rod will need to be renewed as the bushes are not obtainable separately. The last point to check is the pivot of the relay or idler arm which supports the centre track trod on the side opposite the steering box. This unit is bolted to the side frame member and any play calls for renewal of the unit.

5 Finally, check the steering box. Make sure the bolts holding the steering box to the side frame members are tight. Obtain assistance to help examine the mechanism. One person should hold the drop arm at the bottom of the steering box while the other turns the steering wheel a little way from side to side. The amount of lost motion between the steering wheel and the drop arm indicates the degree of wear somewhere in the steering box mechanism. This check should be carried out with the wheels first in the straight ahead position and then at nearly full lock on each side. If the play only occurs noticeably in the straight ahead position then the wear is most probably in the worm and/or nut. If it occurs at all positions then the wear is probably in the rocker shaft bush. An oil leak at this point is another indication of such wear. In either case the steering box will need removal for closer examination and repair.

6 Many owners consider removing shims at one of the two places they are fitted, thinking thereby to compensate for wear. This can be done but the beneficial results, if any, will be very short lived. The wear which has taken place and which will be taken up by removal of the shims will not be properly compensated. The top cover shims, which control rocker shaft endfloat, will not rectify wear in the bush. Their removal will merely keep the shaft running out of alignment, albeit with less play initially. But stiffness will probably result and wear will continue at an accelerated rate until the situation will soon be worse than it was originally. The other shims, between the column flange and the box, pre-load the two ball races (which are not adjustable) on the shaft inside the box. If there is noticeable endfloat on the shaft due to worn bearings, the removal of shims will take up the float but the already worn bearings will wear much faster as a result. It must be understood that the shims are used for initial setting up of new components. They are not designed as a means of subsequent adjustment to compensate for wear. If used in this manner, play will be

removed initially (with the likelihood of stiffness and steering irregularity), but wear will accelerate and result in an equal or increased amount of play.

## 12 Steering linkage – removal and refitting

1 The balljoints on the two outer track rods and the swivel bushes on the centre track rod are fitted into their respective locations by means of a taper pin in a tapered hole, secured by a self-locking nut. In the case of the four balljoints (two on each side of the outer track rods) they are screwed onto the rod and held by a locknut. The two other balljoints have left-hand threads.

2 To remove the taper pin, remove the self-locking nut. On rare occasions the taper pins have been known to simply pull out. More often they are well wedged in position and a clamp or slotted steel wedges may be driven between the ball unit and the arm to release the joint. Another method is to place the head of a hammer (or other solid metal article) on one side of the hole in the arm in which the pin is fitted. Then hit the arm smartly with a hammer on the opposite side. This has the effect of squeezing the taper out and usually works, provided one can get a good swing at it.

3 When the taper pin is free, grip the shank of the joint and back off the locknut. Move this locknut just sufficiently to unlock the shank as its position is a guide to fitting a new joint. Screw the balljoint off the rod.

4 It is important when fitting new balljoints to ensure they are screwed on to the rod for the correct distance and then, before tightening the locknut, they are correctly angled. So, after connecting up and before tightening the locknuts, set the steering in the straight ahead position and see that the socket of the balljoint is square with the axis of the ball taper pin. If this is not done the joint could be under extreme strain when the steering is on only partial lock.

5 If the centre track rod bushes require that the track rod be renewed then it will be necessary first to detach the inner balljoints of the outer track rods from it. The two swivel joints can then be removed from the drop arm and idler arm respectively and the unit removed (photos).

6 As mentioned already, any play in the idler arm bush means that the centre track rod should be detached from it and the whole unit unbolted from the side frame and renewed.

7 When any part of the steering linkage is renewed, have the alignment of the steering checked at a garage equipped with the proper equipment.

## 13 Steering column cowling – removal and refitting

1 Undo the two rear screws beneath the lower cowling. Detach the upper cowling.

2 Remove the two front screws. Remove the clip and lower cowling.

3 To refit, reverse the removal sequence. Check the lower cowl locating dowel enters the column recess.

## 14 Direction indicator switch – removal and refitting

1 Disconnect the battery.

2 Remove the steering column cowling, as described in Section 13.

3 Remove the two screws and clip. Remove the switch.

4 Reverse the removal sequence to refit. Ensure the front wheels are in the straight-ahead position.

## 15 Steering gear – removal and refitting

1 The steering gear (or steering box) is integral with the steering column and shaft. Removal and refitting are not quick jobs. Do not therefore start dismantling it without having first decided what is needed to put it right. If the bush is worn out the new one may need reaming out and this involves specialist tools. If the unit is badly worn it is almost certain that the quickest and cheapest repair is going to be the fitting of another one. It is unusual for only one part to be worn and the cost of the component parts together would be little less than that for the assembly.

2 On right-hand drive cars it is necessary to lower the front

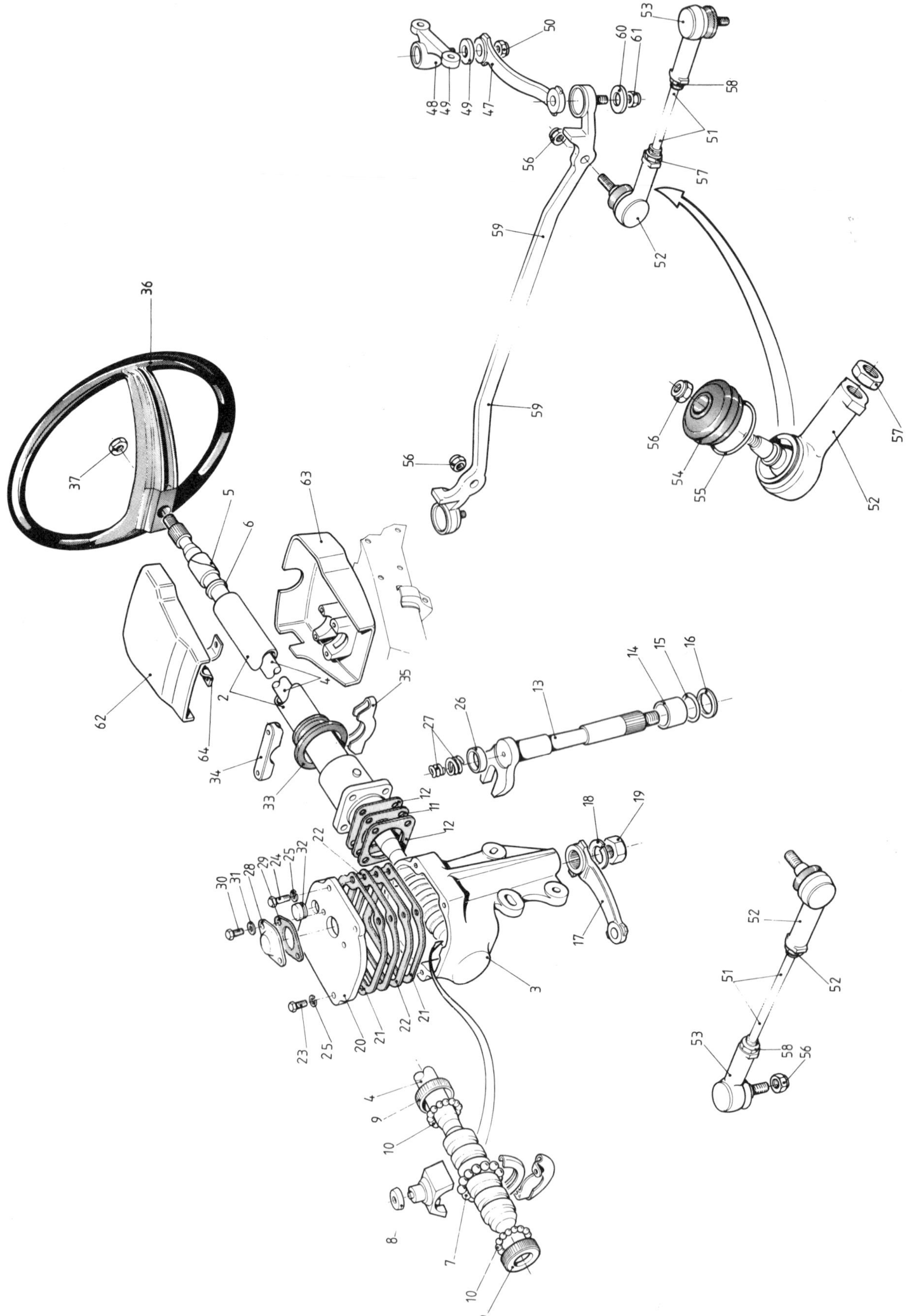

2
3
4
5
6
7
8
9
10
11
12
13
14
15
16
17
18
19
20
21
22
23
24
25
26
27
28
29
30
31
32
33
34
35
36
37
47
48
49
50
51
52
53
54
55
56
57
58
59
60
61
62
63
64

**Fig. 11.8 Steering box, column and linkage (Sec 11)**

2  Outer column tube
3  Steering box
4  Inner column shaft and worm gear
5  Felt bush
6  Retaining washer
7  Recirculating balls
8  Nut guide roller
9  Bearing race
10  Bearing balls
11  Shim
12  Gaskets

13  Rocker shaft
14  Bush
15  Seal
16  Seal retainer
17  Drop arm
18  Lockwasher
19  Nut
20  Top cover
21  Gaskets
22  Shims
23  Screw
24  Dowel screw

25  Spring washer
26  Thrust button
27  Thrust springs
28  Retaining cap
29  Joint
30  Cap screw
31  Star washer
32  Filler plug
33  Grommet
34  Clamping bracket – upper half

35  Clamping bracket – lower half
36  Steering wheel
37  Nut
47  Idler (relay) arm
48  Idler pivot
49  Dust cover
50  Self-locking nut
51  Outer track rod
52  Balljoint right-hand thread
53  Balljoint left-hand thread
54  Rubber boot

55  Retainer ring
56  Self-locking nut
57  Rod locknut right-hand thread
58  Rod locknut left-hand thread
59  Centre track rod
60  Dust cover
61  Self-locking nut
62  Cowl (upper half)
63  Cowl (lower half)
64  Cowl clamp

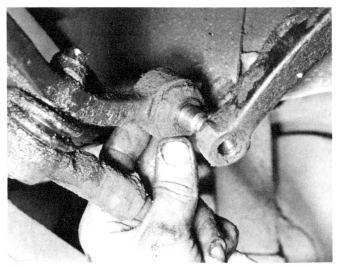

12.5a Refitting the centre track rod to the drop arm

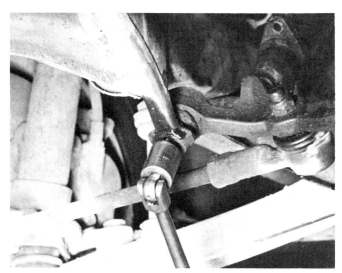

12.5b Refitting the centre track rod to the idler arm

crossmember to provide sufficient clearance to get the whole unit out from under the car. It is also necessary to have at least two feet ground clearance in order to get the column out.

3   First disconnect the battery and then remove the upper and lower halves of the cowl around the upper end of the steering column by taking out the screws from underneath. Then detach the direction indicator switch and overdrive switch if fitted.

4   Next remove the steering wheel. This can be done by first prising out the motif in the centre. Then mark the position of the wheel in relation to the shaft – which will simplify refitting if the same shaft is being put back. Undo the nut and the wheel can be pulled off. Remove the steering column lock, if fitted, as described in Section 19.

5   Move the front seat right back and pull the carpet back from the scuttle. Remove the screws and clips holding the parcel shelf in position. Undo the two clamps holding the column.

6   To lower the front crossmembr means detaching the engine from its forward mounting so the weight will have to be supported by other means. As the car has to be raised much higher than usual at the front it is not really practicable or safe to support the engine from underneath . It is better to support it from above by lifting tackle suspended from a beam or some suitably padded strut across the top of the engine compartment, from which a hook or sling may be attached to the slinging eye at the front of the engine.

7   With the car raised on stands and the weight of the engine supported, the engine mounting bolts should be removed. Then the

two bolts on each side which hold the crossmember to the side frame should be taken out and the crossmember allowed to come down as far as it can.

8   Detach the end of the centre track rod from the drop arm.

9   The three bolts holding the steering box to the side frame should now be slackened and, before removal, the position of any shims between the box and the wheel arch noted. The shims must be retained. They should go back as before even if a new box is fitted.

10  The steering box and column can now be manoeuvred out from under the car.

11  On left-hand drive models, the removal of the crossmember is unnecessary. If the air cleaner and clutch slave cylinder are taken off, the whole column can be swung to the horizontal. Guard against oil coming out of the upper end. Lift the box upwards in the engine compartment and draw the assembly out.

12  Refitting is a reversal of the removal procedure with the following points borne in mind. Assemble all the mounting bolts and column clamping brackets loosely before tightening anything. The shims between the box and wing panel should be in position and the rubber grommet round the column where it passes through the scuttle. The

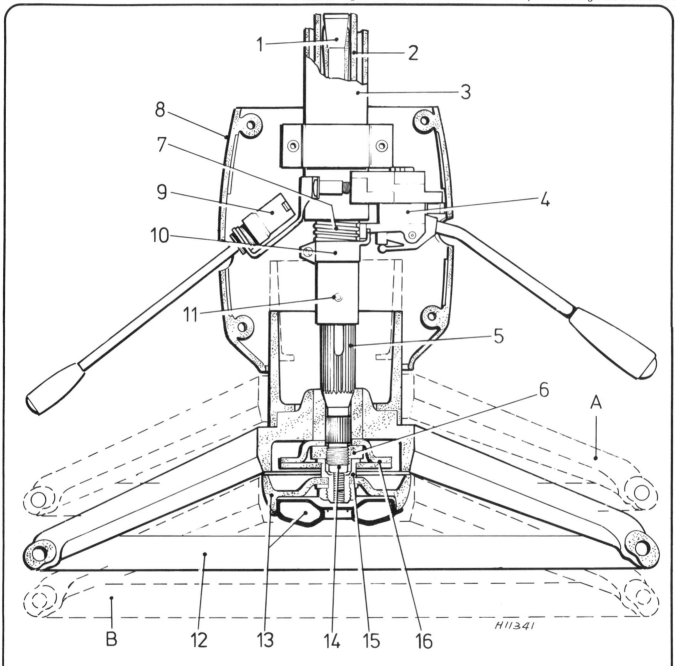

**Fig. 11.9 Adjustable steering column, upper section – sectional drawing (Sec 18)**

| | | | |
|---|---|---|---|
| 1  Expander bolt | 7  Bearing spring | 12  Steering wheel | 16  Circular pressure plate |
| 2  Inner column | 8  Column cowl | 13  Hand control and cap | A   Lowest position of steering |
| 3  Outer column | 9  Overdrive switch (where | 14  Nylon circlip | wheel |
| 4  Direction indicator switch | fitted) | 15  Expander bolt adjusting | B   Highest position of steering |
| 5  Splined extension | 10  Indicator striker | nut | wheel |
| 6  Steering wheel nut | 11  Dowel | | |

alignment of the column with the upper and lower clamps is important as when everything is tight there should be no twist or stresses built up. This is why it may be necessary to increase or reduce the shims at the steering box mounting. Fill the box with oil on completion. Check the front wheel alignment.

## 16 Burman adjustable steering gear – removal and refitting

The procedure for removal of the adjustable steering gear is similar to that for the conventional steering gear as described in Section 15 with the exception of the removal of the steering wheel, which is described in Section 18.

## 17 Steering gear with column lock – removal and refitting

Initially, remove the steering lock as described in Section 19, then follow the procedure for the conventional steering gear.

## 18 Steering wheel with adjustable steering unit – removal and refitting

1   Carefully prise off the steering wheel hub cap using a screwdriver in the slot under the cap outer edge.
2   Unscrew the nut and washer securing the hand control nut to the inner squared expander bolt adjusting nut.
3   Carefully withdraw the hand control nut.
4   Unscrew the three crosshead screws which retain the circular pressure plate; withdraw the plate.
5   Undo and remove the inner squared expander bolt adjusting nut.
6   Set the roadwheels to the straight-ahead position.
7   Loosen the large nut securing the steering wheel to the splined inner column extension.
8   Rock the steering wheel a little from side to side to loosen it on its splines, then remove the steering wheel nut and pull off the wheel.
9   Refitting is a reversal of the removal procedure, but particular attention should be paid to the following points:

   *(a) The inner column should be set to its lowest position and the nylon circlip fitted to the top expander bolt*
   *(b) Ensure that the roadwheels are in the straight-ahead position*
   *(c) Align the spokes of the steering wheel as it is being fitted*

## 19 Steering lock and ignition switch – removal and refitting

1   To remove the switch only, remove the battery earth lead, then apply thumb pressure to lever off the plastic ring on the back of the unit. The switch can then be carefully withdrawn from its location by pulling on the cables.
2   To remove the complete lock and switch, first remove the battery earth lead.
3   Withdraw the gaiter from the rear of the switch, then disconnect the cables.
4   Remove the front parcel tray, then take off the steering column cowling. Disconnect the steering column supporting brackets.
5   Loosen the bolts which retain the steering unit to the car frame, then remove them all except for one.
6   Lower the top end of the column to gain access to the steering lock fixing bolts.
7   Using a sharp centre punch, mark the centre of the domed head of the shear head bolts, then drill out the bolts to a depth of $\frac{1}{8}$ in (3 mm) using a $\frac{1}{4}$ in (7 mm) drill. This will release the bolt head from the shank.
8   Remove the slot-headed screws from the fixing clamp and withdraw the unit from the column.
9   Using suitable grips, unscrew the bolt shanks remaining in the body of the unit.
10   To refit the lock unit, set to the park position with the locking plunger disengaged.
11   With the clamp removed, fit the unit to the column ensuring that the spigot registers squarely in the location hole.
12   Secure the unit to the column by fitting the clamp, fixing screws

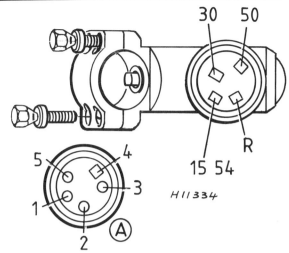

Fig. 11.10 Steering lock and ignition switch – rear view, showing terminals and shear head bolts (Inset: A alternative terminal markings) (Sec 19)

| Terminal No | Connection to | Cable colour |
|---|---|---|
| 50 or 1 | Starter solenoid | White/red |
| 30 or 2 | Battery | Brown (without ammeter); Brown/white (with ammeter) |
| 15/54 or 3 | Fuse 1 | White |
| 4 | Buzzer | Black/brown |
| R or 5 | Accessories | Green |

and bolts, taking care not to shear the heads of the special bolts at this stage.
13   Check the operation of the lock and, if satisfactory, tighten the shear head bolts fully, shearing the bolt heads.
14   Refit the steering column in its original position. Refit the parcel tray.
15   Reconnect the wires to the rear of the switch. Refit the rubber gaiter.
16   Reconnect the battery earth lead.

## 20 Steering column upper felt bush – removal and refitting

1   The felt bush normally requires no attention in service. However, rattling of the column or unreliable operation of the direction indicator switch can result from the bush becoming worn.
2   To renew the bush, remove the steering column cowls, direction indicator switch and striker. See appropriate Sections.
3   Withdraw the felt bush using an appropriate probe.
4   Chamfer one edge of the bush to facilitate fitting, and soak in graphited oil for six hours.
5   Place the strip round the inner column, chamfered edge downwards and on the outside. Persuade the felt down between the inner and outer columns until it is 0.25 in (6 mm) below the top of the outer column.
6   Refit all parts.

## 21 Front wheel bearings – adjustment

1   Jack up the front wheels and remove the hub caps. Check the bearings as described in Section 11 to verify that they need adjusting. Prise off the bearing dust cap. This can usually be dislodged by a few sideways taps with a hammer.
2   When the bearing nut is exposed withdraw the split pin and the castellated lock cap.
3   If a torque wrench is available, tighten the bearing nut, spinning the wheel all the while, to a torque of 15 to 20 lbf ft. Then back off one flat and refit the lock cap and fit a new split pin. If no torque wrench is available tighten the nut with a tubular spanner as much as you can without using a tommy bar and then continue as described.

4    If, during the adjustment and afterwards, the bearing feels rough or the wheel tends to bind in any position it is possible that one or both of the hub bearing races is worn out in which case they should be renewed.

5    Refit all items in reverse sequence. Do not fill the dust cap with grease.

## 22  Front hubs and bearings – removal and refitting

1    When the 15 000 mile service calls for repacking the hubs with grease, the hubs must be taken off the spindles. To renew the bearings is a procedure following on from this.

2    Jack up the car, support it on stands and remove the front wheels.

3    Detach the brake callipers from the discs as detailed in Chapter 9.

4    Remove the bearing dust covers. Take out the split pin and remove the castellated lock cap followed by the nut and washer.

5    The hub and disc assembly may be drawn off and the roller bearing taken out from each side of the hub.

6    If flushing and repacking is all that is being done, the inside of the hub should be cleaned with paraffin to remove old grease. The roller bearings should be cleaned similarly. Dry them off thoroughly and work new grease into the bearings. The hub should be packed with grease only as indicated in the cross-section drawing. Clean the spindle and make sure the grease seal is in good condition. Remove the seal and distance piece if the bearings are being renewed.

7    If the bearings are being renewed, the inner races of each one will have to be driven out of the hub. This can be done with a suitable drift through the bore of the hub. Be careful to drive the races out straight and square and do not damage the bore of the hub where they fit. Fit the inner races of the new bearings into the hub, making sure that the larger internal diameter of each race faces outwards.

8    Pack the rollers and hub with grease as previously described. Place the rollers of the inner bearing in position.

9    The bearing seal should be pressed into the hub with the lip towards the bearing. Push the special distance piece into the centre of the seal with the bevelled side facing outwards.

10   Refit the hub on the axle spindle and fit the rollers of the outer bearing, followed by the washer and nut.

11   Adjust the bearings as described in Section 21. Refit the dust cap.

12   Refit the brake calliper and roadwheel.

## 23  Wheel studs – removal and refitting

1    Do not attempt to drive studs out with the hub in place, as damage will be caused to the bearings.

2    Employ special tool No 18G 1063 to press out the defective stud. Alternatively, remove the hubs then support the areas on either side of the stud head and carefully drive the stud through.

3    To fit the new stud, employ the special tool after carefully aligning the splines. Alternatively, the stud may be drawn through, using a wheel nut with a washer beneath it.

## 24  Steering alignment

1    To obtain accurate steering, correct front wheel alignment is essential. Misalignment can be very dangerous and causes rapid tyre wear.

2    Before assuming a steering defect exists, check the following points:

  (a)  Tyre pressures are correct
  (b)  Wheels – truth and balance
  (c)  Wheel bearings – adjustment and wear
  (d)  Steering linkage – balljoints and swivels
  (e)  Steering box – wear

3    A proper check of steering alignment consists of an examination of the following:

  (a)  Toe-in
  (b)  Camber angle
  (c)  Castor angle
  (d)  Steering axis inclination angle
  (e)  Wheel angles on turns

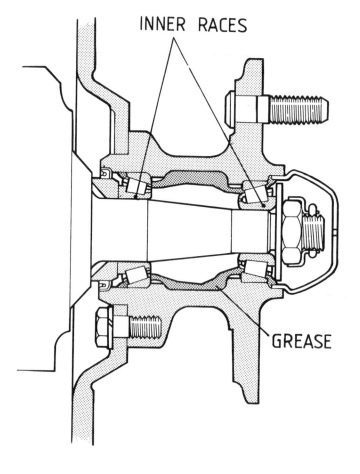

Fig. 11.11 Front wheel hub assembly (Sec 22)

Of this total of five alignment features, only one can be adjusted – namely, toe-in. Toe-in is adjusted by the outer track rods. All other angles are controlled by the angles and dimensions of the component parts of the steering and the bushes and balljoints which link them together.

4    It is not possible to check the steering alignment without proper gauge equipment. It is imperative that any checking is done on the correct equipment and one is advised to go to an authorised agent for this service. This is because in addition to the alignment measuring gear, the suspension at front and rear has to be pre-set to a fixed datum before checking begins. (This is done by loading the body and fitting special dimension blocks at certain points). The steering geometry alters under different loads and attitudes and the specifications are at datum position. If the agents should advise that after setting the toe-in correctly some other aspect of the steering geometry is incorrect then it means that one or more components have been distorted (provided of course that all the joints and bushes are in order). In such circumstances the components which affect the alignment will have to be removed and their dimensions individually checked. Details of the components and their dimensions are given in Figs. 11.12, 11.13 and 11.14.

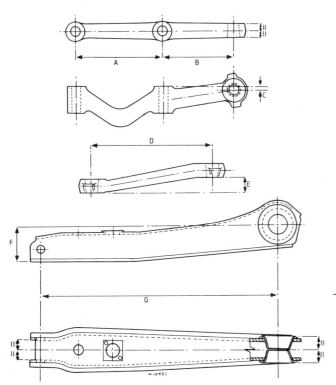

**Fig. 11.12 Dimensions – idler arm, steering arm and track control arm (Sec 24)**

Steering arm:
- A    3.8 in (96.52 mm)
- B    3.02 in (76.71 mm)
- C    0.14 in (3.56 mm)

Idler arm:
- D    5.0 in (127 mm) hole centre lines parallel
- E    0.7 in (17.78 mm)

Track control (lower suspension) arm:
- F    1.88 in (47.75 mm)
- G    12.1 in (307.34 mm)

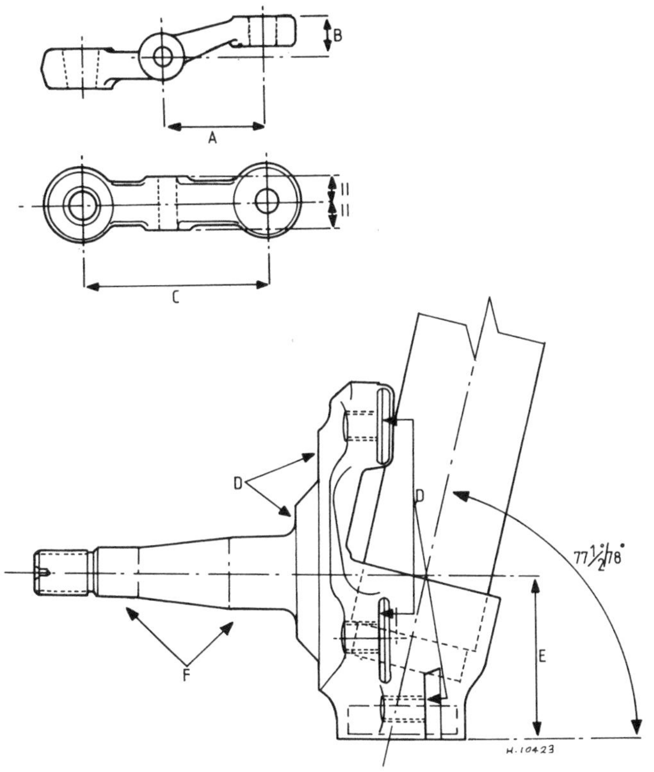

**Fig. 11.13 Dimensions – stub axle and track control arm balljoint carrier (Sec 24)**

Track control arm balljoint carrier:
- A    1.96 in (49.78 mm)
- B    0.72 in (18.29 mm)
- C    3.58 in (90.93 mm)

Stub axle:
- D    Faces parallel at right angles to spindle centre line
- E    2.45 in (62.23 mm)
- F    Concentric bearing surfaces

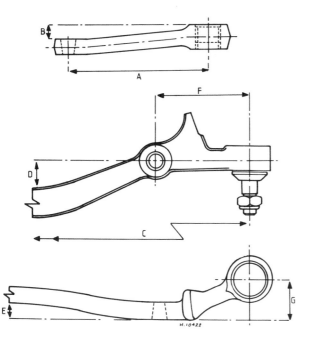

**Fig. 11.14 Dimensions – centre track rod and drop arm (Sec 24)**

- A    5.0 in (127 mm) hole centre lines parallel
- B    0.5 in (12.7 mm)

Centre track rod:
- C    23.75 in (603.25 mm) between ball pin centres
- D    0.94 in (23.88 mm)
- E    0.54 in (13.72 mm)
- F    3.21 in (81.53 mm)
- G    1.28 in (32.51 mm)

## 25 Fault diagnosis – suspension and steering

| Symptom | Reason(s) |
| --- | --- |
| Steering feels vague | Tyre pressures uneven and otherwise incorrect |
| Vehicle wanders or floats at speed | Defective dampers<br>Wear in steering linkage<br>Excessive play in steering box<br>Steering box loose<br>Hub bearings worn or loose<br>Body misalignment |
| Stiff or heavy steering | Tyre pressures too low<br>Wear or seizure in steering linkage<br>Front wheel toe-in incorrect<br>Steering column misaligned |
| Wheel wobble or vibration | Wheel nuts loose<br>Front wheels and tyres out of balance<br>Steering linkage worn<br>Steering box worn<br>Hub bearings worn<br>Springs weak or broken<br>Wheels buckled |

# Chapter 12 Bodywork and fittings

## Contents

| | |
|---|---|
| Body mouldings – removal and refitting | 16 |
| Bonnet – removal aand refitting | 8 |
| Boot lid – removal and refitting | 9 |
| Bumpers and rubbing strips – removal and refitting | 13 |
| Centre console and front parcel tray – removal and refitting | 24 |
| Directional air diffusers – removal and refitting | 21 |
| Doors and fittings – maintenance, removal and refitting | 7 |
| Facia crash roll – removal and refitting | 22 |
| Facia panel – removal | 23 |
| General description | 1 |
| Heater controls and cables – removal and refitting | 28 |
| Heater unit and controls (later models) – removal and refitting | 30 |
| Heater unit, blowers and water valve (early models) – removal and refitting | 29 |
| Heating and ventilating system – description and adjustment | 27 |
| Maintenance – bodywork and underframe | 2 |

| | |
|---|---|
| Maintenance – upholstery and carpets | 3 |
| Major bodywork damage – repair | 5 |
| Minor bodywork damage – repair | 4 |
| Name badges – removal and refitting | 12 |
| Radiator grilles – removal and refitting | 11 |
| Rear embellisher assembly (later models) – removal and refitting | 14 |
| Rear number plate – correct fitment | 15 |
| Roof cover and simulated wood finish (where fitted) | 18 |
| Roof lining | 25 |
| Roof rack – description, removal and refitting | 20 |
| Seat belts | 26 |
| Seats – removal and refitting | 6 |
| Spare wheel carrier (saloon and estate models) | 19 |
| Weatherstrips – refitting | 17 |
| Windscreen and windows – removal and refitting | 10 |

## 1 General description

The combined bodyshell and underframe is a welded structure of steel pressings. Openings provide for the engine compartment, luggage boot, doors and windows. The rear suspension is bolted to the side frame at each end of the leaf springs. A detachable crossmember is bolted to the side members at the bottom of the engine compartment. This braces the structure, supports the forward end of the engine/gearbox unit and provides the lower attachment points for the front suspension struts. A shorter transverse member is bolted across the transmission tunnel, to the rear of the engine compartment. This is the third support point for the engine/gearbox unit, the gearbox rear extension being flexibly mounted on it. All models have four doors and there are estate versions having an additional rear door hinged at the top. The wing aprons are reinforced where the upper bearing thrust units of the suspension strut assemblies are bolted to the bodywork.

## 2 Maintenance – bodywork and underframe

1   The general condition of a car's bodywork is the thing that significantly affects it value. Maintenance is easy but needs to be regular. Neglect, particularly after minor damage, can lead quickly to further deterioration and costly repair bills. It is important also to keep watch on those parts of the car not immediately visible, for instance the underside, inside all the wheel arches and the lower part of the engine compartment.

2   The basic maintenance routine for the bodywork is washing – preferably with a lot of water, from a hose. This will remove all the loose solids which may have stuck to the car. It is important to flush these off in such a way as to prevent grit from scratching the finish. The wheel arches and underframe need washing in the same way to remove any accumulated mud which will retain moisture and tend to encourage rust. Paradoxically enough, the best time to clean the underframe and wheel arches is in wet weather when the mud is thoroughly wet and soft. In very wet weather the underframe is usually cleaned of large accumulations automatically and this is a good time for inspection.

3   Periodically, it is a good idea to have the whole of the underframe of the car steam cleaned, engine compartment included, so that a thorough inspection can be carried out to see what minor repairs and renovations are necessary. Steam cleaning is available at many garages and is necessary for removal of the accumulation of oily grime which sometimes is allowed to become thick in certain areas. If steam cleaning facilities are not available, there are one or two excellent grease solvents available which can be brush applied. The dirt can then be simply hosed off.

4   After washing paintwork, wipe off with a chamois leather to give an unspotted clear finish. A coat of clear protective wax polish will give added protection against chemical pollutants in the air. If the paintwork sheen has dulled or oxidised, use a cleaner/polisher com-

bination to restore the brilliance of the shine. This requires a little effort, but such dulling is usually caused because regular washing has been neglected. Always check that the door and ventilator opening drain holes and pipes are completely clear so that water can be drained out. Bright work should be treated in the same way as paintwork. Windscreens and windows can be kept clear of the smeary film which often appears, by adding a little ammonia to the water. If they are scratched, a good rub with a proprietary metal polish will often clear them. Never use any form of wax or other body or chromium polish on glass.

## 3 Maintenance – upholstery and carpets

1   Mats and carpets should be brushed or vacuum cleaned regularly to keep them free of grit. If they are badly stained remove them from the car for scrubbing or sponging and make quite sure they are dry before refitting. Seats and interior trim panels can be kept clean by a wipe over with a damp cloth. If they do become stained (which can be more apparent on light coloured upholstery) use a little liquid detergent and a soft nail brush to scour the grime out of the grain of the material. Do not forget to keep the head lining clean in the same way as the upholstery. When using liquid cleaners inside the car do not over-wet the surfaces being cleaned. Excessive damp could get into the seams and padded interior causing stains, offensive odours or even rot. If the inside of the car gets wet accidentally it is worthwhile taking some trouble to dry it out properly, particularly where carpets are involved. *Do not leave oil or electric heaters inside the car for this purpose.*

## 4 Minor body damage – repair

*The photographic sequences on pages 222 and 223 illustrate the operations detailed in the following sub-sections.*

### Repair of minor scratches in the car's bodywork

If the scratch is very superficial, and does not penetrate to the metal of the bodywork, repair is very simple. Lightly rub the area of the scratch with a paintwork renovator, or a very fine cutting paste, to remove loose paint from the scratch and to clear the surrounding bodywork of wax polish. Rinse the area with clean water.

Apply touch-up paint to the scratch using a thin paint brush; continue to apply thin layers of paint until the surface of the paint in the scratch is level with the surrounding paintwork. Allow the new paint at least two weeks to harden: then blend it into the surrounding paintwork by rubbing the paintwork, in the scratch area, with a paintwork renovator or a very fine cutting paste. Finally, apply wax polish.

Where the scratch has penetrated right through to the metal of the bodywork, causing the metal to rust, a different repair technique is

This sequence of photographs deals with the repair of the dent and paintwork damage shown in this photo. The procedure will be similar for the repair of a hole. It should be noted that the procedures given here are simplified – more explicit instructions will be found in the text

In the case of a dent the first job – after removing surrounding trim – is to hammer out the dent where access is possible. This will minimise filling. Here, the large dent having been hammered out, the damaged area is being made slightly concave

Now all paint must be removed from the damaged area, by rubbing with coarse abrasive paper. Alternatively, a wire brush or abrasive pad can be used in a power drill. Where the repair area meets good paintwork, the edge of the paintwork should be 'feathered', using a finer grade of abrasive paper

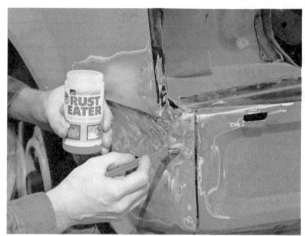

In the case of a hole caused by rusting, all damaged sheet-metal should be cut away before proceeding to this stage. Here, the damaged area is being treated with rust remover and inhibitor before being filled

Mix the body filler according to its manufacturer's instructions. In the case of corrosion damage, it will be necessary to block off any large holes before filling – this can be done with zinc gauze or aluminium tape. Make sure the area is absolutely clean before...

...applying the filler. Filler should be applied with a flexible applicator, as shown, for best results; the wooden spatula being used for confined areas. Apply thin layers of filler at 20-minute intervals, until the surface of the filler is slightly proud of the surrounding bodywork

Initial shaping can be done with a Surform plane or Dreadnought file. Then, using progressively finer grades of wet-and-dry paper, wrapped around a sanding block, and copious amounts of clean water, rub down the filler until really smooth and flat. Again, feather the edges of adjoining paintwork

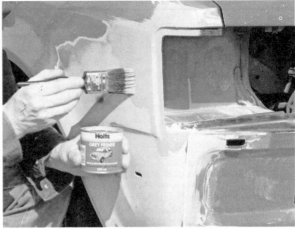

The whole repair area can now be sprayed or brush-painted with primer. If spraying, ensure adjoining areas are protected from over-spray. Note that at least one inch of the surrounding sound paintwork should be coated with primer. Primer has a 'thick' consistency, so will fill small imperfections

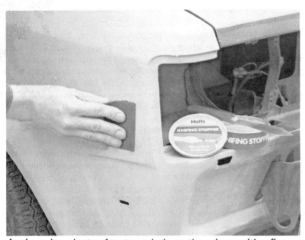

Again, using plenty of water, rub down the primer with a fine grade of wet-and-dry paper (400 grade is probably best) until it is really smooth and well blended into the surrounding paintwork. Any remaining imperfections can now be filled by carefully applied knifing stopper paste

When the stopper has hardened, rub down the repair area again before applying the final coat of primer. Before rubbing down this last coat of primer, ensure the repair area is blemish-free — use more stopper if necessary. To ensure that the surface of the primer is really smooth use some finishing compound

The top coat can now be applied. When working out of doors, pick a dry, warm and wind-free day. Ensure surrounding areas are protected from over-spray. Agitate the aerosol thoroughly, then spray the centre of the repair area, working outwards with a circular motion. Apply the paint as several thin coats

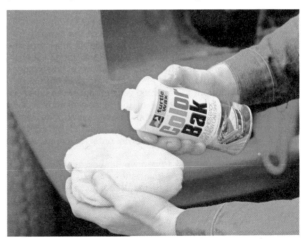

After a period of about two weeks, which the paint needs to harden fully, the surface of the repaired area can be 'cut' with a mild cutting compound prior to wax polishing. When carrying out bodywork repairs, remember that the quality of the finished job is proportional to the time and effort expended

required. Remove any loose rust from the bottom of the scratch with a penknife, then apply rust inhibiting paint to prevent the formation of rust in the future. Using a rubber or nylon applicator fill the scratch with bodystopper paste. If required, this paste can be mixed with cellulose thinners to provide a very thin paste which is ideal for filling narrow scratches. Before the stopper-paste in the scratch hardens, wrap a piece of smooth cotton rag around the top of a finger. Dip the finger in cellulose thinners and then quickly sweep it across the surface of the stopper-paste in the scratch; this will ensure that the surface of the stopper-paste is slightly hollowed. The scratch can now be painted over as described earlier in this Section.

### Repair of dents in the car's bodywork

When deep denting of the vehicle's bodywork has taken place, the first task is to pull the dent out, until the affected bodywork almost attains its original shape. There is little point in trying to restore the original shape completely, as the metal in the damaged area will have stretched on impact and cannot be reshaped fully to its original contour. It is better to bring the level of the dent up to a point which is about $\frac{1}{8}$ in (3 mm) below the level of the surrounding bodywork. In cases where the dent is very shallow anyway, it is not worth trying to pull it out at all. If the underside of the dent is accessible, it can be hammered out gently from behind, using a mallet with a wooden or plastic head. Whilst doing this, hold a suitable block of wood firmly against the outside of the panel to absorb the impact from the hammer blows and thus prevent a large area of the bodywork from being 'belled-out'.

Should the dent be in a section of the bodywork which has double skin or some other factor making it inaccessible from behind, a different technique is called for. Drill several small holes through the metal inside the area – particularly in the deeper section. Then screw long self-tapping screws into the holes just sufficiently for them to gain a good purchase in the metal. Now the dent can be pulled out by pulling on the protruding heads of the screws with a pair of pliers.

The next stage of the repair is the removal of the paint from the damaged area, and from an inch or so of the surrounding 'sound' bodywork. This is accomplished most easily by using a wire brush or abrasive pad on a power drill, although it can be done just as effectively by hand using sheets of abrasive paper. To complete the preparation for filling, score the surface of the bare metal with a screwdriver or the tang of a file, or alternatively, drill small holes in the affected area. This will provide a really good 'key' for the filler paste.

To complete the repair see the Section on filling and re-spraying.

### Repair of rust holes or gashes in the car's bodywork

Remove all paint from the affected area and from an inch or so of the surrounding 'sound' bodywork, using an abrasive pad or a wire brush on a power drill. If these are not available a few sheets of abrasive paper will do the job just as effectively. With the paint removed you will be able to gauge the severity of the corrosion and therefore decide whether to renew the whole panel (if this is possible) or to repair the affected area. New body panels are not as expensive as most people think and it is often quicker and more satisfactory to fit a new panel than to attempt to repair large areas of corrosion.

Remove all fittings from the affected area except those which will act as a guide to the original shape of the damaged bodywork (eg headlamp shells etc). Then, using tin snips or a hacksaw blade, remove all loose metal and any other metal badly affected by corrosion. Hammer the edges of the hole inwards in order to create a slight depression for the filler paste.

Wire brush the affected area to remove the powdery rust from the surface of the remaining metal. Paint the affected area with rust inhibiting paint; if the back of the rusted area is accessible treat this also.

Before filling can take place it will be necessary to block the hole in some way. This can be achieved by the use of zinc gauze or aluminium tape.

Zinc gauze is probably the best material to use for a large hole. Cut a piece to the approximate size and shape of the hole to be filled, then position it in the hole so that its edges are below the level of the surrounding bodywork. It can be retained in position by several blobs of filler paste around its periphery.

Aluminium tape should be used for small or very narrow holes. Pull a piece off the roll and trim it to the approximate size and shape required, then pull off the backing paper (if used) and stick the tape

over the hole; it can be overlapped if the thickness of one piece is insufficient. Burnish down the edges of the tape with the handle of a screwdriver or similar, to ensure that the tape is securely attached to the metal underneath.

### Bodywork repairs – filling and re-spraying

Before using this Section, see the Sections on dent, deep scratch, rust holes and gash repairs.

Many types of bodyfiller are available, but generally speaking those proprietary kits which contain a tin of filler paste and a tube of resin hardener are best for this type of repair. A wide, flexible plastic or nylon applicator will be found invaluable for imparting a smooth and well contoured finish to the surface of the filler.

Mix up a little filler on a clean piece of card or board – measure the hardener carefully (follow the maker's instructions on the pack) otherwise the filler will set too rapidly or too slowly.

Using the applicator apply the filler paste to the prepared area; draw the applicator across the surface of the filler to achieve the correct contour and to level the filler surface. As soon as a contour that approximates the correct one is achieved, stop working the paste – if you carry on too long the paste will become sticky and begin to 'pick up' on the applicator. Continue to add thin layers of filler paste at twenty-minute intervals until the level of the filler is just proud of the surrounding bodywork.

Once the filler has hardened, excess can be removed using a metal plane or file. From then on, progressively finer grades of sandpaper should be used, starting with a 40 grade production paper and finishing with 400 grade wet-and-dry paper. Always wrap the abrasive paper around a flat rubber, cork, or wooden block – otherwise the surface of the filler will not be completely flat. During the smoothing of the filler surface the wet-and-dry paper should be periodically rinsed in water. This will ensure that a very smooth finish is imparted to the filler at the final stage.

At this stage the 'repair area' should be surrounded by a ring of bare metal, which in turn should be encircled by the finely 'feathered' edge of the good paintwork. Rinse the repair area with clean water, until all of the dust produced by the rubbing-down operation has gone.

Spray the whole repair area with a light coat of primer – this will show up any imperfections in the surface of the filler. Repair these imperfections with fresh filler paste or bodystopper, and once more smooth the surface with abrasive paper. If bodystopper is used, it can be mixed with cellulose thinners to form a really thin paste which is ideal for filling small holes. Repeat this spray and repair procedure until you are satisfied that the surface of the filler, and the feathered edge of the paintwork are perfect. Clean the repair area with clean water and allow to dry fully.

The repair area is now ready for final spraying. Paint spraying must be carried out in a warm, dry, windless and dust free atmosphere. This condition can be created artificially if you have access to a large indoor working area, but if you are forced to work in the open, you will have to pick your day very carefully. If you are working indoors, dousing the floor in the work area with water will help to settle the dust which would otherwise be in the atmosphere. If the repair area is confined to one body panel, mask off the surrounding panels; this will help to minimise the effects of a slight mis-match in paint colours. Bodywork fittings (eg chrome strips, door handles etc) will also need to be masked off. Use genuine masking tape and several thicknesses of newspaper for the masking operations.

Before commencing to spray, agitate the aerosol can thoroughly, then spray a test area (an old tin, or similar) until the technique is mastered. Cover the repair area with a thick coat of primer; the thickness should be built up using several thin layers of paint rather than one thick one. Using 400 grade wet-and-dry paper, rub down the surface of the primer until it is really smooth. While doing this, the work area should be thoroughly doused with water, and the wet-and-dry paper periodically rinsed in water. Allow to dry before spraying on more paint.

Spray on the top coat, again building up the thickness by using several thin layers of paint. Start spraying in the centre of the repair area and then, using a circular motion, work outwards until the whole repair area and about 2 inches of the surrounding original paintwork is covered. Remove all masking material 10 to 15 minutes after spraying on the final coat of paint.

Allow the new paint at least two weeks to harden, then, using a paintwork renovator or a very fine cutting paste, blend the edges of the paint into the existing paintwork. Finally, apply wax polish.

## 5 Major body damage – repair

Where serious damage has occurred or large areas need renewal due to neglect, it means that completely new sections or panels will need welding in and this is best left to professionals. If the damage is due to impact it will also be necessary to completely check the alignment of the bodyshell structure. Due to the principle of construction, the strength and shape of the whole vehicle can be affected by damage to a part. In such instances the services of an agent with specialist checking jigs are essential. If a body is left misaligned it is first of all dangerous as the car will not handle properly, and secondly uneven stresses will be imposed on the steering, engine and transmission, causing abnormal wear or complete failure. Tyre wear may also be excessive.

## 6 Seats – removal and refitting

1   To remove a front seat, place it in the rearward position and remove the two seat runner front bolts. Push the seat forward and remove the two rear bolts (employ a socket of reduced height, with a lever welded to the side to remove the inboard bolt). Lift out the seat, noting the position of the stop plate if fitted. Retain the nylon packing pieces from the outside runner. Refit in reverse order.
2   To remove a rear seat cushion (except on Sceptre and estate models), raise the front edge of the cushion to clear the retaining valance, and remove.
3   On Sceptre models, remove the ashtray, withdraw the screw, and remove the tray housing. Proceed as for other models.
4   On estate cars, rotate the cushion to the vertical, remove the four screws securing each hinge and remove the cushion.
5   To remove the rear seat squab (all except estate models) remove the cushion, remove the two retaining screws (one from each wheel area), and lift the squab up and away from the three retaining clips.
6   To remove the rear squab (estate models only), undo the screws securing the hinges to the wheel arch.
7   Refitting of all cushions and squabs is a reversal of the removal sequence.

## 7 Doors and fittings – maintenance, removal and refitting

1   The hinges and door latches should be wiped clean and a few drops of light oil applied occasionally. An oil with a graphite additive is particularly good. Do not over-oil as the excesss runs out and collects dirt. Wipe after oiling. Other places which stiffen up and need oiling are the bonnet and boot lid hinges, bonnet release and safety catches.
2   If a rattle appears to be coming from a door, check first that it is not loose on its hinges and that the latch is holding it firmly closed. The hinges can be checked by rocking the door up and down when open to detect any play. If the hinges are worn at the pin the whole hinge will need renewal. When the door is closed the panel should be flush with the pillar. If not, the hinges or latch striker plate need adjustment. The door hinges are held to the door and frame by three studs on each hinge plate. Access to the nuts is from behind the door and body and the trim should be removed as described in paragraph 5. The fitting of new hinges requires assistance if damage to the paintwork is to be avoided. To adjust the setting of the door catch, slacken the screws holding the striker plate to the door pillar just enough so that it can be moved but will hold its position. Close the door with the latch button pressed then release the latch. This is so that the striker plate position is not disturbed on closing the door. Then set the door position by moving it without touching the catch, so that the panel is flush with the bodywork. This will set the striker plate in the proper place. Carefully release the catch so as not to disturb the striker plate, open the door and tighten the screws. Rattles within the door will be due to loose fixtures or missing anti-rattle pads.
3   To remove the window winder handle, press back the circular escutcheon behind it and push out the pin thus exposed. Pull off the handle and escutcheon ring.
4   Remove the arm rest (where fitted) by removing the nuts and withdrawing the rest.
5   Remove the trim panel by moving a flat blade along behind the bottom edge of the panel until it strikes a clip. Lever the clip out.

Continue in this manner, making sure the leverage is applied close to the clips; otherwise, they may pull out of the panel. When the clips are free, pull the panel down to free the top edge from the garnish rail. On rear doors, the panel is held by the three screws at the bottom. Remove these before drawing the panel down.
6   To remove the garnish rail, first remove the door pull where fitted, by removing the two screws and taking away the handle. Remove the garnish rail screws, lift the rail free of the top edge of the door and ease it over the interior door handle. Watch that the locking slide does not fall from the handle.
7   The remote handle may now be detached by removing the link clip and taking out the handle securing bolts.
8   To remove the window winder mechanism, undo the bottom stop bracket screw and take out the stop bracket. Refit the winder handle temporarily and lower the window to the bottom of the door. Remove the screws holding the winder mechanism and slide the operating arm out of the channel at the bottom of the glass. Lift the glass up to the door and prop it in position there. Lift out the winder mechanism from the bottom of the door.
9   To remove the door exterior handle, undo the two nuts securing it inside the door outer panel.
10   To remove the lock mechanism disconnect the remove lever link, and after undoing the screws, take the lock out from inside the door.
11   To adjust the striker, loosen the screws and adjust as necessary. Tighten the screws.
12   Whichever window (quarter light or main window) needs to be removed from the front door, the quarterlight has to come out first and a pop rivet has to be drilled out which will need renewal. Lower the window after removing the bottom stop bracket, then remove the screw which holds the lower end of the vertical dividing strip btween the quarterlight and main window. Remove the operating arm from the channel at the bottom of the glass. Remove the rubber weatherstrip from the outside of the door sill and the felt strip from the inside edge. Take the rubber channel from the window frame. At the top of the vertical dividing strip a pop rivet secures it to the door frame. Drill this out and undo the screw which holds the top quarterlight hinge to the door frame. The quarterlight complete with strip may then be lifted out

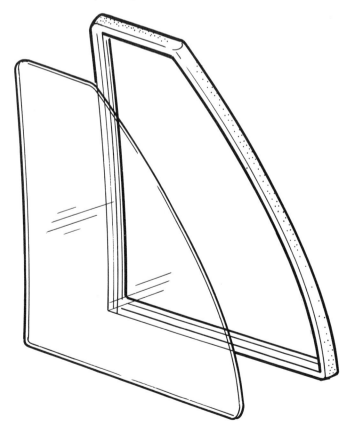

**Fig. 12.1 Rear light – estate models (Sec 7)**

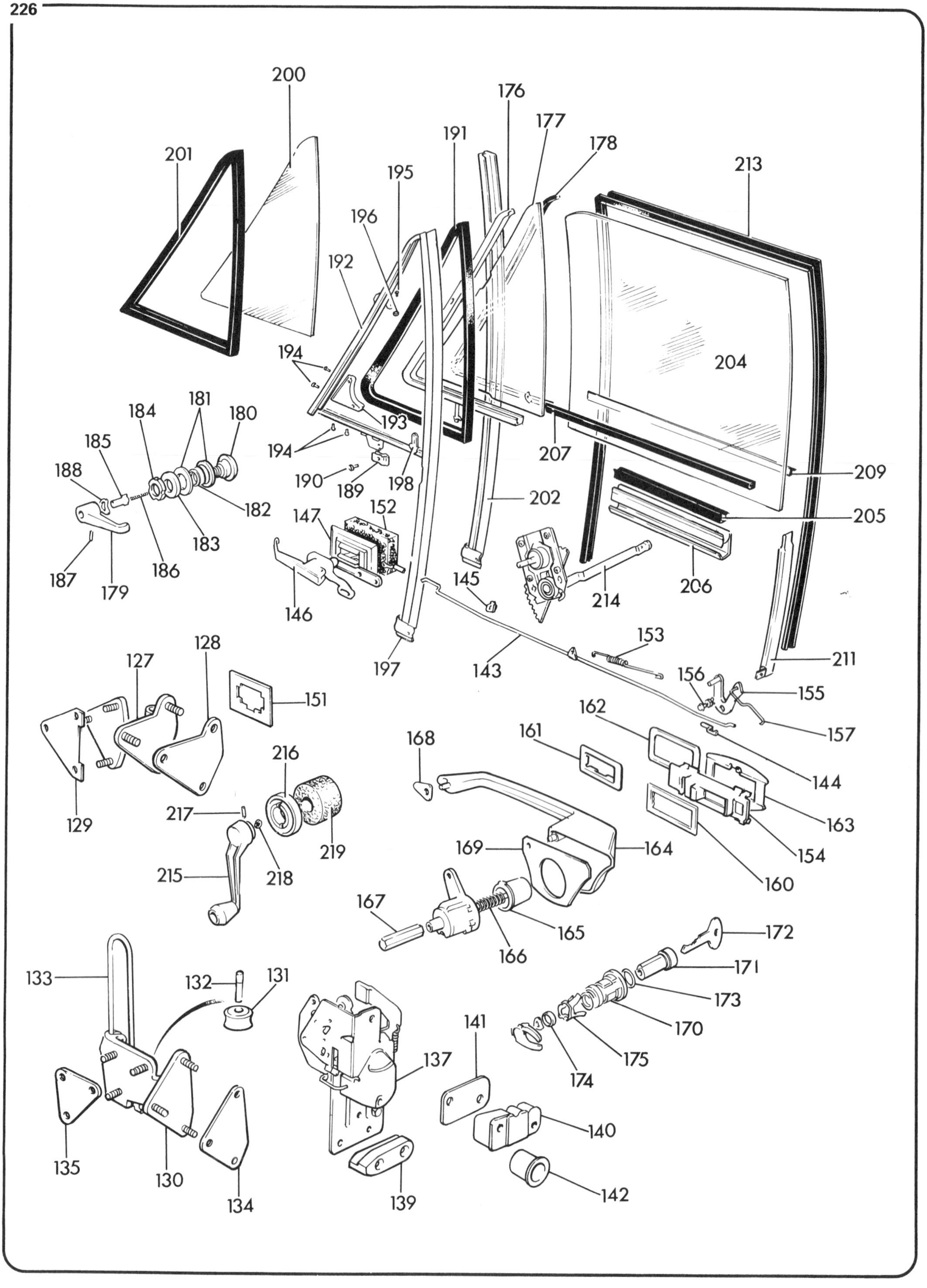
200
201
176
177
191
178
213
195
196
192
194
204
184
181
180
185
193
188
194
207
209
190
189
198
182
202
183
147
152
205
187
179
186
146
145
214
206
153
128
127
197
143
211
151
156
155
162
157
161
168
144
216
129
217
163
219
154
169
164
215
218
160
167
165
172
166
133
132
131
171
173
170
141
137
175
174
140
135
130
134
139
142

of the door. On back doors, the quarterlight is fixed and does not need to be removed before the main window. However, the vertical dividing strip which is held by a screw and pop rivet, as in the front door, has to be taken out in the same way. To remove the main window of both front and rear doors turn it through 90° so that the bottom edge is towards the door centre and then lift it out. If the rear quarterlight glass is to be removed, pull it out of the rubber channel strip. When refitting it, seal the glass into the channel with a proprietary sealing compound. Refitting of all door components is a reversal of the removal sequence. When refixing the vertical dividing strip make sure the main window runs up and down easily before tightening the lower fixing screw.

13 To remove the bonnet lock (internal release type), drain off the coolant and detach the hoses at the radiator. Remove radiator fixings and then the radiator. Remove the spring and cable nipple from the catch, remove the bolts and the lock assembly.

14 To remove the bonnet lock (Sceptre models, internal release type), remove the grille centre section (see Section 11). Proceed as given in paragraph 13.

15 To remove the bonnet lock (external release) proceed as given in paragraph 13. However, note that there is no control cable.

16 Remove the bonnet hinges by removing the nut beneath the facia, and withdrawing the pivot bolt. When reassembling, check the hinge after fitting for freedom of operation.

17 To remove the boot lid lock, withdraw the plastic studs to partially remove the trim (if relevant). Take out the bolts and withdraw the lock. If necessary, remove the lock barrel by releasing the two-legged spring clip. Refit in the reverse order.

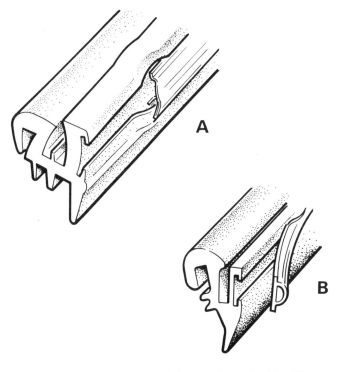

**Fig. 12.3 Windscreen to window sealing strips (Sec 7)**

A  Metal mouldings       B  Plastic mouldings

**Fig. 12.2 Front door fittings (Sec 7)**

| | |
|---|---|
| 127 | Upper hinge |
| 128 | Spreader plate to door |
| 129 | Spreader plate to body |
| 130 | Lower hinge |
| 131 | Check link roller |
| 132 | Retainer pin |
| 133 | Torsion spring |
| 134 | Spreader plate to door |
| 135 | Spreader plate to body |
| 137 | Lock assembly |
| 139 | Dovetail |
| 140 | Striker plate |
| 141 | Anti-burst plate |
| 142 | Dovetail striker |
| 143 | Remote control rod |
| 144 | Clip |
| 145 | Anti-rattle clip |
| 146 | Inside handle |
| 147 | Escutcheon |
| 151 | Escutcheon retainer |
| 152 | Seal |
| 153 | Handle return spring |
| 154 | Locking bolt |
| 155 | Lever locking bolt |
| 156 | Pivot |
| 157 | Locking link |
| 160 | Escutcheon |
| 161 | Escutcheon |
| 162 | Retainer |
| 163 | Retainer |
| 164 | Outside handle |
| 165 | Push button screw |
| 166 | Spring |
| 167 | Contact nut |
| 168 | Seating washer |
| 169 | Seating washer |
| 170 | Lock |
| 171 | Lock cylinder |
| 172 | Key |
| 173 | Seating washer |
| 174 | Pin retainer |
| 175 | 4-prong retainer |
| 176 | Frame |
| 177 | Quarterlight |
| 178 | Glazing rubber |
| 179 | Locking handle (quarterlight) |
| 180 | Boss and peg |
| 181 | Sealing washer |
| 182 | Cone washer |
| 183 | Special washer |
| 184 | Locking ring |
| 185 | Push button |
| 186 | Spring |
| 187 | Spring pin |
| 188 | Wave washer |
| 189 | Clip |
| 190 | Screw |
| 191 | Weatherstrip |
| 192 | Frame and vertical divider strip |
| 193 | Corner block |
| 194 | Screw |
| 195 | Pivot pin |
| 196 | Spacer |
| 197 | Division channel |
| 198 | Catch plate |
| 200 | Fixed glass |
| 201 | Weatherstrip |
| 202 | Division channel |
| 204 | Main glass |
| 205 | Glazing rubber |
| 206 | Lifting channel |
| 207 | Inner sill seal |
| 209 | Outer sill seal |
| 211 | Support channel |
| 213 | Glass rim channel |
| 214 | Regulator |
| 215 | Handle |
| 216 | Escutcheon |
| 217 | Cross pin |
| 218 | Rubber pad |
| 219 | Foam pad |

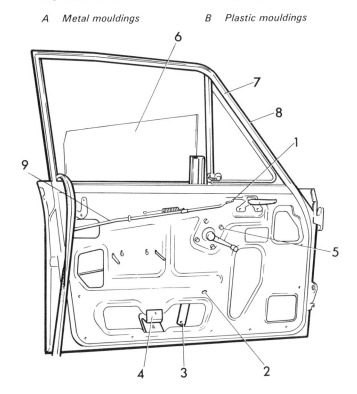

**Fig. 12.4 Front door, showing main items affected when removing windows and locks (Sec 7)**

| | | | |
|---|---|---|---|
| 1 | Remote control link coupling | 5 | Regulator fixing screw |
| 2 | Locating screw (dividing channel) | 6 | Door glass |
| | | 7 | Pop rivet (frame support) |
| 3 | Regulator arm | 8 | Quarterlight top hinge screw |
| 4 | Bottom stop bracket screw | 9 | Remote control link |

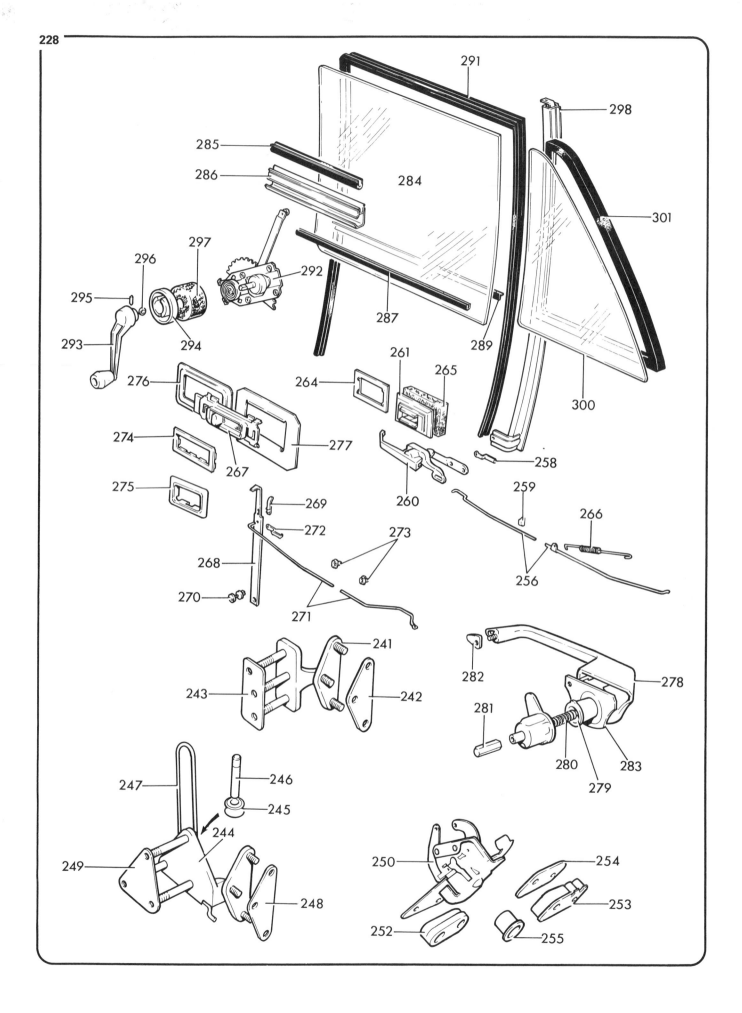

18  Rear door hinges (estate models) are removed by withdrawing the cover plate at the rear of the roof. Remove the door from the hinges, and the clip retaining the springs. Remove the hinges from the body. Refit in the reverse order.

19  To remove the rear door lock (estate models), remove the three screws holding the lock cover, and then the three screws holding the lock to the cover. Press down the lever to release the plastic thimble from the press button. Withdraw the lock button and cylinder after removing the two screws and retainer clip. Refit in reverse, bearing in mind that the countersunk screw with the flat head which holds the lock to the cover is fitted in the centre.

20  To remove the striker plate (estate models), remove the three screws. To adjust the plate position, loosen the screws and move the plate as required.

## 8   Bonnet – removal and refitting

1   When in position and closed the bonnet should fit centrally in the aperture and be flush with the surrounding bodywork. The fore and aft and vertical positions at the hinge end can be adjusted by repositioning the vertical slotted bonnet bracket on the horizontally slotted hinge plate. The forward end is adjusted by the position of the catch post in the centre of the bonnet. By undoing the locknut where it is mounted on the bonnet, it can be screwed in or out as necessary, altering the height at which it hooks under the release catch.

2   To remove the bonnet, it should be propped open and cloth placed under the rear corners to protect the paintwork. Two people are needed to remove the bonnet easily as support is required while the hinge bolts are undone. However, it is possible for one person to do it by supporting the rear corners on wooden blocks while undoing the

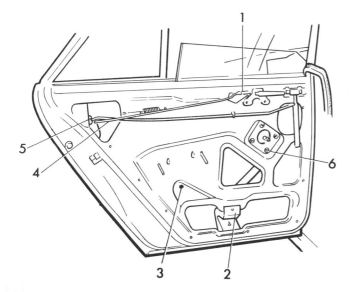

**Fig. 12.6 Rear door, showing main items affected when removing windows and locks (Sec 7)**

1   Remote control link coupling
2   Locating screw (bottom stop bracket)
3   Locating screw (dividing channel)
4   Remove control link
5   Remote control lock coupling
6   Regulator fixing screws

**Fig. 12.5 Rear door fittings (Sec 7)**

| | | | |
|---|---|---|---|
| 241 | Upper hinge | 272 | Clip |
| 242 | Spreader plate to door | 273 | Anti-rattle clip |
| 243 | Spreader plate to body | 274 | Escutcheon |
| 244 | Lower hinge and check link | 275 | Escutcheon |
| 245 | Check link roller | 276 | Retainer |
| 246 | Retainer pin | 277 | Retainer |
| 247 | Torsion hinge | 278 | Outside handle |
| 248 | Spreader plate to door | 279 | Push button screw |
| 249 | Spreader plate to body | 280 | Spring |
| 250 | Door lock assembly | 281 | Contact nut |
| 252 | Dovetail | 282 | Seating washer (front) |
| 253 | Striker plate | 283 | Seating washer (rear) |
| 254 | Anti-burst plate | 284 | Main glass |
| 255 | Dovetail striker | 285 | Glazing rubber |
| 256 | Remote control rod | 286 | Lifting channel |
| 258 | Clip | 287 | Inner sill seal |
| 259 | Anti-rattle clip | 289 | Outer sill seal |
| 260 | Inside door handle | 291 | Glass rim channel |
| 261 | Escutcheon | 292 | Regulator |
| 264 | Retainer | 293 | Handle |
| 265 | Seal | 294 | Escutcheon |
| 266 | Return spring | 295 | Cross pin |
| 267 | Locking bolt | 296 | Rubber pad |
| 268 | Locking bolt lever | 297 | Foam pad |
| 269 | Lever pad | 298 | Division channel |
| 270 | Pivot | 300 | Fixed glass (saloon) |
| 271 | Locking link | 301 | Weather strip |
| | | 303 | Fixed glass (estate) |

8.2a Bonnet propped by a wooden block on each side

8.2b Bonnet hinge bolts – removal

hinge bolts. Care is needed as the whole bonnet tends to pitch to one side off the front prop stay. Before slackening the hinge bolts, mark the positions of the two brackets so that the need for adjustment is minimised on refitting (photos).

### 9  Boot lid – removal and refitting

The fitting of the lid into the aperture follows the same principles as for the bonnet and the hinge end is adjusted in the same way. The height of the closing end is adjusted by raising or lowering the catch post which is clamped to the inner edge of the compartment rear panel.

### 10  Windscreen and windows – removal and refitting

1    The fitting of replacement screens can give considerable difficulty to those who do not possess the specialised knowledge and items of equipment normally required for this work. It is therefore advised that the assistance of one of the many specialists in this field should be sought.

2    If a water leak should develop at one of the screens, it may be possible to seal this by employing a proprietary sealing compound inserted into the weatherstrip. However, if deterioration of the weatherstrip is the cause of the problem, it is unlikely that anything other than renewal will be effective.

### 11  Radiator grilles – removal and refitting

1    Grilles are held in place by self-tapping screws, located as shown in Fig. 12.8. When refitting, start all screws by one or two turns, and then tighten them all evenly.

2    On twin headlamp models, detach the grille by removing the retaining screws arrowed in white (Fig. 12.8). The black arrows indicate the screws which retain the headlamp finisher panel.

### 12  Name badges – removal and refitting

To remove, lever off very carefully. Push into place to refit.

### 13  Bumpers and rubbing strips – removal and refitting

1    Disconnect electrical connections at the nearest snap connectors. Remove the bolts and nuts, then remove the bumpers. Refit in the reverse sequence.

2    To remove the front bumper rubbing strip, first remove the fifteen nuts behind the bumper, and pull the strip clear. If fitting a replacement, change over to bolts. Do not overtighten the nuts.

3    To remove the rear bumper rubbing strip, remove the bumper. Remove the thirteen nuts securing the rear bumper strip. Then proceed as for the front bumper.

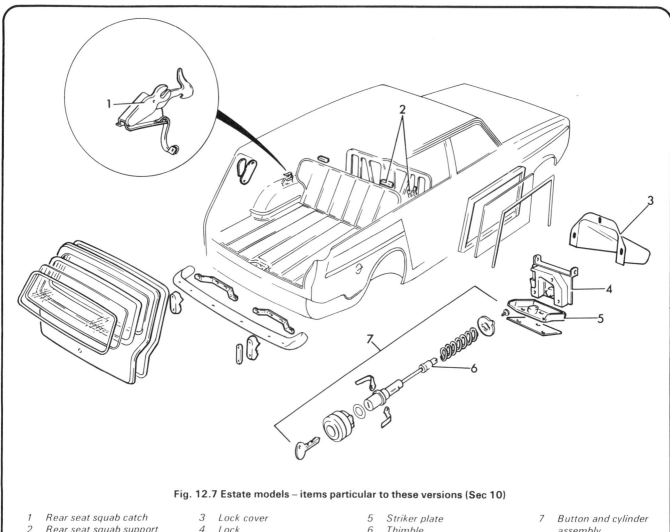

**Fig. 12.7 Estate models – items particular to these versions (Sec 10)**

| | | | |
|---|---|---|---|
| 1  Rear seat squab catch | 3  Lock cover | 5  Striker plate | 7  Button and cylinder |
| 2  Rear seat squab support | 4  Lock | 6  Thimble | assembly |

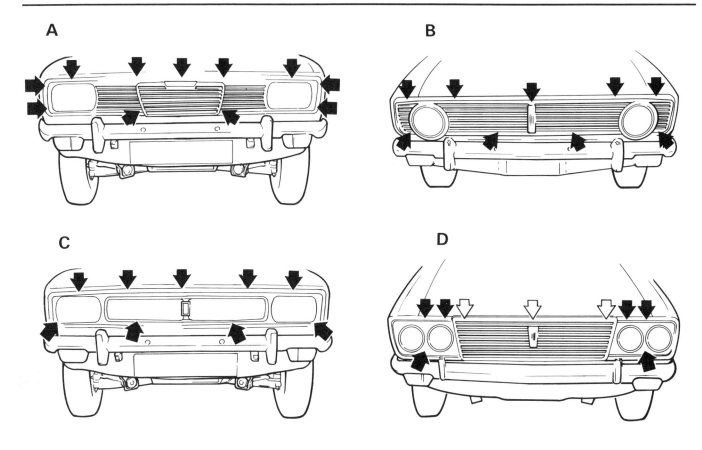

**Fig. 12.8 Radiator grille – fixing points (Sec 11)**

A   *Vogue and Gazelle*          B   *Minx and early Hunter*          C   *Later type Hunter*          D   *Sceptre*

## 14 Rear embellisher assembly (later models) – removal and refitting

1    From inside the luggage compartment gently pull back the trim on the rear quarter panel on both sides of the compartment, exposing the three nuts and bolts per side which secure the corner chrome moulding to the top of the rear wings. Remove the nuts, plain washers and water sealing washers and lift off the top corner moulding.
2    Remove one nut and washer and one self-tapping screw from just below the moulding points and lift off the corner embellisher.
3    Remove the three screws which secure the boot lid lock to the inner side of the rear panel and remove.
4    Release the circular spring from the rear of the boot lock barrel, also the washer securing the lock shaft. Separate the lock barrel and the lock shaft before removing the barrel and draw the lock barrel forward clear of the panel.
5    Remove three self-tapping screws from along the top of the embellisher. From inside the boot remove four self-tapping screws, one at each end of the panel, one in the centre, and one just left of the centre line.
6    Lower the petrol filler flap and from inside the panel, remove two nuts located just below the filler neck. Do not remove the screws as these are held by double nuts. Now pull forward the whole embellisher and petrol filler flap compartment clear of the vehicle.
7    Refitting is a reverse of the removal procedure.

## 15 Rear number plate – correct fitment

To conform to regulations, the plate should be fitted with at least 1.3 in (8 mm) between the lowest point of the number plate lamp cover and the top of the letters on the plate.

## 16 Body mouldings – removal and refitting

1    Start at both ends of the moulding, lifting them over the edge of the retaining clips (or, if applicable, drill out the pop rivets). Slide the moulding off the remaining clips. Refit damaged clips by punching out the centre peg of the old clip, pressing a new clip into the hole, and fitting and driving home a new peg. Ensure the long side of the clip is at the bottom.
2    To refit the moulding, hold the lower edge over the long side of the clip and tap the moulding to snap it over completely.

## 17 Weatherstrips – refitting

1    'Weatherstrip' is the term used to describe the rubber mouldings used in places such as door openings, to provide a seal against the elements.
2    Suitable adhesives for attaching weatherstrip can be obtained from most motor factors or authorised agents.
3    The surfaces to be joined must be completely free from foreign matter. Wipe with white spirit.
4    Employ the adhesive as specified in the instructions which normally accompany the pack. Clean any surplus adhesive from adjacent surfaces with a lightly moistened rag, using petrol or white spirit.

## 18 Roof cover and simulated wood finish (where fitted)

Removing and refitting the leathercloth cover involves a certain amount of skill, and in addition, preferably the use of a paint oven to improve the working nature of the leathercloth. It is therefore advised that a competent body shop be asked to carry out such work. The same basic remarks apply to the renewal of simulated wood items.

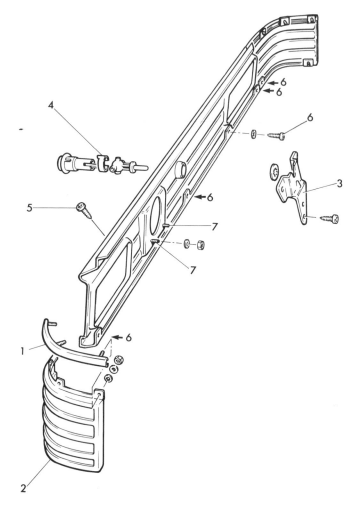

**Fig. 12.9 Rear embellisher assembly – exploded view (Sec 14)**

| 1 | Moulding | 5 | Screw |
|---|----------|---|-------|
| 2 | Embellisher | 6 | Screw |
| 3 | Boot lock | 7 | Studs |
| 4 | Circular spring | | |

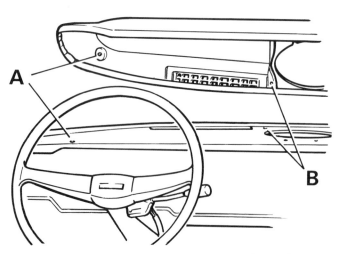

**Fig. 12.10 Facia crash roll – removal (Sec 22)**

| A | Crash roll nuts | B | Screw locations |
|---|-----------------|---|-----------------|

## 19 Spare wheel carrier – saloon and estate models

1    On saloon cars, unhook the catch, remove the spare wheel, and spring the wire frame ends out of the lugs. Remove the carrier. Refit in reverse order. Screw the knurled adjuster in or out as necessary, to obtain the correct tension on the catch.
2    On estate cars, lower the carrier fully and remove the spare wheel. Remove the split pins at the pivot points. Remove the carrier. Employ new split pins when reassembling.

## 20 Roof rack – description, removal and refitting

1    The rack is a factory option on the Hunter Estate, and standard on the Sceptre Estate. It should not be removed unless accident or repair work dictates this be done.
2    Remove the eight screws from the rack feet. The sealing compound employed on these may cause some stiffness. Lift the rack away.
3    Clean the screw threads and recoat with a suitable sealing compound. Fit the pads under the feet, and refit and tighten the screws.
4    The roof rubbing strips may be removed by taking out the securing screws, three per strip.

## 21 Directional air diffusers – removal and refitting

1    Take off the outer facia panel after removing the retaining screws.
2    Press the clips which retain the diffusers against the body of the vent from behind the facia, then withdraw the vent from the front. Take great care with this operation since the clips can readily be damaged and thus render the unit unfit for further service.
3    Refitting is a reversal of the removal procedure.

## 22 Facia crash roll – removal and refitting

1    From beneath the facia, remove the two nuts (A in Fig. 12.10), then unscrew the two self-tapping screws (B) from the inner ends of the grilles over the heater vents.
2    Insert a thin piece of plastic or card between the A-post trim and each end of the roll, then remove the latter upwards and outwards, taking care that the windscreen weatherstrip is not damaged.
3    Refitting is a reversal of the removal procedure.

## 23 Facia panel – removal

The instrument panel and the end facia panels are retained by screws, which, when removed, permit the panel to be withdrawn to give access to the panel items.

## 24 Centre console and front parcel tray – removal and refitting

1    To remove the console, disconnect the battery, remove the gear lever knob and locknut, and remove the retaining screws. Lift the console, disconnect the clock lamp holder from the clock, disconnect the supply leads, and lift out the console followed by the insulating pad. Refit in the reverse order.
2    On Sceptre models only, the main portion comes away leaving the rearmost section in place. To remove the remaining section, release the fixing screws under the open pocket.
3    To remove the front parcel tray, remove the centre console. Remove the retaining nut at each end of the tray, pull out the plastic peg at each end, and withdraw the tray.

## 25 Roof lining

The removal and refitting of the roof lining, a complicated enough operation on its own, is made more difficult by the need to remove the front and rear windscreens. It is therefore felt that this work should be entrusted to a competent body repair shop.

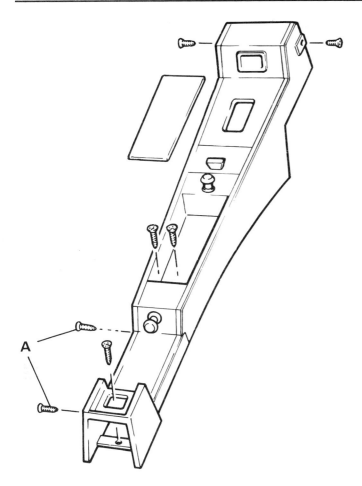

**Fig. 12.11 Centre console – fixing screws (Note: Screws A are used on Sceptre models only) (Sec 24)**

A

### 26 Seat belts

1   Figs. 12.12 to 12.15 inclusive show the types of seat belt which have been employed, together with the relevant fixings, and these are self explanatory.

2   If an accident has been suffered, the belts should be renewed if they have been subjected to any shock load. The anchorages should also be examined.

### 27 Heating and ventilating system – description and adjustment

1   The system comprises a water heated matrix, linked into the engine radiator circuit, but not controlled by the thermostat, so that hot water reaches the heater as soon as available. Air enters the system through the grille over the scuttle and, depending on the control settings, is either partially or wholly heated and directed to screen, interior or both. The controls operate the mixing valve, distribution valve and water valve. The top lever of the two marked 'off, screen, car' controls the distribution flap. In the 'off' position no air passes to either the car or screen. In the 'screen' position all air is directed to the screen vents for demisting and in the 'car' position most air is directed into the car with some bled off towards the screen. The other lever, marked 'cold - hot' operates both the air 'mixing' flap and the water valve. They operate simultaneously when the lever is moved away from cold. The water valve lets hot water into the heater matrix and the mixing flap lets a proportion of the inlet air past the heater. In the 'hot' position all air flows past the heater. The water valve is fully open before the mixer flap completely cuts off the cold air inlet. The air flow is boosted when necessary by the twin rotor blow fan. A pair of independent fresh air inlet ducts, with outlets one at each end of the dashboard, is also installed. This is not affected by the controls and cannot be heated. The direction and flow of the air is controlled by the air valves at the ends of the ducts.

2   If the heater seems to be faulty, ensure that a thermostat is fitted and working properly (see Chapter 2).

3   In order to make sure that the air valves are working they can be checked and adjusted at the heater ends of the cables. Release the cable at the lever trunnion ('A' in Fig. 12.18) and set the mixing flap control to 'cold'. The lever should then be set as far as it will go in a clockwise direction (as arrowed in Fig. 12.18) and the cable clamped up. The water valve, operated by the same cable, should be set at the same time by undoing the trunnion clamp ('B' in Fig. 12.18) and pressing the top arm down (as arrowed). Tighten the clamp.

4   The distributor valve cable is set in the same manner but the lever is moved as far as possible clockwise ('C' in Fig. 12.18). Check the full range of operation after adjustment to ensure the flap valves are seating correctly at each extremity.

5   The heater air intake is under the grille on the scuttle. Access is obtained by removing the screws, then the grille.

### 28 Heater controls and cables – removal and refitting

1   To renew either cable, withdraw the control assembly from the facia. Disconnect the battery and disconnect both cables at the heater and adjustment trunnions.

2   Remove the radio, console, parcel shelf and the escutcheon (held by two screws) round the control levers. On later models, take off the detachable knobs.

3   Two screws, accessible through the aperture, hold the assembly in position and when these are removed it can be drawn forward, bringing the cables with it. Each cable is clamped. It can be detached and the inner cable lifted off the lever peg.

4   When fitting a cable, make sure the end of the outer does not project beyond the edge of the clamp (or spring clip). Adjust the levers, after refitting, as described in Section 27.

### 29 Heater unit, blowers and water valve (early models) – removal and refitting

1   Disconnect the battery. Partially drain the cooling system. Disconnect the inlet and outlet hoses from the water valve.

2   Remove the controls as described in Section 28.

3   Remove the face vent air hoses from the heater end and the demist tubes which run up to the windscreen.

4   Disconnect the two blower cables at the snap connections. Release the cable harness where it is clipped to the body of the heater unit.

5   Release the four screws, two on each side, which hold the unit in place. Move it carefully to one side and lift out.

6   To remove the water valve, disconnect the short hose between the valve and matrix and release the operating link at the trunnion. The two crosshead securing screws should be removed and the valve withdrawn. Note the O-ring seal which fits between the valve and matrix. This must be renewed when refitting the valve.

7   To remove the heater matrix (having removed the unit from the car and taken off the water valve) take off the air mixing valve shaft retainer clip from the end opposite the lever and remove all the screws holding the end cover in position. The end cover, together with the mixing valve, can be withdrawn and the matrix lifted out.

8   The blower units are serviced as complete assemblies and no spares are supplied by the manufacturers. They are assembled and balanced on original assembly and the clearances between rotors and casings are very fine. Dismantling is not, therefore, recommended. To remove the blowers the heater unit should be taken from the car. Attach a draw wire to each of the cables and remove the six screws holding the blowers to the casing. The draw wires should be left in position on the casing for refitting the leads when refitting the blowers. Note the earth wire attached to one of the centre screws.

9   When reassembling the unit it is important for quietness and proper operation that all sealed joints are made good and that the foam padding is in good condition and correctly positioned.

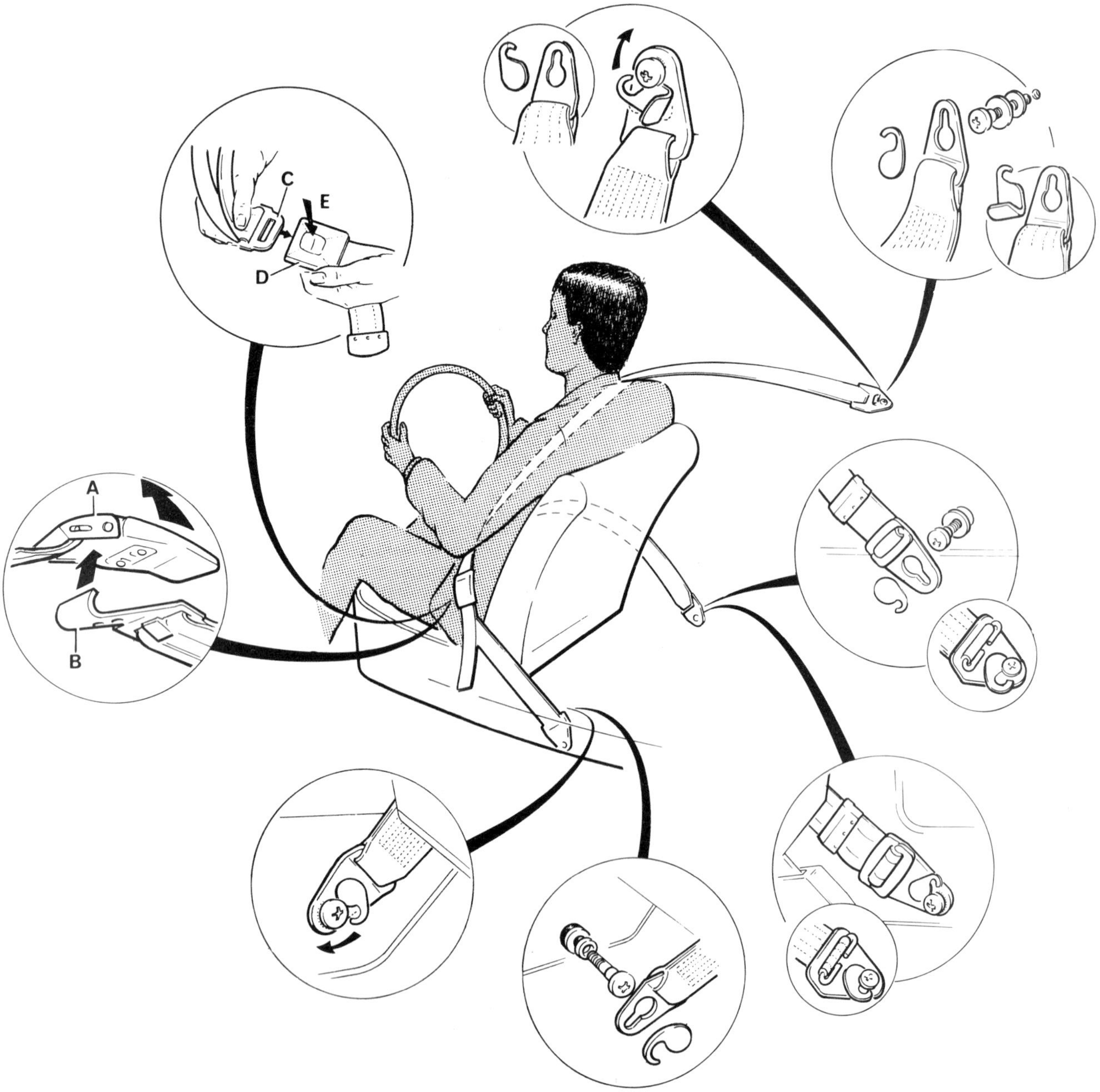

**Fig. 12.12 Safety belt – early, magnetic buckle type (Sec 26)**

A   Magnetic buckle
B   Connector (magnetic buckle)
C   Connector (latch buckle)

D   Latch buckle
E   Release button

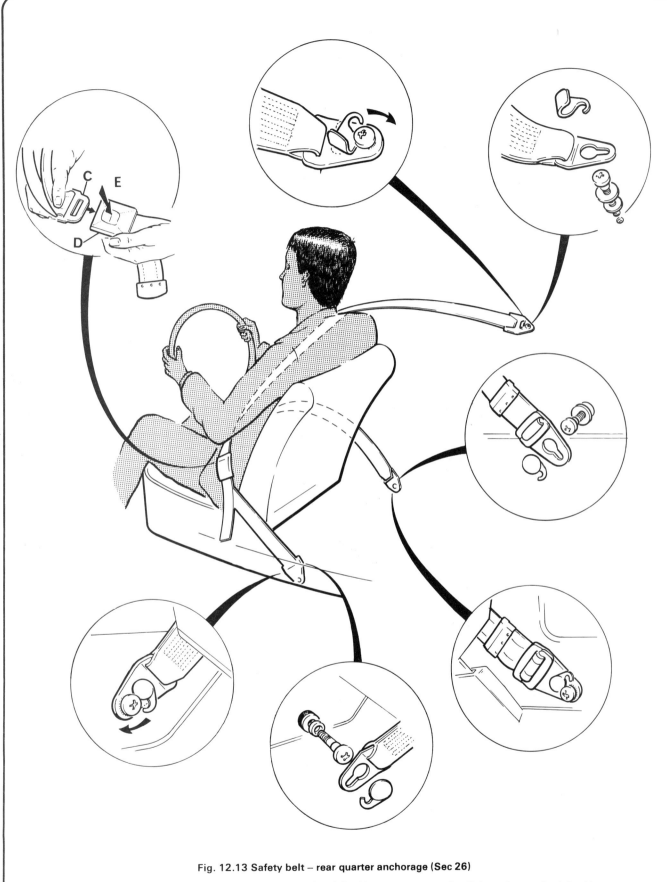

**Fig. 12.13 Safety belt – rear quarter anchorage (Sec 26)**

C   *Connector, latch buckle*       D   *Latch buckle*       E   *Release button, latch buckle*

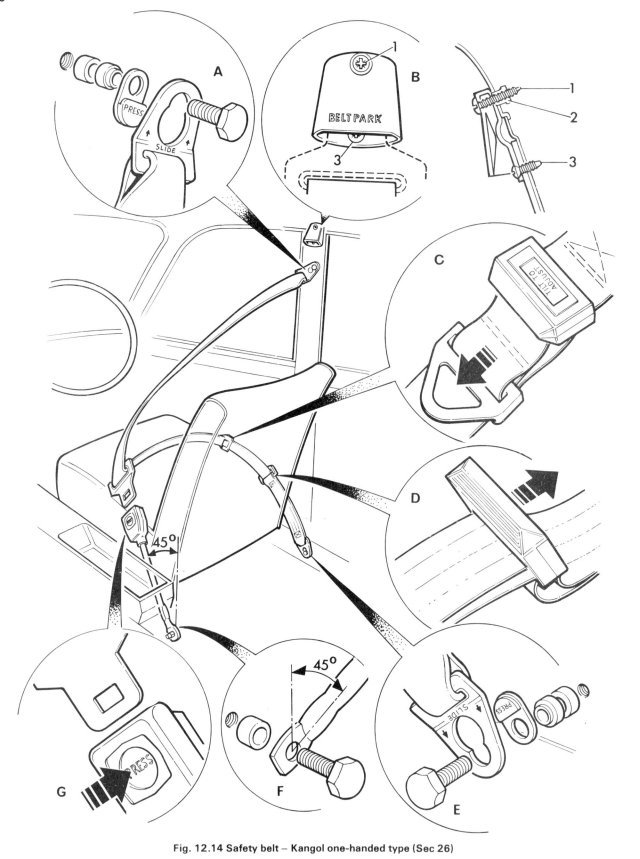

Fig. 12.14 Safety belt – Kangol one-handed type (Sec 26)

A   Pillar anchorage
B   Stowage fixing
C   Adjuster
D   Adjuster
E   Lower outer anchorage
F   Tunnel anchorage
G   Locking assembly
1   Large screw
2   Insert
3   Small screw

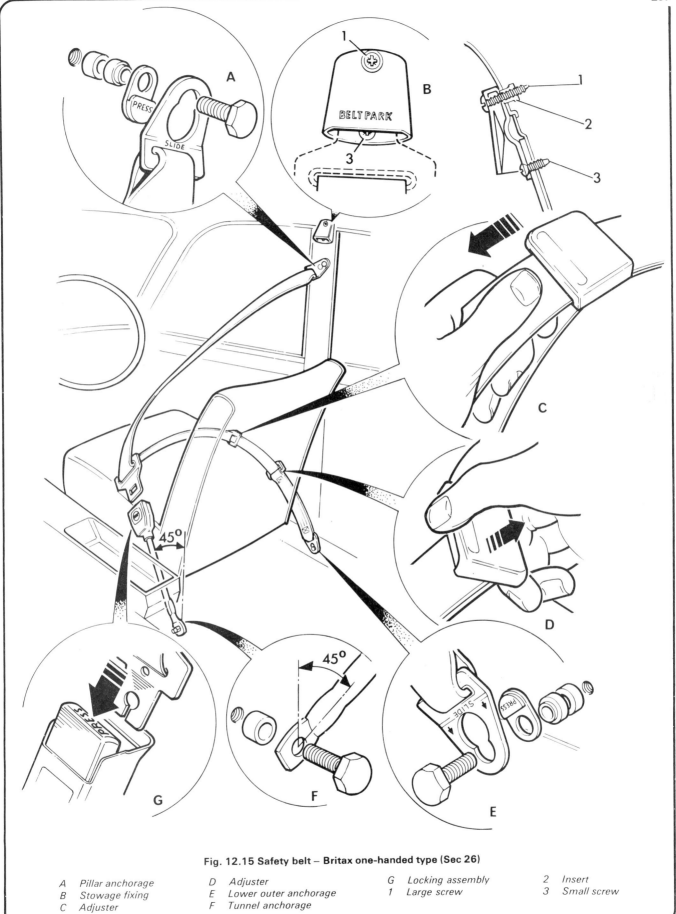

**Fig. 12.15 Safety belt – Britax one-handed type (Sec 26)**

| | | | |
|---|---|---|---|
| A  Pillar anchorage | D  Adjuster | G  Locking assembly | 2  Insert |
| B  Stowage fixing | E  Lower outer anchorage | 1  Large screw | 3  Small screw |
| C  Adjuster | F  Tunnel anchorage | | |

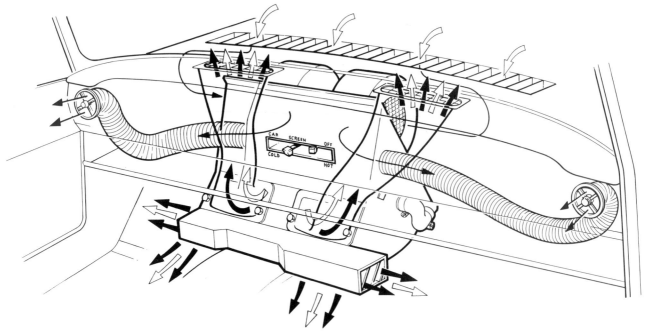

**Fig. 12.16 Ventilation air flow (Sec 27)**

➡ 1   *Heated outside air*      ➡ 2   *Outside air to face vents*      ⇨ 3   *Cool outside air*

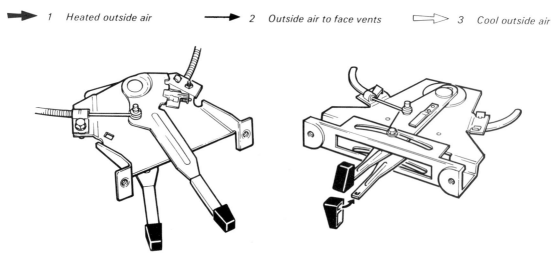

**Fig. 12.17 Heater control details, showing the two types fitted (Sec 27)**

## 30 Heater unit and controls (later models) – removal and refitting

The information contained in this section applies to the following models:

*Hunter De Luxe from chassis No LH 064 7*
*Hunter De Luxe Estate from chassis No LH 160 7*
*Hunter Super from chassis No LH 075 7*
*Hunter GL from chassis No LH 059 7*
*Hunter GL Estate from chassis No LH 150 7*
*Hunter GLS from chassis No 040 7*
*Hunter GT from chassis No LH 831 7*

1   Disconnect the battery.
2   Partially drain the cooling system, then disconnect the heater inlet and outlet hoses.
3   Working from inside the vehicle, remove the radio and centre console.
4   Pull the rubber cover away from the ignition switch/steering lock wiring socket, extract the screw and uncouple the socket.
5   Remove the parcel shelf and heater control knobs.

6   If an oil pressure gauge is fitted, disconnect the oil pipe from the rear of the gauge.
7   Extract the two screws and withdraw the facia centre panel as far as it will come without straining the electrical leads.
8   Release the heater control cables from the heater by loosening the lever transmission screws and prising off the outer cable clips. Remove the heater control assembly (two screws).
9   Unscrew the two securing nuts from each of the two demister tube assemblies. Remove the tubes.
10   Remove the two hoses between the heater and the facia.
11   Disconnect the blower leads at the snap connectors, and unclip them from the heater casing.
12   Remove the steering column upper shroud (two screws) and unclip the flasher unit from the lower shroud.
13   Extract the six facia screws so the facia can be moved slightly upwards as the heater assembly is withdrawn.
14   Extract the four heater securing screws and withdraw the heater from under the facia, toward the passenger side of the vehicle.
15   Refitting is the reverse of the removal procedure, but adjust the control cables as described in Section 27.
16   Refill the cooling system and check for leaks.

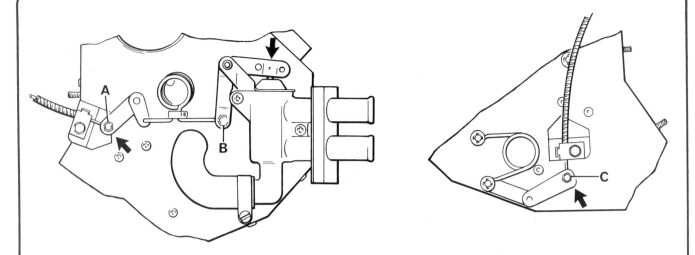

**Fig. 12.18 Heater cable adjustment points (Sec 27)**

A   Mixing valve              B   Water valve              C   Distributor valve

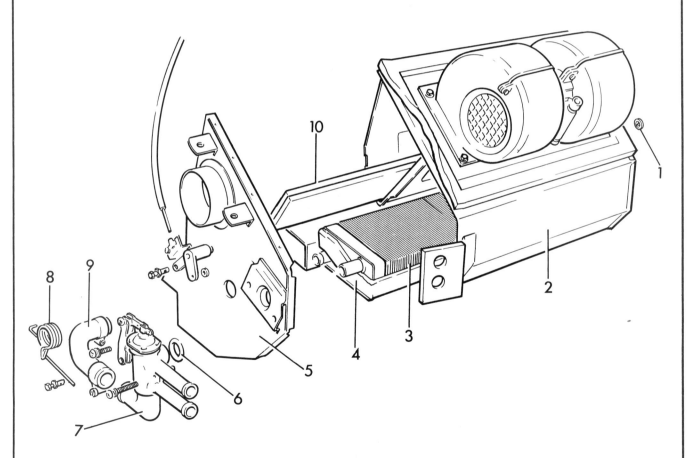

**Fig. 12.19 Heater and blower unit (Sec 29)**

| | | | | |
|---|---|---|---|---|
| 1 | Mixing valve shaft retainer clip | 3 Heater matrix | 6 O-ring seal | 9 Hose valve to matrix |
| 2 | Heater casing | 4 Seal | 7 Water valve | 10 Mixing valve flap |
| | | 5 End cover | 8 Valve operating link | |

# Conversion factors

## Length (distance)
| | | | | | |
|---|---|---|---|---|---|
| Inches (in) | X | 25.4 | = Millimetres (mm) | X 0.039 | = Inches (in) |
| Feet (ft) | X | 0.305 | = Metres (m) | X 3.281 | = Feet (ft) |
| Miles | X | 1.609 | = Kilometres (km) | X 0.621 | = Miles |

## Volume (capacity)
| | | | | | |
|---|---|---|---|---|---|
| Cubic inches (cu in; in³) | X | 16.387 | = Cubic centimetres (cc; cm³) | X 0.061 | = Cubic inches (cu in; in³) |
| Imperial pints (Imp pt) | X | 0.568 | = Litres (l) | X 1.76 | = Imperial pints (Imp pt) |
| Imperial quarts (Imp qt) | X | 1.137 | = Litres (l) | X 0.88 | = Imperial quarts (Imp qt) |
| Imperial quarts (Imp qt) | X | 1.201 | = US quarts (US qt) | X 0.833 | = Imperial quarts (Imp qt) |
| US quarts (US qt) | X | 0.946 | = Litres (l) | X 1.057 | = US quarts (US qt) |
| Imperial gallons (Imp gal) | X | 4.546 | = Litres (l) | X 0.22 | = Imperial gallons (Imp gal) |
| Imperial gallons (Imp gal) | X | 1.201 | = US gallons (US gal) | X 0.833 | = Imperial gallons (Imp gal) |
| US gallons (US gal) | X | 3.785 | = Litres (l) | X 0.264 | = US gallons (US gal) |

## Mass (weight)
| | | | | | |
|---|---|---|---|---|---|
| Ounces (oz) | X | 28.35 | = Grams (g) | X 0.035 | = Ounces (oz) |
| Pounds (lb) | X | 0.454 | = Kilograms (kg) | X 2.205 | = Pounds (lb) |

## Force
| | | | | | |
|---|---|---|---|---|---|
| Ounces-force (ozf; oz) | X | 0.278 | = Newtons (N) | X 3.6 | = Ounces-force (ozf; oz) |
| Pounds-force (lbf; lb) | X | 4.448 | = Newtons (N) | X 0.225 | = Pounds-force (lbf; lb) |
| Newtons (N) | X | 0.1 | = Kilograms-force (kgf; kg) | X 9.81 | = Newtons (N) |

## Pressure
| | | | | | |
|---|---|---|---|---|---|
| Pounds-force per square inch (psi; lbf/in²; lb/in²) | X | 0.070 | = Kilograms-force per square centimetre (kgf/cm²; kg/cm²) | X 14.223 | = Pounds-force per square inch (psi; lbf/in²; lb/in²) |
| Pounds-force per square inch (psi; lbf/in²; lb/in²) | X | 0.068 | = Atmospheres (atm) | X 14.696 | = Pounds-force per square inch (psi; lbf/in²; lb/in²) |
| Pounds-force per square inch (psi; lbf/in²; lb/in²) | X | 0.069 | = Bars | X 14.5 | = Pounds-force per square inch (psi; lbf/in²; lb/in²) |
| Pounds-force per square inch (psi; lbf/in²; lb/in²) | X | 6.895 | = Kilopascals (kPa) | X 0.145 | = Pounds-force per square inch (psi; lbf/in²; lb/in²) |
| Kilopascals (kPa) | X | 0.01 | = Kilograms-force per square centimetre (kgf/cm²; kg/cm²) | X 98.1 | = Kilopascals (kPa) |

## Torque (moment of force)
| | | | | | |
|---|---|---|---|---|---|
| Pounds-force inches (lbf in; lb in) | X | 1.152 | = Kilograms-force centimetre (kgf cm; kg cm) | X 0.868 | = Pounds-force inches (lbf in; lb in) |
| Pounds-force inches (lbf in; lb in) | X | 0.113 | = Newton metres (Nm) | X 8.85 | = Pounds-force inches (lbf in; lb in) |
| Pounds-force inches (lbf in; lb in) | X | 0.083 | = Pounds-force feet (lbf ft; lb ft) | X 12 | = Pounds-force inches (lbf in; lb in) |
| Pounds-force feet (lbf ft; lb ft) | X | 0.138 | = Kilograms-force metres (kgf m; kg m) | X 7.233 | = Pounds-force feet (lbf ft; lb ft) |
| Pounds-force feet (lbf ft; lb ft) | X | 1.356 | = Newton metres (Nm) | X 0.738 | = Pounds-force feet (lbf ft; lb ft) |
| Newton metres (Nm) | X | 0.102 | = Kilograms-force metres (kgf m; kg m) | X 9.804 | = Newton metres (Nm) |

## Power
| | | | | | |
|---|---|---|---|---|---|
| Horsepower (hp) | X | 745.7 | = Watts (W) | X 0.0013 | = Horsepower (hp) |

## Velocity (speed)
| | | | | | |
|---|---|---|---|---|---|
| Miles per hour (miles/hr; mph) | X | 1.609 | = Kilometres per hour (km/hr; kph) | X 0.621 | = Miles per hour (miles/hr; mph) |

## Fuel consumption*
| | | | | | |
|---|---|---|---|---|---|
| Miles per gallon, Imperial (mpg) | X | 0.354 | = Kilometres per litre (km/l) | X 2.825 | = Miles per gallon, Imperial (mpg) |
| Miles per gallon, US (mpg) | X | 0.425 | = Kilometres per litre (km/l) | X 2.352 | = Miles per gallon, US (mpg) |

## Temperature
Degrees Fahrenheit (°F) $= (°C \times \frac{9}{5}) + 32$

Degrees Celsius
(Degrees Centigrade; °C) $= (°F - 32) \times \frac{5}{9}$

*It is common practice to convert from miles per gallon (mpg) to litres/100 kilometres (l/100km), where mpg (Imperial) x l/100 km = 282 and mpg (US) x l/100 km = 235

# Index

## A

**Air cleaner**
    Stromberg 150 CDS – 62
    Stromberg 150 CDSE – 62
    Stromberg 150 CD3 – 62
    SU HS4 – 63
    SU HS4C – 63
    twin Stromberg 150 CDS – 62
    twin Weber 40 DCOE – 62
**Alternator control** – 11
**Alternator (Delco Remy type DN460)**
    description – 173
    testing in the car – 174
**Alternator (Lucas type 10AC)**
    description and maintenance – 169
    dismantling and reassembly – 170
    precautions and testing – 169
    removal and refitting – 170
**Alternator (Lucas types 16AC, 15ACR and 16ACR)**
    general information – 171
    servicing – 173
    testing in the car – 172
**Anti-freeze** – 58
**Automatic transmission**
    accelerator linkage – 138
    description – 136
    downshift cable – 136
    fault diagnosis – 141
    fluid level – 136
    removal and refitting – 141
    selector lever linkage – 138
    specifications – 111
    starter inhibitor/reversing light switch – 140
    torque wrench settings – 113

## B

**Battery** – 167
**Big-end bearings**
    refitting – 44
    removal – 34
    renovation – 38
**Bodywork and fittings**
    centre console and front parcel tray – 232
    description – 221
    directional air diffusers – 232
    facia crash roll – 232
    facia panel – 232
    maintenance – 221
    mouldings – 231
    name badges – 230
    rear embellisher assembly (later models) – 231
    repairs
        major damage – 225
        minor damage – 221
    weatherstrips – 231
**Bonnet** – 229
**Boot lid** – 230
**Braking system**
    brake drums and shoes – 153
    description – 150
    disc calliper – 158
    disc pads – 151
    discs – 153
    dual braking system – 162
    dual hydraulic system bleeding – 163
    fault diagnosis – 164
    handbrake – 155
    hydraulic fluid pipes – 155
    hydraulic system bleeding – 161
    hydraulic wheel cylinders (rear) – 157
    maintenance, routine – 150
    master cylinder
        single circuit system – 158
        tandem – 163
    pedal – 162
    pressure failure switch – 163
    servo unit – 159
    specifications – 150
    stop light switch – 162
    torque wrench settings – 150
**Bumpers** – 230

## C

**Camshaft**
    refitting – 44
    removal – 35
    renovation – 40
**Carburettors (Stromberg 150 CDS twin)**
    choke control – 70
    removal and refitting – 70
    slow running and synchronization – 69
**Carburettors (Stromberg 150 CD-3 twin)** – 76
**Carburettor (Stromberg 150 CDS)**
    description and principle of operation – 63
    dismantling and reassembly – 68
    removal and refitting – 65
    setting and adjustments – 67
Carburettor (Stromberg 150 CD-3) – 74
Carburettor (SU HS4)
    adjustments and tuning – 80
    description – 77
    dismantling and reassembly – 77
    examination and repair – 79
    float chamber
        flooding – 79
        fuel level adjustment – 79
    float needle sticking – 79
    jet centering – 80
    needle renewal – 80
    piston sticking – 79
    removal and refitting – 77
**Carburettor (SU HS4C)** – 81
**Carburettors (Weber 40 DCOE)**
    adjustments – 70
    description – 70
    dismantling – 73
    removal and refitting – 73
**Carpets maintenance** – 221
**Closed crankshaft ventilation system** – 37
**Clutch**
    bleeding the hydraulic system – 104
    description – 104
    fault diagnosis – 110
    maintenance, routine – 104
    master cylinder – 107
    operating cylinder – 107
    operating lever and thrust release bearing – 109
    pedal – 108
    refitting – 109
    removal – 108
    renovation – 108
    specifications – 104
**Connecting rods**
    reassembly – 43
    refitting – 44
    removal – 34
    renovation – 39
**Control box (Lucas type RB 340)**
    current regulator adjustment – 181

cut-out adjustment – 181
description – 180
maintenance – 180
voltage regulator adjustment – 180
**Cooling system**
description – 53
draining – 54
fault diagnosis – 59
filling – 55
flushing – 54
maintenance, routine – 53
specifications – 53
torque wrench settings – 53
**Crankshaft**
reassembly – 41
removal – 36
renovation – 37
**Crankshaft pulley**
refitting – 47
removal – 33
**Cylinder bores renovation – 38**
**Cylinder head**
refitting – 48
removal – 32
renovation – 39

**D**

**Decarbonisation – 40**
**Dimensions, general – 8**
**Direction indicator system – 182**
**Distributor (Ducellier) – 100**
**Distributor (Lucas 25 D4)**
condenser – 94
contact breaker points – 93
dismantling and reassembly – 94
ignition timing – 95
removal and refitting – 94
**Distributor (Lucas 23 D4) – 96**
**Distributors (Lucas 43 D4 and 45 D4)**
dismantling and reassembly – 98
general note – 96
ignition timing – 96
maintenance and adjustment – 96
removal and refitting – 98
**Doors – 225**
**Dynamo**
maintenance and testing – 167
removal and refitting – 167
repair – 168

**E**

**Electrical system**
description – 166
fault diagnosis – 193
specifications – 165
wiring diagrams – 195 to 205
**Engine**
ancillaries
dismantling – 31
reassembly – 51
description – 23
dismantling – 30
examination – 37
fault diagnosis – 52
maintenance, routine – 26
mountings and damper
removal and refitting – 37
operations possible with engine in place – 26
operations requiring engine removal – 26
reassembly – 41
refitting – 51
removal – 26

specifications – 19
torque wrench settings – 21
**Exhaust emission control – 83**
**Exhaust system – 88**

**F**

**Fanbelt – 58**
**Fan, viscous type – 57**
**Flasher units – 183, 188, 189**
**Flywheel**
refitting – 47
removal – 34
renovation – 40
**Fuel gauge – 88**
**Fuel pump – 86**
**Fuel system**
description – 61
fault diagnosis – 90
maintenance, routine – 62
specifications – 60
**Fuel tank – 88**
**Fuse unit – 182**

**G**

**Gearbox, manual**
description – 113
dismantling – 117
examination – 118
fault diagnosis – 125
input shaft bearing – 119
mainshaft – 119
maintenance, routine – 113
rear cover – 120
reassembly – 120
removal and refitting – 113
specifications – 111
torque wrench settings – 112
**Gudgeon pins**
reassembly – 43
removal – 34

**H**

**Headlamps**
2 FR type (rectangular) – 186
4 FR type (rectangular) – 187
Cibie type (rectangular) – 188
Lucas type F575 (dual system) – 187
**Heater**
controls and cables – 233
description – 233
removal and refitting
early models – 233
later models – 238
**Horn – 186**
**Hubs and bearings, front – 218**

**I**

**Ignition system**
description – 92
fault diagnosis – 102
maintenance, routine – 93
specifications – 91
**Instrument panel and instruments – 190**

**J**

**Jacking – 13**

**L**

Lights – 186 to 189
Lubricants, recommended – 15
Lubrication chart – 15

**M**

Main bearings
    reassembly – 41
    removal – 36
    renovation – 37
Maintenance, routine – 17
Manifolds, inlet and exhaust
    inspection – 40
    refitting – 48
    removal – 31
Manual gearbox *see* Gearbox, manual

**N**

Number plate, rear – 231

**O**

Oil filter – 36
Oil pump
    refitting – 37
    removal – 34
    renovation – 40
Overdrive
    specifications – 111
    torque wrench settings – 112
Overdrive (type D)
    description – 125
    fault diagnosis – 129
    maintenance, routine – 129
    operating lever – 128
    overhaul – 126
    relief valve, non-return valve and operating valve – 129
    removal and refitting – 126
Overdrive (type 'J')
    description – 130
    fault diagnosis – 136
    maintenance, routine – 135
    overhaul – 131
    pressure filter – 135
    pump non-return valve – 135
    relief valve and dashpot – 134
    removal and refitting – 130
    solenoid control valve – 134

**P**

Piston rings
    refitting – 44
    renovation – 39
Pistons
    reassembly – 43
    refitting – 44
    removal – 34
    renovation – 39
Propeller shaft
    centre bearing (two-piece shaft) – 142
    description – 142
    maintenance, routine – 142
    removal and refitting – 142
    specifications – 142
    torque wrench settings – 142
    universal joints
        dismantling and fitting new bearings – 145
        repair – 144

**R**

Radiator – 55
Radiator grille – 230
Rear axle
    description – 148
    differential carrier – 148
    differential, crownwheel and pinion – 148
    fault diagnosis – 149
    halfshafts, bearings and oil seals – 148
    maintenance, routine – 148
    removal and refitting – 148
    specifications – 146
    torque wrench settings – 146
Roof cover and simulated wood finish – 231
Roof lining – 232
Roof rack – 232
Routine maintenance – 17

**S**

Safety – 16
Seat belts – 233
Seats – 225
Spare parts, buying – 10
Spare wheel carrier – 232
Spark plugs and HT leads – 102
Starter motor (Lucas type 35G-1)
    circuit testing – 174
    description – 174
    drive pinion – 176
    removal and refitting – 175
    repair – 175
Starter motor (Lucas type 35J)
    description – 176
    overhaul – 177
    removal and refitting – 177
Starter motor (Lucas type M35G– pre-engaged) – 178
Starter motor (Lucas type M35J PE) – 179
Steering
    alignment – 218
    column
        cowling – 213
        upper bush – 217
    description – 208
    direction indicator switch – 213
    fault diagnosis – 220
    gear – 213
    gear, Burman adjustable – 217
    gear with column lock – 217
    linkage – 213
    lock and ignition switch – 217
    maintenance, routine – 208
    specifications – 206
    torque wrench settings – 207
    wheel with adjustable steering unit – 217
Sump
    refitting – 47
    removal – 32
Suspension
    description – 208
    fault diagnosis – 220
    maintenance, routine – 208
    specifications – 206
    springs and dampers inspection – 208
    springs and dampers (rear)
        removal and refitting – 211
    stabilizer bar – 210
    strut assembly, front – 210
    strut replacement damper cartridge, front – 211
    torque wrench settings – 207
    track control arm and bushes – 210
    track control arm balljoint – 210
Switches – 189

## T

Tappets
   refitting – 44
   removal – 35
   renovation – 40
Thermostat – 55
Timing chain and sprockets renovation – 40
Timing chain tensioner, sprockets and cover refitting – 44
Timing gear and cover removal – 32
Tools – 11
Towing – 13
Tyre sizes and pressures – 207

## U

Upholstery maintenance – 221

## V

Valve rocker clearances
   checking and adjustment – 51

Valve rocker gear
   reassembly and refitting – 48
   removal – 31
   renovation – 39
Valves
   reassembly to cylinder head – 47
   removal and renovation – 39
Vehicle identification numbers – 10

## W

Water pump – 56
Water temperature gauge – 58
Weights, general – 8
Wheel bearings, front – 217
Wheel types and sizes – 207
Wheel studs – 218
Windscreen and windows – 230
Windscreen washer – 185
Windscreen wiper
   Lucas type DL3A – 183
   Lucas type DL5A – 183
   Lucas type 15W – 185
Wiring diagrams – 195 to 205
Working facilities – 11

Printed by
Haynes Publishing Group
Sparkford Yeovil Somerset
England